Modulation and Codin

for Wireless Communications

M000240285

We work with leading authors to develop the strongest educational materials in engineering, bringing cutting-edge thinking and best learning practice to a global market.

Under a range of well-known imprints, including Prentice Hall, we craft high quality print and electronic publications which help readers to understand and apply their content, whether studying or at work.

To find out more about the complete range of our publishing please visit us on the World Wide Web at: www.pearsoneduc.com

Modulation and Coding
for Wireless Communications

Alister Burr

An imprint of **Pearson Education**

Harlow, England · London · New York · Reading, Massachusetts · San Francisco
Toronto · Don Mills, Ontario · Sydney · Tokyo · Singapore · Hong Kong · Seoul
Taipei · Cape Town · Madrid · Mexico City · Amsterdam · Munich · Paris · Milan

Pearson Education Limited

Edinburgh Gate
Harlow
Essex CM20 2JE
England

and Associated Companies around the world

Visit us on the World Wide Web at:
www.pearsoneduc.com

First published 2001

© Pearson Education Limited 2001

ISBN 0 201 39857 5

British Library Cataloguing-in-Publication Data
A catalogue record for this book can be obtained from the British Library

Library of Congress Cataloging-in-Publication Data
A catalog record for this book can be obtained from the Library of Congress

10 9 8 7 6 5 4 3 2 1
05 04 03 02 01

Typeset by 60
Printed and bound in Great Britain by
T.J. International Ltd., Padstow, Cornwall

To
Anna, Miriam and Jonathan,
and my assistant
Minou

Contents

Chapter 3 Modulation for non-linear systems   51

Chapter 4 Modem design   77

Chapter 5 Principles of FEC Coding   112

Chapter 6 Cyclic block codes 141

Contents

Chapter 9 Modulation and coding on multipath channels 241

Chapter 10 OFDM 283

Preface

It is superfluous to expatiate here on the importance of wireless communications in the modern world. However, the central role of modulation and coding in wireless communications is the main subject of this book. Modulation and coding provide the fundamental link between the user (the customer) and the wireless channel, and determine the performance of the system and its use of the resources of bandwidth and signal power. I write this preface shortly after the auction of the third generation mobile radio spectrum in the UK for in excess of £20 billion, after which no-one can doubt the monetary value of these resources!

This book, then, is concerned with the principles of modulation and coding as they apply to wireless systems (although other systems are also mentioned), and with the actual modulation and coding schemes that are found in modern wireless systems. It is therefore pitched at a somewhat higher level than most introductory undergraduate textbooks on communications, in order to provide the necessary theoretical underpinning for these schemes.

In fact, the book has developed from the notes of a successful MSc module (also taken as a week-long stand-alone short course for industry), which I have taught for some years at the University of York and elsewhere. This in turn developed from a final year MEng course on 'Advanced Modulation and Coding' at York, as well as from 15 years of research in wireless communications. The book is thus aimed primarily at final year undergraduate or Master's level postgraduate students, with the implication that some prior exposure to basic communication principles would be helpful. In an academic context, then, I hope it will support courses towards the end of a Bachelor's programme (or an equivalent first degree in Europe), or Master's level courses or in support of Doctoral programmes. While it is designed as an integrated whole, many of the chapters will stand alone, so it could also be used in courses on modulation or coding only.

However, it is also my hope that it will be suitable for practising communications engineers, both to provide an introduction to the more advanced topics in this area, and also to give practical guidance in developing and applying the schemes described. To this end a number of practical examples are included, as well as tables and graphs and a full chapter on implementation issues.

The implicit premise behind the book is that modulation and coding are best regarded as a single process, rather than as two separate processes. This implies not only that they should be implemented jointly, but also that they should be taught jointly. We then find, serendipitously, that there are a plethora of common principles between the two aspects, which greatly aid understanding. It also provides a natural basis for such techniques as coded modulation and coded orthogonal frequency division multiplexing (OFDM), in which coding and modulation are inextricably combined.

Modulation and (especially) coding are notorious for being heavily mathematical subjects. I suspect this reputation is not entirely accurate – or it would be beyond my understanding! I have, therefore, tried to keep the mathematical content of the book to an absolute minimum (but not below!), and to make use of graphical and verbal explanations of the sort I have myself found helpful. Mathematics has been included either where it actually aids understanding, or where it is essential to allow numerical calculations. Detailed derivations of results have generally been omitted, with reference to the original literature for the interested reader. In a couple of cases mathematical detail has been relegated to appendices.

An important motivation for the book has been to provide the basis for understanding the modulation and coding schemes actually used in modern wireless systems, and as mentioned above, this has largely dictated the level of the book. With such a rapidly developing field, however, it is impossible to keep up, and there have been some significant developments even during the gestation of the book which I have had to leave out. However, I have been able to include such advanced techniques as OFDM and turbo-codes, which are now appearing in 'live' systems and which are not well covered in other texts. Other content, such as the effect of multipath and of non-linear amplifiers, is peculiar to wireless systems and again is not often included in books of this sort. I should emphasize here, however, that 'coding' in this book refers to error control coding, and in particular to forward error correcting coding. Other very important types of code, such as speech/video coding and cryptography, are outside its scope.

The book is accompanied by a Companion Web Site, hosted by Pearson Education at www.booksites.net/burr. This will include a variety of material, which I hope will helpfully supplement the book. In particular it will include worked solutions to the problems, which are included in all but the two final chapters. These problems, by the way, are intended not only as exercises for students when the book is used as a course text, but also to extend the material presented in the book in ways which may be of use to practising engineers. The web site will also contain some of the *Mathematica* scripts that were used in obtaining results presented in the text, in the hope that they may be of use in obtaining new results.

This book would certainly not exist were it not for the MSc course mentioned above, which obliged me to record in more cogent form the notes on which it is based. For this reason I am particularly grateful to the University of York for permission to use that material. Other material has also been adapted from a residential course run by the Institution of Electrical Engineers.

I am also grateful to several generations of students at York, and one class at the Technical University of Vienna, for feedback over the years which has refined and much improved the material. Many colleagues, both at York and elsewhere, have had a formative effect on my understanding, which has also influenced this book. I would like to single out Tim Tozer at York and Professor Paddy Farrell (now at Lancaster), for help and encouragement. A number of research students have helped to develop my understanding, and have contributed specific results, notably James Aldis, Tim Lunn, Dan Verdin, John Sheppard, Paul Thorlby and George White.

I am also grateful for the patience of my editors at Pearson Education during the course of a gestation which turned out to be much longer than I had hoped, and of my family who had also to put up with long hours spent at the computer.

Abbreviations

3-RC	3 (symbol period) raised cosine (continuous phase modulation)
8-AMPM	8-state amplitude and phase modulation
8-PSK	8-state phase-shift keying
16-PSK	16-state phase-shift keying
16-QAM	16-state quadrature amplitude modulation
32-AMPM	32-state amplitude and phase modulation
32-CROSS	32-state cross-shaped (modulation constellation)
64-QAM	64-state quadrature amplitude modulation
256-QAM	256-state quadrature amplitude modulation
a.c.f.	auto correlation function
ACG	asymptotic coding gain
ACI	adjacent channel interference
ACS	add, compare, select (operations)
ADC	analog to digital conversion
ADSL	asymmetric digital subscriber line
AM–AM	amplitude modulation to amplitude modulation
AMP	amplitude modulated pulses
AM–PM	amplitude modulation to phase modulation
AMPM	amplitude and phase modulation
ASIC	application-specific integrated circuit
ASK	amplitude-shift keying
AWGN	additive white Gaussian noise
BCC	body-centred cubic (lattice)
BCH	Bose–Chaudhuri–Hocquenghem
BCJR	Bahl–Cocke–Jelinek–Raviv
BCM	block coded modulation
BER	bit error ratio
BPSK	binary phase-shift keying
BT	time–bandwidth product
BU	bad urban (COST 207 mobile channel model)
C–M	carrier-to-multipath ratio
CCI	co-channel interference
CCITT	Consultative Committee on International Telecommunications
CCSDS	Consultative Committee on Space Data Systems
CD	compact disk

CDMA	code division multiple access
COFDM	coded orthogonal frequency division multiplexing
COST 207	COllaboration in Science and Technology – European research programme responsible for mobile channel models
CP-FSK	continuous phase frequency-shift keying
CPM	continuous phase modulation
CSI	channel-state information
DAB	digital audio broadcast
DBPSK	differential binary phase-shift keying
DECT	digitally enhanced cordless telecommunications
DFE	decision-feedback equalization
DFT	discrete Fourier transform
DPSK	differential phase-shift keying
DQPSK	differential quadrature phase-shift keying
DSL	digital subscriber line
DSP	digital signal processing
DVB	digital video broadcast
DVB-T	digital video broadcasting (terrestrial)
EGC	equal gain combining
ETSI	European Telecommunication Standards Institute
FDMA	frequency division multiple access
FEC	forward error correction
FIR	finite impulse response
FM	frequency modulation
FPGA	field programmable gate array
FSK	frequency-shift keying
FSM	finite state machine
GF	Galois field
GMSK	Gaussian minimum-shift keying
GSM	global system for mobile communications
GWSSUS	Gaussian wide-sense stationary uncorrelated scatterers
HF	high frequency
HPA	high power amplifier
HT	hilly terrain (COST 207 mobile channel model)
i.c.i.	inter-channel interference
i.s.i.	inter-symbol interference
IDFT	inverse discrete Fourier transform
IF	intermediate frequency
IIR	infinite impulse response
IMT-2000	international mobile telecommunications 2000
I/Q	in-phase and quadrature (modulator/demodulator)
IS-54	Interim Standard 54 (American second generation mobile standard)

IS-136	Interim Standard 136 (American second generation mobile standard)
ITU-T	International Telecommunications Union – Telecommunications
JPL	Jet Propulsion Laboratory
LCM	least common multiple
LLC	logical link control
LLR	log likelihood ratio
LNA	low noise amplifier
LO	local oscillator
LSB	least significant bit
MAC	medium access control
MAP	maximum a posteriori
M-FSK	M-ary frequency-shift keying
ML	maximum likelihood
ML-TCM	multilevel turbo-coded modulation
MLCM	multilevel coded modulation
MLSD	maximum likelihood sequence detection
MLSE	maximum likelihood sequence estimation
MMSE	minimum mean-square error
MPEG	Motion Picture Experts Group (coded video standard)
M-PSK	M-ary phase-shift keying
MRC	maximum ratio combining
MSB	most significant bit
MSK	minimum-shift keying
NASA	North American Space Administration
OFDM	orthogonal frequency division multiplexing
OQPSK	offset quadrature phase-shift keying
OSI	open systems interconnect
p.d.f.	probability density function
p.s.d.	power spectral density
$\pi/4$ QPSK	pi-by-4 quadrature phase-shift keying
PACS-UB	Personal Access Communication System – Unlicensed Band (American second generation mobile/cordless standard)
PC-RSC	parallel concatenated recursive-systematic convolutional codes
PCTCM	version of trellis turbo-coded modulation
PD	phase detector
PLL	phase-locked loop
PMR	private mobile radio
QAM	quadrature amplitude modulation
QPSK	quadrature phase-shift keying

r.m.s.	root mean square
RA	rural area (COST 207 mobile channel model)
RAKE	spread spectrum receiver (not an acronym)
RF	radio frequency
RM	Reed–Muller
RPE-LPC	regular pulse excited linear predictive coding
RS	Reed–Solomon
RSC	recursive-systematic convolutional
RSSE	reduced-state sequence estimation
RS-TCM	recursive-systematic turbo-coded modulation
RX	receiver
S-random	spread random
SC	switched (or selection) combining
SEP	symbol error probability
SFH	slow frequency hopping
SFN	single frequency network
SISO	soft in, soft out
SNR	signal-to-noise ratio
SOVA	soft output Viterbi algorithm
SPC	single parity check
STAR-QAM	star quadrature amplitude modulation
TCM	trellis coded modulation
TDMA	time division multiple access
TETRA	terrestrial trunked radio
TFM	tamed frequency modulation
TOI	third-order intercept
T-TCM	turbo trellis coded modulation
TU	typical urban (COST 207 mobile channel model)
TWT	travelling wave tube
TX	transmitter
UHF	ultra high frequency (i.e. 300 MHz–3 GHz)
UMTS	universal mobile telecommunications system
V.32, V.32(bis), V.34	ITU-T voiceband modem standards
VCC	voltage-controlled clock
VCO	voltage-controlled oscillator
WER	word error ratio
WLAN	wireless local area networks
XOR	exclusive-OR (logic function)
ZF	zero-forcing

Chapter 1

Introduction to modulation and coding

Wireless communications has become one of the most rapidly growing industries in the world, and its products are now exerting an impact in all our lives. This is most obvious in the form of the mobile phone; but many other advances, such as digital broadcasting and the 'wireless Internet', will very soon be making their influence felt. In the developing world, wireless communications is also bringing telecommunications to millions (and potentially to billions) who have never yet made a telephone call. This book concerns one of the most fundamental aspects of wireless, or radio communications: the modulation and coding schemes that enable information to be transmitted over the radio channel.

Our purpose in this first chapter is to set the scene for the remainder of the book. We begin in Section 1.1 by placing modulation and coding in the context of a complete radio communication system, outlining its rôle in the transmitter and receiver, and its position in the open systems interconnect (OSI) model, which is often used to describe telecommunication systems. We also show that coding and modulation, although traditionally regarded as separate functions, should actually be treated jointly. We then, in Section 1.2, consider the parameters by which the performance of a modulation and coding scheme can be assessed, and how they impact on the performance of the communication system as a whole. This gives us the tools that will be used to assess the performance of schemes in the following chapters. The most important of these parameters are bandwidth and power requirements, upon which we focus in Section 1.3. This leads to a description in Section 1.4 of the system-level advantages which can result from improvements in modulation and coding schemes, using the advanced techniques to be described in this book. Finally, we give an outline of the remainder of the book.

1.1 Role of modulation and coding

Modulation and coding play a fundamental rôle in any communication system, and perhaps especially in a radio system. We begin this book by considering where modulation and coding fit in a general communication system, of which a very abstract outline is shown in Fig. 1.1.

The most fundamental part of any communication system must be the *channel*, which is the physical medium by which information-bearing signals are transferred from the *source* of the information (any entity having informa- tion to transmit), to the *sink*, i.e. the end-user of the information. In a radio system this channel is of course the propagation of radio waves in free space. However, in nearly all cases some equipment is required to translate the information-bearing signal into a suitable form for transmission over the channel, and then back into a form that is comprehensible to the end-user. This equipment is the transmitter and the receiver, and the task of the commu- nication system engineer is to design suitable apparatus. The receiver does not simply perform the inverse translation to the transmitter: it also has the task of overcoming the distortions and disturbances that occur on the channel, and thus it is usually more difficult to design than the transmitter.

We now consider in more detail what sub-systems are required in the trans- mitter and receiver, specifically for a radio system. We describe the structure of the transmitter here (Fig. 1.2), since the receiver mirrors the transmitter (despite its more difficult job).

A radio transmitter most fundamentally requires an *antenna* (or aerial), which converts the electrical signal into a radio wave propagating in free space. Note that any conductor will in fact function to some degree as an antenna, but for efficient operation it should be carefully designed. To generate

Figure 1.1   Outline of a communication system

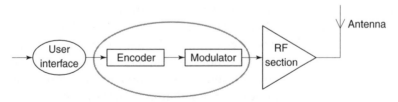

Figure 1.2   Structure of the transmitter for a radio system

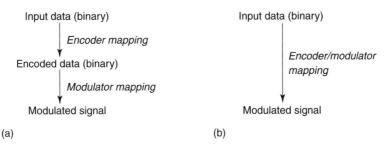

Figure 1.3   Encoder/modulator function: (a) separate, and (b) integrated

a signal of sufficient power at the required frequency is the task of the *RF section* of the transmitter, which typically contains a *high power amplifier* (HPA), a *local oscillator* (LO), and an *up-converter*. However, typically the RF (Radio Frequency) section only amplifies and frequency-converts the signal.

At the input of the transmitter the *user interface* interacts with the user (the information source) and in a digital system, in particular, converts the information into a suitable digital data stream. It is then the function of the encoder and the modulator to bridge the gap between the digital data and the electrical signal required at the input to the RF section.

This signal must occupy a defined narrow band of frequencies around the system carrier frequency. It is therefore obtained by taking a sine wave at the required frequency and using the data to modify its characteristics in some way, which is the process known as *modulation*. The encoder (more specifically the *channel encoder*) acts on the data stream converting it into a form that is more resistant to the degradations introduced by the channel. For some time now, however, it has been realized that modulation and coding should properly (and more effectively) be considered as a single integrated entity, as shown in Fig. 1.3. For more detail on this see Chapter 8.

We may regard the encoder/modulator, then, as a single sub-system that maps data presented to it by the user interface onto a modulated RF carrier for subsequent processing, amplification and transmission by the RF section. The demodulator/decoder conversely takes the received RF signal and performs the inverse mapping back to a data stream for onward transmission. This view underlines the importance of the process: it is the encoding and modulation that determines, for example, the bandwidth occupied by the transmitted signal, and it is the demodulator/decoder that determines the quality of the resulting data service, in terms of bit error ratio (BER), availability and delay. It also determines the robustness of the system to channel impairments, due both to the RF sub-systems (such as phase noise and non-linearity) and the RF channel (such as multipath dispersion and fading). Thus the correct choice for the modulation/coding scheme is vital for the efficient operation of the whole system.

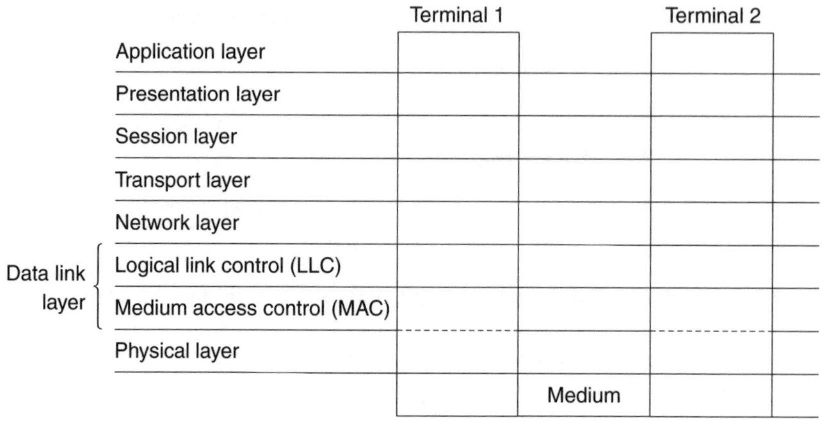

	Terminal 1		Terminal 2	
Application layer				
Presentation layer				
Session layer				
Transport layer				
Network layer				
Logical link control (LLC)				
Medium access control (MAC)				
Physical layer				
		Medium		

Data link layer: Logical link control (LLC), Medium access control (MAC)

Figure 1.4   The OSI seven-layer model

Another useful framework for the consideration of digital communication systems, this time from a much more software-oriented viewpoint, is the OSI seven-layer protocol model [1.1], illustrated in Fig. 1.4. The principle here is that each layer can communicate with the corresponding layer in another terminal via the lower layers of the protocol stack, which appear transparent to it. Lower layers pass on information from higher layers unchanged, adding their own control information, which is then stripped out in the same layer of the receiving terminal, as the data are passed back up the stack. We are interested here in only the lowest levels of the stack, whose functions are given in Table 1.1. This shows that modulation and coding is the primary task of the physical layer, which adapts the information transmitted to it from the higher layers into a form that can be transmitted over the physical medium. Note, however, that some functions which are best integrated with modulation and coding, such as error control and multiple access, appear higher up the stack, which suggests that the model should not in fact be adhered to too strictly in implementing radio systems.

Layer	Function
Network layer	Routing
Data link layer	
Logical link control	Error control
Medium access control	Multiple access protocols
Physical layer	Modulation, FEC, equalization, synchronization, etc.
Medium	Radio propagation mechanisms

Table 1.1   Functions of the lower layers of the OSI model

1.2 Performance parameters

We next consider the parameters of a modulation/coding scheme by which its effectiveness may be judged. These can then be used to provide a set of specifications for the scheme and the sub-systems that implement it.

Perhaps the most important parameter is the bandwidth requirement of the scheme, since a deficiency in this respect cannot be overcome anywhere else in the system. Usually, a radio system will be strictly limited by the regulatory authorities to a certain frequency band. Often, too, this band will be shared among users of the system by means of *frequency division multiple access* (FDMA), and hence the narrower the bandwidth occupied by each user, the more users can be accommodated.

Bandwidth requirement is determined by the *spectrum* of the modulated signal, usually presented as a plot of power spectral density (p.s.d.) against frequency (Fig. 1.5). Ideally, of course, the p.s.d. should be zero outside the band occupied. In practice, however, this can never be so, and the spectrum extends to infinity beyond the band. This is either because of the inherent characteristics of the modulation scheme (see below), or because of the practical implementation of filters (which must have a finite roll-off rate). Hence, we must define the bandwidth W such that the signal power falling outside the band is below a specified threshold (as shown). In practice, this threshold is determined by the tolerance of the system (and any others sharing the band) to adjacent channel interference (ACI), which is itself a feature of the modulation/coding scheme.

The bandwidth requirement determines the *bandwidth efficiency* (also known interchangeably as *spectrum efficiency* or *spectral efficiency*) of a modulation/coding scheme. This is defined as the channel data rate r_b per unit bandwidth occupied, and is measured in bits s^{-1} Hz^{-1}:

$$\eta = \frac{r_b}{W} \tag{1.1}$$

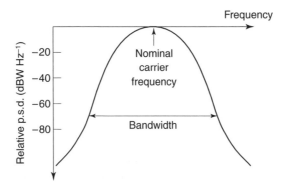

Figure 1.5 Spectrum of modulated signal

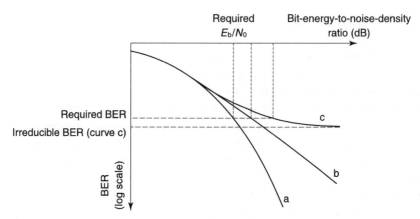

Figure 1.6   Curves of BER (log scale) against bit-energy-to-noise-density ratio: (a) white

The other main parameter of a modulation/coding scheme is its *bit error ratio* (BER) performance.

> The BER is defined as the ratio of erroneous bits received to the total number of bits received.

BER is also known more loosely as the 'error rate', and is equal to the probability of bit error, P_b. BER is frequently plotted as a logarithmic plot against signal-to-noise ratio (SNR, in dB), leading to the well-known 'waterfall curve' (Fig. 1.6). In fact the ordinate of the graph is normally the *bit-energy-to-noise-density ratio* E_b/N_0, since this results in a more system-independent measure. The noise power spectral density N_0 is usually a fundamental feature of a channel, due, for example, to the thermal noise that is inevitably generated in any receiver (unless it is kept at absolute zero temperature), and unlike the noise power it is independent of the bandwidth of the system. Since N_0 has dimensions of $W\,Hz^{-1}$, which is the same as J, E_b/N_0 is dimensionless.

The shape of these curves depends on the channel and on the modulation scheme. Curve (a) is the typical curve for the ideal white Gaussian noise (AWGN) channel. Curve (b) is the shape that often occurs on fading channels, see p. 775 of [1.2], while curve (c) shows an 'error rate floor', where the BER tends to a finite limit however much the bit-energy-to-noise-density ratio is increased. This can occur, for example, on channels subject to dispersion or due to synchronization errors. The level of the 'floor' is called the *irreducible BER*. We will encounter BER curves like these later in the book, for example in Chapters 4 and 9.

Again we would ideally like the BER of the service offered to the user to be zero, but this is not possible in practice. Hence, we must specify a required BER. This will in general be different for different services. For example, digital speech services can usually tolerate a BER of 10^{-3} or higher, while for data transfer the standard may be 10^{-9} (to be equivalent to fixed services), or 10^{-6} in some systems [1.3]. Then, for the given required BER, the curve can be used to obtain the required bit-energy-to-noise-density ratio, which informs the link budget calculation.

Note that the 'noise' here may not only be thermal noise. In a cellular system, co-channel interference (CCI) from users in other cells is in fact much more important. It can, however, in many cases be adequately modelled as white Gaussian noise. In this case, the required bit-energy-to-noise-density ratio determines the sensitivity of the system to CCI, and hence the necessary re-use distance, and thus the cluster size.

There is an inherent trade-off between the bandwidth efficiency and the bit-energy-to-noise-density requirement of a modulation/coding scheme. The greater the bandwidth efficiency, the greater the required E_b/N_0 is likely to be. Hence, it is usually possible to increase the capacity of a system for a given bandwidth allocation by increasing the signal power. A fundamental bound on the capacity was given by Shannon [1.4–1.6]:

$$\frac{E_b}{N_0} \geq \frac{2^\eta - 1}{\eta} \tag{1.2}$$

This is plotted in Fig. 1.7, showing the minimum bit-energy-to-noise-density ratio required on an AWGN channel for a given bandwidth efficiency, although in practice it is very difficult to approach this bound. Most radio systems operate up to about 2 bits s^{-1} Hz^{-1}, and may be up to 10 dB from the bound. Note that the intercept with the horizontal axis is at -1.6 dB, which sets an absolute limit on the E_b/N_0 requirement for any system. This bound and its implications will be considered in more detail in Chapter 8.

There are a number of other characteristics of a modulation/coding scheme that are also of particular importance in radio systems [1.7].

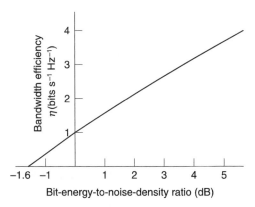

Figure 1.7   **Shannon bound on required bit-energy-to-noise-density ratio versus bandwidth efficiency**

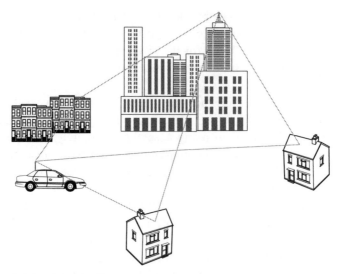

Figure 1.8   Origin of multipath

(1) The high power amplifiers (HPAs) used in many systems, for example in mobile radio handsets, are usually highly non-linear, because of the requirement for power efficiency. These amplifiers give rise to amplitude modulation–amplitude modulation (AM–AM) and amplitude modulation–phase modulation (AM–PM) conversion, which may result in an irreducible BER floor. The optimum solution is to use a constant envelope modulation scheme, which does not give rise to these effects. This means that phase-only modulation should be used. However, some schemes are used that are not truly constant envelope, but which have been designed to minimize envelope variations. Note that the requirement for true constant envelope modulation inherently gives rise to a spectrum of un-limited bandwidth. This will be considered in more detail in Chapter 3.

(2) Many radio channels are subject to *multipath* effects, due to interference between signals following different propagation paths, as illustrated in Fig. 1.8. These cause *fading* and *dispersion*, which may degrade perfor-mance very significantly. The former causes increased error rates, and may create difficulties in synchronization (see Chapter 4), while the latter is likely to require *equalization* in the receiver. This is dealt with in some detail in Chapter 9.

1.3   Power- and bandwidth-efficient schemes

The Shannon bound illustrated in Fig. 1.7 shows that it is possible to trade-off bandwidth efficiency η for power efficiency (required E_b/N_0). This tends to lead to two types of coding/modulation schemes, optimized either for power or for bandwidth efficiency. Which is preferred depends on whether the communication system in question is *power-limited* or *bandwidth-limited*. We will illustrate this distinction by means of an example.

Example 1.1

A fixed microwave link uses binary phase-shift keying (BPSK) modulation. The basic BPSK signal is filtered using a sixth-order Butterworth filter to reduce the signal bandwidth. The system parameters are:

Transmit power, mW	100
Link path loss, dB	100
Receiver noise figure, dB	2
Absolute temperature, K	290
Required BER	10^{-6}
Out-of-band signal threshold, dB	-40
Allocated bandwidth, MHz	300

Figure 1.9 shows the signal spectrum (against frequency offset from carrier, normalized to data rate), and Fig. 1.10 the BER performance. Find the maximum data rate.

Solution   Power budget, $S/N_0 = S_T \times [(1/L)/(kT \times F)]$:

Transmit power (S_T), dBW	-10
Path (loss) $(1/L)$, dB	-100
Received signal power (S), dBW	$\overline{-110}$
Thermal noise (kT), dBW Hz^{-1}	$-(-204)$
Noise figure (F), dB	-2
Received signal-to-noise-density ratio, dB Hz	$\overline{92}$

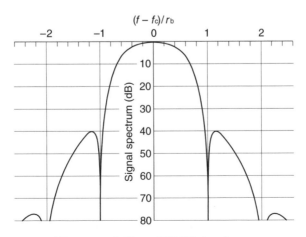

Figure 1.9   Spectrum of Butterworth-filtered BPSK signal

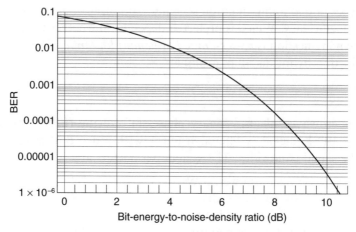

Figure 1.10   BER versus bit-energy-to-noise-density ratio performance for BPSK system

The out-of-band signal requirement gives signal bandwidth $W \geq 2r_b$. The BER requirement gives $E_b/N_0 = 10.6\,\text{dB}$.

$$\frac{S}{N_0} = r_b \frac{E_b}{N_0} \quad \therefore \ r_b(\text{max}) = \frac{S/N_0}{E_b/N_0}$$

$$= 92 - 10.6 = 81.4\,\text{dB}\,(\text{bit s}^{-1}) \text{ or } \sim 140\,\text{Mbit s}^{-1} \qquad (1.3)$$

Bandwidth is $2 \times 140 = 280\,\text{MHz}$

This is within the bandwidth allocation of the system, and hence it is power limited. Any increase in transmitter power (or other improvement of the power budget) would increase the data capacity. Conversely, a small change in the bandwidth allocation would not change the capacity.

Example 1.2

The system of Example 1.1 is now required to operate in a bandwidth allocation of 200 MHz. Find the maximum data rate.

Solution   The power-limited maximum data rate is as above. The bandwidth limitation on data rate is now $(200\,\text{MHz})/2 = 100\,\text{Mbit s}^{-1}$.

The system is now bandwidth limited: a change in transmit power will not change the capacity, but it is now sensitive to the bandwidth allocation.

In Example 1.1 capacity could be increased by a scheme which required a lower bit-energy-to-noise-density ratio for a given BER: a more bandwidth-efficient modulation/coding scheme. This could be implemented by the addition of FEC coding (see Chapter 5). In Example 1.2, a capacity increase could be obtained by means of a more bandwidth-efficient modulation scheme (Chapter 2), even if the required E_b/N_0 was somewhat higher. In this case, the use of quadrature phase-shift keying (QPSK) would double the bandwidth efficiency without increasing the required E_b/N_0, and would thus allow a capacity of 140 Mbit s^{-1} once again. Even higher capacities might be possible by means of bandwidth-efficient coded modulation (Chapter 8).

1.4 Advantages of advanced modulation and coding

A comparison of this example with the Shannon bound, re-drawn in Fig. 1.11, shows the potential advantages of the application of coding and/or more advanced modulation schemes, such as are described in this book, in radio systems. The spectral efficiency of the filtered BPSK signal is 0.5 bits s^{-1} Hz^{-1}, and the required bit-energy-to-noise-density ratio is 10.6 dB. The Shannon bound on η for $E_b/N_0 = 10.6$ dB is 6.2 bits s^{-1} Hz^{-1}. A more bandwidth-efficient scheme could therefore transmit the same information in a much reduced bandwidth. Conversely, the bound on E_b/N_0 to maintain $\eta = 0.5$ is −0.9 dB, and therefore a much more power-efficient scheme is possible, which might, for example, require much less transmitter power.

The curve labelled '$W = 300$ MHz' in Fig. 1.11 allows the maximum system capacity to be calculated by means of a graphical solution of Equation (1.3) (putting $\eta = r_b(\max)/W$) together with the Shannon bound. This gives a bandwidth efficiency of 2.7 bits s^{-1} Hz^{-1} at $E_b/N_0 = 3.0$ dB, which would in principle allow a data rate of 810 Mbit s^{-1}. Both a power- and bandwidth-efficient scheme would be required to achieve this maximum. Current coding and modulation techniques cannot of course approach this very closely, but highly significant improvements are possible with quite simple schemes, as we shall see in later chapters.

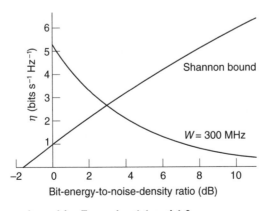

Figure 1.11   Shannon bound for Examples 1.1 and 1.2

This example has shown some of the system benefits that may be obtained in radio communications by the use of more advanced forms of modulation and coding: others are listed below:

- Capacity increase (higher data rates, or more users)
- Improved bandwidth efficiency (smaller spectrum pricing costs in mobile radio)
- Reduced power requirements:
  - reduced transmitter power
  - reduced antenna gain required (e.g. smaller dish size in satellite systems)
  - increased path loss tolerated (range increase)
- Improved tolerance to co-channel interference:
  - reduced re-use distance in cellular systems ⇒ increased overall capacity
  - essential in CDMA systems to overcome intra-cell interference
- Improved tolerance to multipath effects

Many of these benefits we will explore later in the book.

1.5 Book outline

The structure of the book is illustrated in Fig. 1.12. Broadly speaking the book divides into two streams, one on advanced modulation techniques (Chapters 2,

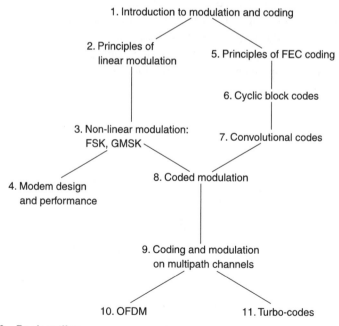

Figure 1.12 Book outline

3 and 4), and one on FEC (Forward Error Correction) coding (5, 6 and 7), which then merge for discussion of coded modulation techniques. In this way the book mirrors the synergy between coding and modulation pointed out above.

Under modulation we consider the two main forms of digital modulation: linear and non-linear, which terms will be explained in the next chapter. We also consider some more practical aspects of the implementation of modems for digital modulation (Chapter 4), and especially the problem of carrier and clock recovery.

Under coding we first introduce the general principles of FEC coding, including bounds on performance, then describe the two main forms of coding: block codes, and in particular cyclic block codes, and convolutional codes. Decoding methods are also described for each. Drawing out the common principles of modulation and coding, we are then in a position to consider coded modulation, and to show how performance improvement can be obtained by integrating coding and modulation. The main practical forms of coded modulation schemes are described.

In a book on modulation and coding for radio it is essential that we consider in detail the effects of multipath, since this is probably the most serious and ubiquitous problem for radio systems. This is covered in Chapter 9, where we describe analytical and simulation models for the multipath channel, and show how performance is affected. Coding and modulation design for the multipath channel are described, as well as its integration with other multipath countermeasures, such as interleaving, diversity and equalization.

Finally, we will describe some of the more recent modulation and coding techniques that are now being introduced in radio systems, such as digital television broadcasting (or digital video broadcasting, DVB), broadband wireless access and the third-generation mobile systems UMTS and IMT-2000. Specifically we consider *orthogonal frequency division multiplexing* (OFDM), which is now being used for DVB and its audio counterpart DAB, and *turbo-codes*, which are likely to be incorporated into the third-generation mobile.

Problems

1.1 A mobile radio system uses a modulation scheme with power spectral density as shown in Fig. 1.13, in which the horizontal axis shows the offset from the carrier frequency divided by the data rate. In any adjacent band the p.s.d. must be more than 20-dB less than the maximum p.s.d. of the wanted signal. However, because of the *near–far effect* (in which the transmitter in an adjacent band may be much closer to the receiver than the wanted signal) the adjacent band signal may be 30-dB greater. If the

Frequency offset from carrier / data rate

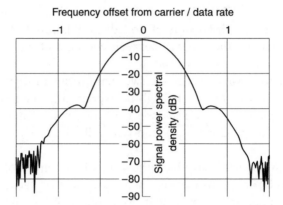

Figure 1.13   Power spectrum of mobile radio modulation scheme for Problem 1.1

data rate is to be $8\,\text{kbit}\,\text{s}^{-1}$, find the minimum spacing between carriers, and the bandwidth efficiency of the system.

1.2 The same system has a maximum transmit power from the mobile handset of 100 mW. The received signal at the base station is subject to thermal noise of p.s.d. $-201\,\text{dBW}\,\text{Hz}^{-1}$. The modulation scheme requires a bit-energy-to-noise-density ratio of 8 dB to maintain the required service BER. If the received signal power at 10 km range is $2 \times 10^{-16}\,\text{W}$, find the maximum data rate possible, assuming the system is power limited.

1.3 Using the Shannon bound, find the maximum data rate possible using a more power-efficient modulation/coding scheme but maintaining the same channel spacing. Would further improvements be possible using a scheme which is also more bandwidth efficient?

References

1.1 Tanenbaum, A. (1981) *Computer Networks*, Prentice-Hall.
1.2 Proakis, J.G. (1995) *Digital Communications*, 3rd Edition, McGraw-Hill.
1.3 Rapeli, J. (1995) UMTS: targets, system concept and standardisation in a global framework. *IEEE Personal Communications Magazine*, **2**(1): 20–8.
1.4 Shannon, C.E. (1948) A mathematical theory of communication. Part 1. *Bell System Technical Journal*, **27**: 379.
1.5 Shannon, C.E. (1948) A mathematical theory of communication. Part 2. *Bell System Technical Journal*, **27**: 623.
1.6 Shannon, C.E. (1949) Communication in the presence of noise. *Proceedings, IRE*, **37**: 10–21.
1.7 Clark, A.P. and Brent, J.B. (1987) Narrow-band digital modems for land-mobile radio. *Journal of the IERE*, **57**(6) (supplement): S293–303.

Chapter 2

Principles of linear modulation

This chapter first introduces the main principles of modulation in general, then those of linear modulation in particular, including the distinction between linear and non-linear modulation schemes. Some important analytical and pictorial tools are described to aid in the understanding of these schemes and in assessing their performance. These include the complex baseband representation of modulated signals, the constellation diagram, and the pulse-superposition model of a communication signal. These may be used to determine the spectrum and the BER performance of the modulation schemes. Some important fundamental concepts are reviewed, including Nyquist filtering and the matched filter. More detail on much of this material is given, for example, in [2.1].

We then describe the most important linear modulation schemes, beginning with the basic schemes, binary phase-shift keying (BPSK) and quadrature phase-shift keying (QPSK), and proceed to *multilevel* modulation schemes, used in bandwidth-efficient systems, including multiphase PSK (M-PSK) and quadrature amplitude modulation (QAM). In each case we determine the spectrum of the signal, and hence its bandwidth efficiency, and the BER performance, providing a measure of power efficiency.

2.1 Modulation principles and analytical tools

The objective of modulation in radio systems, as described in the previous chapter, is to translate the information-bearing signal into a form in which it can be transmitted over the radio channel. Fundamentally, this means frequency-conversion to a suitable transmission frequency.

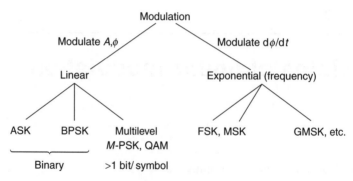

Figure 2.1   Classification of modulation schemes

This is performed by taking a signal that already lies at the required frequency, i.e. a sine wave at the carrier frequency, and modifying it in some way according to the information to be conveyed. A general sine wave can be written as a function of time, t:

$$a(t) = A\cos(\omega_c t + \phi) \tag{2.1}$$

where A is the *amplitude*, $\omega_c = 2\pi f_c$ is the carrier frequency, and ϕ is the instantaneous phase.

We may vary the two parameters A and/or ϕ in order to convey the information, and this is the basis of all modulation schemes. The type of scheme depends on which parameter(s) are varied, and in exactly what way. Note that the instantaneous frequency of the signal:

$$\omega_{inst} = \frac{d(\omega_c t + \phi)}{dt} = \omega_c + \frac{d\phi}{dt} \tag{2.2}$$

that is, the instantaneous frequency deviation from the carrier frequency is equal to the derivative of the phase. Thus, frequency modulation can be viewed simply as a variant of phase modulation. Figure 2.1 illustrates the classification of modulation schemes according to the means by which the parameters are varied. This chapter will deal with linear modulation schemes; the next with non-linear, or *exponential*, schemes. The basis of this distinction between linear and non-linear schemes, and the meaning of the terms, will be clarified in Section 2.2.

2.1.1   The complex baseband representation

In this section we show how any modulated signal (or indeed any band-limited signal) may be represented as the product of a sinusoidal complex exponential function (representing the carrier) with a *complex baseband signal*. This baseband signal then includes all the important information about the modulated signal apart from the carrier frequency, and thus provides a compact

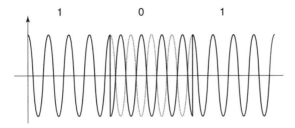

Figure 2.2 BPSK modulated signal

representation of the modulated signal. It is especially useful for simulation of radio communication systems.

Consider first one of the simplest possible modulation schemes: BPSK (Fig. 2.2). In BPSK we modulate the phase of the carrier according to the data to be transmitted:

$$\begin{aligned} '0', \quad \phi = \pi \\ '1', \quad \phi = 0 \end{aligned} \tag{2.3}$$

This is illustrated in Fig. 1.2, in which the nominal carrier waveform is shown in grey.

This can equally well be modelled as the product of the carrier signal and a polar binary *equivalent baseband signal*, $b(t)$ (Fig. 2.3). This of course mirrors the way in which BPSK is normally generated (Fig. 2.4).

The equivalent baseband signal then gives most of the important information about the modulated signal. As we shall see, its spectrum can be used directly to derive the modulated signal spectrum, and we shall also show how the BER

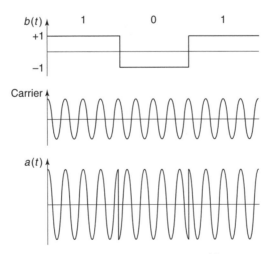

Figure 2.3 Generation of BPSK modulated signals, $a(t)$, by equivalent baseband signal, $b(t)$

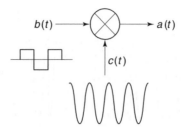

Figure 2.4   Generation of BPSK

may be determined. However, the BPSK model as it stands is not capable of generating phase shifts other than 0 and π, and therefore may not be used for general modulated signals. This requires a generalization of the model.

Such a model is illustrated in Fig. 2.5. We add to the modulator of Fig. 2.4 a *quadrature branch*, in which a quadrature version of the carrier (at a phase angle $\pi/2$ from the in-phase carrier) is modulated by an independent baseband signal. The output of the two branches is then added together. In this way a resultant signal with any given phase and amplitude may be generated. The whole structure is known as an *I/Q modulator*.

Thus, the single equivalent baseband signal of the BPSK model is replaced by a pair of signals, $b_{\mathrm{p}}(t)$ and $b_{\mathrm{q}}(t)$ (the in-**p**hase and **q**uadrature baseband signals).

$$a(t) = b_{\mathrm{p}}(t)\cos(\omega_{\mathrm{c}}t) + b_{\mathrm{q}}(t)\cos\left(\omega_{\mathrm{c}}t + \frac{\pi}{2}\right)$$

$$= b_{\mathrm{p}}(t)\cos(\omega_{\mathrm{c}}t) - b_{\mathrm{q}}(t)\sin(\omega_{\mathrm{c}}t) \tag{2.4}$$

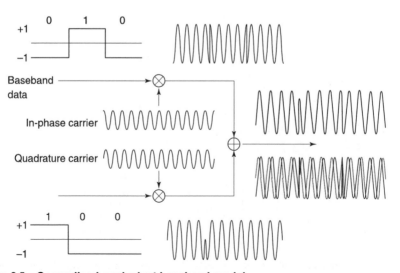

Figure 2.5   Generalized equivalent baseband model

These may conveniently be combined into one complex signal:

$$b(t) = b_p(t) + jb_q(t) \qquad (2.5)$$

Then the modulated signal, $a(t)$, can be written as:

$$
\begin{aligned}
a(t) &= \text{Re}[b(t)\exp(j\omega_c t)] = \text{Re}\{b(t)[\cos(\omega_c t) + j\sin(\omega_c t)]\} \\
&= \text{Re}\{b_p(t)\cos\omega_c t - b_q(t)\sin\omega_c t + j[b_p(t)\sin\omega_c t - b_q(t)\cos\omega_c t]\} \\
&= b_p(t)\cos\omega_c t - b_q(t)\sin\omega_c t \qquad (2.6)
\end{aligned}
$$

We may also show mathematically how a general modulated signal may be represented in these terms:

$$
\begin{aligned}
a(t) &= A(t)\cos[\omega_c t + \phi(t)] \\
&= \underbrace{A(t)\cos\phi(t)}_{b_p(t)}\cos\omega_c t - \underbrace{A(t)\sin\phi(t)}_{b_q(t)}\sin\omega_c t \\
&= \text{Re}[b(t)\exp(j\omega_c t)] \qquad (2.7)
\end{aligned}
$$

2.1.2 The constellation diagram

It is convenient to draw a plot of $b_q(t)$ against $b_p(t)$ for a modulated signal. This is equivalent to an Argand diagram (a plot of imaginary *versus* real part) of the complex baseband signal $b(t)$. The diagram will consist of points, which indicate the possible states of amplitude and phase of the signal, and is known as the *constellation* of the modulated signal. The constellation of the modulated signal of Fig. 2.5 (which in fact is QPSK) is shown together with that of BPSK in Fig. 2.6, indicating the four possible phase states (with transitions between them shown in grey).

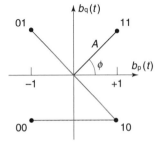

Figure 2.6 Constellation diagrams for BPSK and QPSK

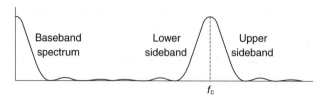

Figure 2.7   Spectrum of BPSK

Since this is effectively a polar diagram, the amplitude of the modulated signal A is given by the distance from the origin, and the phase ϕ is the angle between the line to the origin and the positive in-phase (real) axis. Thus, we note that the QPSK signal has four possible states, all with the same amplitude (here $\sqrt{2}$) and with phases $\pi/4$, $3\pi/4$, $5\pi/4$ and $7\pi/4$.

2.1.3   Spectrum of modulated signal

We now show how the spectrum of the modulated signal relates to that of the complex baseband signal. Consider first the spectrum of BPSK. It is well-known [2.2, p. 223] that the spectrum of a modulated signal consists of a frequency-shifted version of the baseband signal spectrum shifted up to lie above the carrier frequency (the *upper sideband*), plus its mirror image shifted up to lie just below the carrier frequency (the *lower sideband*). In this case the baseband signal is a polar rectangular data waveform, which has a $\sin(x)/x$ spectrum [2.1, p. 54]. Hence the modulated signal has a double-sided $\sin(x)/x$ spectrum (see Fig. 2.7). Now, since mathematically the spectrum of the baseband signal (as obtained using the Fourier transform) is double-sided, with a symmetrical extension in negative frequency (as any real signal must [2.1, p. 50]), the modulated signal spectrum consists simply of the baseband spectrum shifted upwards by the carrier frequency, ω_c.

In fact, the modulated signal itself has a symmetrical extension in negative frequency, and hence for a general real modulating signal the resulting spectrum is as shown in Fig. 2.8. The extension in negative frequency is, for practical purposes, a 'mathematical fiction', which is indistinguishable from the positive frequency part.

The complex baseband signal, however, is not a real signal, and is therefore not constrained to have a symmetrical spectrum: its extension in negative frequency

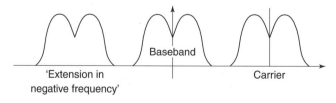

Figure 2.8   Double-sided spectrum of signal modulated by real baseband signal

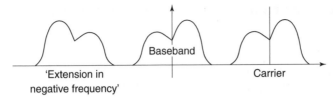

Figure 2.9 Double-sided spectrum of signal modulated by complex baseband signal

may not be a mirror image, as shown in Fig. 2.9. This means that the upper and lower sidebands may also no longer be mirror images of one another.

Mathematically, we may write the modulated signal:

$$a(t) = \text{Re}[b(t)\exp j\omega_c t] = \frac{1}{2}\left[b(t)\exp(j\omega_c t) + \overbrace{b^*(t)\exp(-j\omega_c t)}^{\text{complex conjugate}} \right] \quad (2.8)$$

To find its spectrum we take the Fourier transform [2.1, p. 48]:

$$A(\omega) = \frac{1}{2}\int_{-\infty}^{\infty} [b(t)\exp(j\omega_c t) + b^*(t)\exp(-j\omega_c t)]\exp(-j\omega t)\,dt$$

$$= \frac{1}{2}\left\{ \int_{-\infty}^{\infty} b(t)\exp[-j(\omega - \omega_c)t]\,dt + \int_{-\infty}^{\infty} b(t)\exp[-j(-\omega - \omega_c)t]\,dt \right\}$$

$$= \tfrac{1}{2}[B(\omega - \omega_c) + B^*(-\omega - \omega_c)] \quad (2.9)$$

in which $B(\omega - \omega_c)$ and $B^*(-\omega - \omega_c)$ are, respectively, the positive frequency spectrum and its extension in negative frequency, as shown in Fig. 2.9. It is clear that $B(\omega - \omega_c)$ is simply the spectrum of the complex baseband signal shifted up by the carrier frequency, ω_c, in the same way as for the BPSK signal discussed above. Hence once again, the complex baseband signal contains all the important information about the modulated signal: to generate the spectrum of the modulated signal we have only to shift the baseband spectrum up to the carrier frequency.

Equation (2.9) also relates the modulated signal power to the power of the complex baseband signal (as is usual, in calculating power we assume unit impedance, so that power is simply amplitude squared):

$$S = \int_{-\infty}^{\infty} |A(\omega)|^2 d\omega = \int_{-\infty}^{\infty} |\tfrac{1}{2}[B(\omega - \omega_c) + B^*(-\omega - \omega_c)]|^2\,d\omega$$

$$= \frac{1}{4}\int_{-\infty}^{\infty} [\,|B(\omega - \omega_c)|^2 + |B^*(-\omega - \omega_c)|^2 + 2|B(\omega - \omega_c)B^*(-\omega - \omega_c)|\,]\,d\omega$$

$$= \frac{1}{2}\int_{-\infty}^{\infty} |B(\omega - \omega_c)|^2 d\omega = \frac{1}{2}\int_{-\infty}^{\infty} |B(\omega)|^2\,d\omega$$

$$= \frac{1}{2}\int_{-\infty}^{\infty} |B(f)|^2\,df = \tfrac{1}{2}(\overline{b_p^2} + \overline{b_q^2}) \quad (2.10)$$

which also follows from Equation (2.6), noting that $\overline{\cos^2(\omega_c t)} = \overline{\sin^2(\omega_c t)} = 1/2$.

2.1.4 Complex baseband representation of noise

It is useful to apply the same representation to band-limited signals other than modulated signals, of which the most important is undoubtedly noise. In a practical radio communication system, noise is picked up by the antenna, or generated within the front end amplifiers of the receiver. The most common model is the additive white Gaussian noise (AWGN) model, which treats noise as having a flat spectrum (white) with power spectral density N_0 (W Hz^{-1}), and a Gaussian probability density function (p.d.f.) $p(n)$, given in (2.11). (In practice, this is a good model for internal noise generated in the receiver, although some forms of external noise may have an impulsive p.d.f., or may not be white.)

$$p(n) = \frac{1}{\sigma\sqrt{2\pi}} \exp\left(-\frac{n^2}{2\sigma^2}\right) \tag{2.11}$$

where σ is the standard deviation of the noise, with the variance:

$$\sigma^2 = \overline{n^2} = P_n \tag{2.12}$$

where P_n is the noise power (on our assumption of a system impedance of $1\,\Omega$).

The receiver contains band-pass filters which limit the bandwidth of the noise to a small range around the carrier frequency, usually of the same order of bandwidth as the modulated signal (Fig. 2.10). This band-limited noise signal can then be modelled in a similar way as the modulated signal itself, by regarding it as a carrier randomly modulated in amplitude and phase (Fig. 2.11):

$$n(t) = A(t)\cos[\omega_c t + \phi(t)] = n_p(t)\cos\omega_c t - n_q(t)\sin\omega_c t \tag{2.13}$$

It may be shown [2.3, p. 161] that if n has a Gaussian p.d.f., then n_p and n_q must be independent and must also be Gaussian distributed with the same variance:

$$\overline{n_p^2(t)} = \overline{n_q^2(t)} = \sigma^2 = P_n \tag{2.14}$$

Equivalently, the phase angle ϕ must be uniformly distributed (as is to be expected) and the amplitude A has the Rayleigh distribution:

$$p(A) = \frac{A}{\sigma^2} \exp\left(-\frac{A^2}{2\sigma^2}\right) \tag{2.15}$$

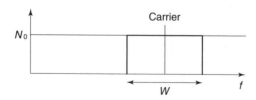

Figure 2.10   Spectrum of band-limited white noise

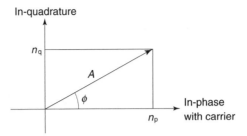

Figure 2.11 Phasor diagram of band-limited noise signal

n_p and n_q are baseband signals with (single-sided) bandwidth $W/2$, and hence the power spectral density (p.s.d.) of each is $2N_0$ (see Fig. 2.12):

2.1.5 The pulse superposition model

Having established the complex baseband signal as a representation of a general modulated signal, we now set up a model for the complex baseband signal itself, applicable to a wide range of modulation schemes (but not all). We model the baseband signal as a superposition of time-shifted pulses, weighted according to the data. For example the rectangular data waveform shown in Fig. 2.13 may be regarded as the sum of the shifted rectangular pulses shown.

In the example, $b(t) = -1 \times g(t) + (+1) \times g(t-T) + (+1) \times g(t-2T) + \cdots$. In general:

$$b(t) = \sum_{i=-\infty}^{\infty} d_i g(t - iT) \tag{2.16}$$

where d_i is the ith symbol value, which may, in general, be complex. For example, in BPSK it takes the values ± 1, whereas in QPSK it takes the four possible values $(\pm 1 \pm j)/\sqrt{2}$.

The symbol $g(t)$ is the *signalling pulse*, or *pulse shaping function*, and is normally real. In the simplest modulation schemes it is a rectangular pulse of

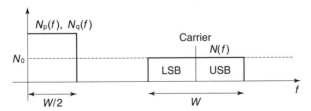

Figure 2.12 Power spectral density of equivalent baseband noise signals (LSB, lower signal baseband; USB, upper signal baseband)

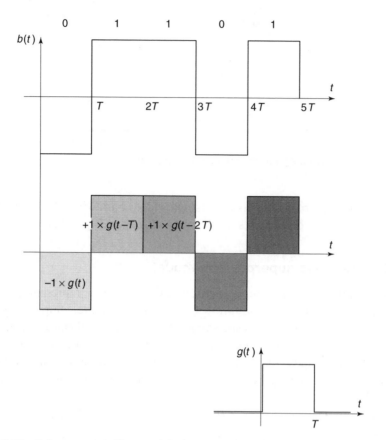

Figure 2.13 Pulse superposition model of rectangular baseband data waveform

duration T, the symbol period. However, the pulses may be longer than one symbol period, and thus may overlap, as shown in Fig. 2.14. A signal like this might result, for example, from low-pass filtering a rectangular baseband data waveform. The signalling pulse shown would then be a filtered version of the rectangular pulse.

This model may readily be used to calculate the spectrum of the complex baseband signal. By the Wiener–Khintchine theorem [2.1, p. 123; 2.4], the power spectrum of any signal is given by the Fourier transform of its auto-correlation function:

$$|B(\omega)|^2 = \mathbf{F}\left\{\int_{-\infty}^{\infty} b(t)b^*(t-\tau)\,dt\right\} = \mathbf{F}[\Phi_{dd}(k) * \Phi_{gg}(\tau)]$$

$$= \mathbf{F}[\Phi_{dd}(k)]\,|G(\omega)|^2 \tag{2.17}$$

where Φ_{dd} and Φ_{gg} denote the autocorrelation function (a.c.f.) of the data and the signalling pulse, respectively; $\mathbf{F}$ denotes the Fourier transform and τ is a

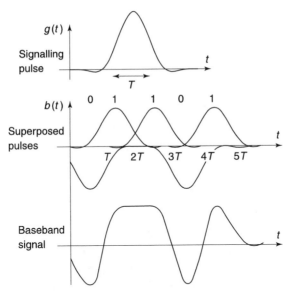

Figure 2.14   Pulse superposition model with overlapping signalling pulses

delay variable. Normally, successive symbols are uncorrelated (the most common exception is where they have been encoded specifically to adapt the signal spectrum, as in line coding) and hence the data a.c.f. is an impulse at the origin, which has a uniform spectrum. Hence, the power spectrum of the baseband signal is simply the squared magnitude spectrum of the signalling pulse, $G(\omega)$.

2.2   Linear and exponential modulation

The pulse superposition model described in Section 2.1 does, in fact, provide a means of distinguishing between the two main types of modulation: *linear* and *non-linear*, or *exponential* modulation. In the model there is a simple linear relationship between the symbol value d_i and the modulated signal, since both Equation (2.16) (which defines the model) and Equation (2.6) (which relates baseband to modulated signal) are linear in d. Thus any scheme to which the pulse superposition model applies is linear.

By appropriate choice of the possible values of d_i, linear modulation can give rise to any desired combination of amplitude and phase, and thus any form of amplitude-shift keying (ASK), PSK, or any combination of the two can be regarded as a linear modulation scheme. However, frequency-shift keying (FSK) involves modulation of rate of change of phase, and thus a phase which is not constant over the symbol period. This cannot, in general, be modelled using the pulse superposition model. However, the complex

25

baseband signal is still applicable. We put:

$$b(t) = \exp(jd_i\omega_d t) \tag{2.18}$$

where in the simplest case the symbol value $d_i = \pm 1$. Then the modulated signal:

$$\left.\begin{aligned} a(t) &= \begin{cases} \operatorname{Re}[\exp(j\omega_d t)\exp(j\omega_c t)] \\ \operatorname{Re}[\exp(-j\omega_d t)\exp(j\omega_c t)] \end{cases} = \begin{cases} \operatorname{Re}\{\exp[j(\omega_c + \omega_d)t]\} \\ \operatorname{Re}\{\exp[j(\omega_c - \omega_d)t]\} \end{cases} \\ &= \begin{cases} \cos[(\omega_c + \omega_d)t], & d_i = +1 \ ('1') \\ \cos[(\omega_c - \omega_d)t], & d_i = -1 \ ('0') \end{cases} \end{aligned}\right\} \tag{2.19}$$

which for data '1' is a sine wave ω_d above the carrier frequency; for data '0' it is ω_d below it. Hence the form of $b(t)$ in Equation (2.18) gives rise to FSK with frequency shift $\pm\omega_d$. In (2.18), the signal now has an exponential relationship with the data value: hence the term *exponential modulation*.

Figure 2.15 illustrates the relationship graphically. The in-phase and the quadrature component of the modulated signal are shown separately, expanding Equation (2.18) as:

$$b(t) = \exp(jd_i\omega_d t) \Rightarrow \begin{aligned} b_p(t) &= \cos(\omega_d t) \\ b_q(t) &= \pm\sin(\omega_d t) \end{aligned} \tag{2.20}$$

It may then be seen that the combination of the two components results in frequency-shifted signals.

It should be noted from Fig. 2.15 and from Equation (2.18) that the amplitude of the signal is constant at all times, whereas with linear modulation it may

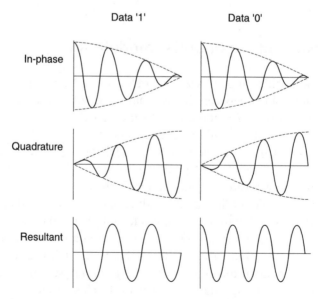

Data '1'   Data '0'

In-phase

Quadrature

Resultant

Figure 2.15   Graphical illustration of exponential modulation

vary. This is an important feature of exponential modulation, leading to several inherent advantages and disadvantages of exponential modulation compared with linear.

These schemes will be explored in more detail in the next chapter.

2.3   Digital transmission fundamentals

In this section we consider two fundamental concepts of digital transmission systems which apply to baseband transmission as well as to digital modulation: Nyquist filtering and the matched filter. We review the principles of the two separately as they apply to the (complex) baseband channel, then consider their joint application to modulated radio systems.

2.3.1   Nyquist filtering

In practice, a communication signal must be accommodated in a limit bandwidth. In radio systems this is usually because a limited spectrum allocation has been assigned by the regulatory authorities. This implies that the complex baseband bandwidth must also be restricted.

Unfortunately, restricting a signal's bandwidth in the frequency domain tends to cause spreading in the time domain [2.3, p. 536]; in fact, the 'uncertainty theorem' inherently implies such spreading. For example, Fig. 2.16 shows the effect of filtering a rectangular pulse of duration T using a third-order Butterworth filter [2.2, p. 80] with cut-off frequency $f_c = 1/2T$. It may be seen that the pulse is delayed, and also *dispersed* in time over three or more times its original duration.

Figure 2.17 shows the effect of a similar filter on a rectangular data waveform, where the cut-off frequency is half the baud rate (which is equivalent to the previous filter). Here we observe that the time dispersion of one signalling pulse results in interference with the next, an effect known as *intersymbol interference* (i.s.i.). In extreme cases this can result directly in data errors and, in

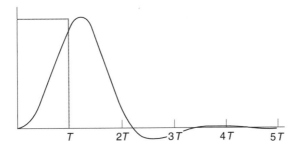

Figure 2.16   Effect of filtering a rectangular pulse (shown in grey)

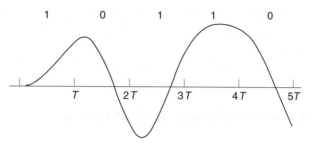

Figure 2.17 Effect of filtering on a rectangular data waveform

general, it will degrade the BER performance of the system in the presence of noise.

The time dispersion effect is an inevitable result of band-limiting the signal. However, it is possible by careful choice of the band-limiting filter to eliminate i.s.i. We note that the receiver will sample the received signal once per symbol, usually at the end of the symbol period (i.e. at integer multiples of T). Hence it may be possible to force the i.s.i. to be zero at these instants, despite the occurrence of time dispersion. This is achieved if the filtered pulse passes through zero at all sampling instants other than its own, as shown in Fig. 2.18, where the individual filtered signalling pulses are shown in grey.

Mathematically, we may write:

$$g(iT) = \begin{cases} 1, & i = 0 \\ 0, & i \neq 0 \end{cases} \tag{2.21}$$

where $g(t)$ is the filtered signalling pulse. This is the *Nyquist criterion* in time domain form [2.1, p. 263; 2.5].

It may be shown [2.3, pp. 542–7; 2.5] that the time domain form of the Nyquist criterion is satisfied if the spectrum of the signalling pulse, $G(f)$, satisfies:

$$\sum_{k=-\infty}^{\infty} G\left(f + \frac{k}{T}\right) = T, \quad |f| \leq \frac{1}{2T} \tag{2.22}$$

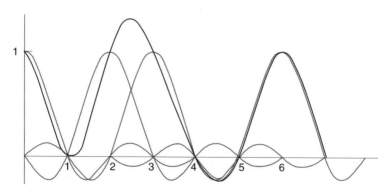

Figure 2.18 Filtered signal with zero i.s.i.

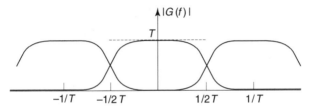

Figure 2.19 Nyquist criterion in the frequency domain

This is the frequency-domain form of the Nyquist criterion. Essentially, it states that the sum of a series of copies of the spectrum shifted by the baud rate must add to a constant value over the frequency range $-1/2T$ to $+1/2T$. This means that the (double-sided) bandwidth of the signal can never be less than $1/T$. Figure 2.19 shows the situation if the bandwidth is less than twice this value (i.e. if there is less than 100% *excess bandwidth*, which is normally the case). The dotted line shows the sum of the signals if the criterion is obeyed.

It will be noted that the magnitude spectrum shown has a certain symmetry in its tails, and that this symmetry must occur if the spectrum itself is symmetrical and the criterion is to be obeyed. It is known as *vestigial symmetry*, and takes the form of an odd symmetry about $f = 1/2T$, as shown in Fig. 2.20.

Most commonly the *raised cosine* Nyquist spectrum is used, in which the roll-off part of the spectrum follows a raised cosine shape. This follows a smooth curve in the frequency domain, which results in better behaviour in the time domain, with reduced overshoot, ringing, etc. Mathematically:

$$|G(f)| = \begin{cases} 1, & |f| \le \frac{1}{2T}(1 - \beta) \\ \frac{1}{2}\left\{1 - \sin\left[\frac{\pi T}{\beta}\left(|f| - \frac{1}{2T}\right)\right]\right\}, & \frac{1}{2T}(1 - \beta) < |f| < \frac{1}{2T}(1 + \beta) \\ 0, & |f| \ge \frac{1}{2T}(1 + \beta) \end{cases}$$

$$(2.23a)$$

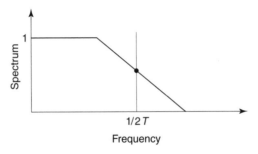

Figure 2.20 Vestigial symmetry

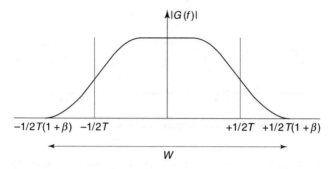

Figure 2.21   Raised cosine spectrum

In the time domain:

$$g(t) = \frac{2\cos(\pi t\beta/T)\sin(\pi t/T)}{t(1 - 4t^2\beta^2/T^2)} \tag{2.23b}$$

The double-sided spectrum is shown in Fig. 2.21, in which the vestigial symmetry is clear. The total bandwidth is given by:

$$W = (1 + \beta)/T = r_s(1 + \beta) \tag{2.24}$$

where r_s is the symbol or baud rate.

The parameter β is called the *roll-off factor*, and may vary between 0 and 1, corresponding to an excess bandwidth of 0–100%. This allows a trade-off between bandwidth and the desirable time-domain properties of the signal. Very low values are difficult to realize in practice, because they require very rapid roll-off in the filter response, and because of the ringing in the time-domain response. Figure 2.22 shows the time-domain response for various values of β.

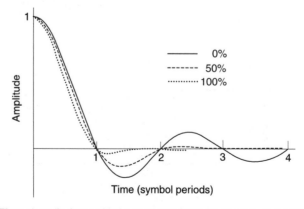

Figure 2.22   Time-domain form of raised cosine Nyquist spectra for various values of β

2.3.2 The matched filter

The structure of a receiver for baseband (binary) data is shown in Fig. 2.23. The received signal is filtered to minimize the noise, then a sample is taken (one per symbol) to provide an estimate of the data signal and, finally, a symbol decision is made. In the binary case, the decision is made simply by comparison with a threshold value. In this section we consider the optimum response for the filter [2.1, p. 279].

The objective of the filter is to maximize the signal-to-noise ratio (SNR) at its output. Because of the sampler, the SNR is of interest only at the sampling instant, which we assume is at the end of the symbol period, at $t = T$. Thus we wish to maximize:

$$SNR_{\text{out}} = \frac{s^2(T)}{\overline{n^2}} \tag{2.25}$$

We therefore choose the filter frequency response, $H(\omega) = H(2\pi f)$, so as to maximize SNR_{out}. We may write $s(T)$ using the inverse Fourier transform evaluated at the sampling instant:

$$s(T) = \int_{-\infty}^{\infty} G(f)H(f)\exp(2\pi jfT)\,df \tag{2.26}$$

where $G(f)$ is the Fourier transform of the signalling pulse, $g(t)$. Similarly, the noise power:

$$\overline{n^2} = \frac{1}{2}\int_{-\infty}^{\infty} N_0|H(f)|\,df \tag{2.27}$$

assuming that the noise is white. The factor $(1/2)$ is required because the integral is double-sided. Invoking the *Cauchy–Schwartz inequality* [2.2, p. 63], which states that for any two functions $X(f)$ and $Y(f)$:

$$\left|\int_{-\infty}^{\infty} X(f)Y(f)\,df\right|^2 \leq \int_{-\infty}^{\infty} |X(f)|^2\,df \int_{-\infty}^{\infty} |Y(f)|^2\,df \tag{2.28}$$

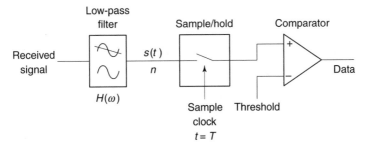

Figure 2.23   Structure of receiver for binary baseband data

and substituting $X(f) = G(f)\exp(2\pi jfT)$ and $Y(f) = H(f)$, we obtain:

$$\frac{s^2(T)}{\overline{n^2}} \leq \frac{\int_{-\infty}^{\infty}|G(f)\exp(2\pi jfT)|^2\,df\int_{-\infty}^{\infty}|H(f)|^2\,df}{\frac{1}{2}\int_{-\infty}^{\infty}N_0|H(f)|^2\,df} \tag{2.29}$$

Since the complex exponential has unit magnitude, $\int_{-\infty}^{\infty}|G(f)\exp(2\pi jfT)|^2\,df$ is simply the energy in the signalling pulse, E. Now equality applies in the Schwartz inequality if and only if $X(f) = kY^*(f)$ (where k is a scalar constant), i.e. if:

$$H(f) = G^*(f)\exp(-2\pi jfT) \tag{2.30}$$

i.e. $|H(f)| = |G(f)|$. In other words, the optimum signal-to-noise ratio is attained if the receive filter response is matched to the signalling pulse spectrum. Thus the optimum filter is called the *matched filter*. (This can be justified intuitively by noting that regions of the received signal spectrum where $|G(f)|$ is small contain mainly noise, and should therefore be suppressed in favour of those regions where $|G(f)|$ is larger.)

In the time domain, (2.30) transforms to:

$$h(t) = g(T - t) \tag{2.31}$$

since the complex conjugation corresponds to a time-reversal, and the exponential term corresponds to a delay, T. Thus the impulse response of the optimum filter should be a time-reversed and delayed copy of the signalling pulse shape, as shown in Fig. 2.24.

If the filter is matched, equality applies in (2.29), and hence:

$$SNR_{\text{out}} = \frac{s^2(T)}{\overline{n^2}} \leq \frac{E\int_{-\infty}^{\infty}|H(f)|^2\,df}{\frac{1}{2}N_0\int_{-\infty}^{\infty}|H(f)|^2\,df} = \frac{2E}{N_0} \tag{2.32}$$

This simple equation applies if the filter is matched, whatever the shape of the signalling pulse.

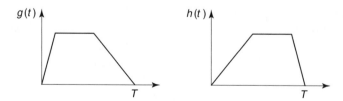

Figure 2.24 Impulse response of matched filter

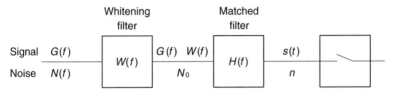

Figure 2.25   Whitened matched filter

If the noise is not white (suppose its power spectrum is $\eta(f) = |N(f)|^2$), we may precede the matched filter with a *whitening filter*, with transfer function magnitude $|W(f)| = 1/\sqrt{|\eta(f)|}$, as shown in Fig. 2.25. The noise at its output is then white, and a matched filter may be added in cascade, matched to the signal after filtering by the whitening filter. The cascade combination is then called a *whitened matched filter*. It is in fact optimum only if the signalling interval is long compared to the inverse bandwidth of the whitening filter, otherwise the filter introduces excessive distortion [2.6, p. 474].

The magnitude response of the matched filter is then:

$$|H(f)| = |G(f)||W(f)| = \frac{|G(f)|}{\sqrt{|\eta(f)|}} \qquad (2.33)$$

and hence the overall magnitude response of the whitened matched filter is:

$$|W(f)G(f)| = |W(f)||H(f)| = \frac{|G(f)|}{|\eta(f)|} \qquad (2.34)$$

2.3.3   Nyquist and matched filtering in radio systems

In a radio system, the Nyquist-filtered baseband signal must of course be modulated onto the carrier, and hence the double-sided baseband spectrum is translated up to the carrier frequency, as described in Section 2.1.3. The spectrum is thus as shown in Fig. 2.21, but centred now around the carrier frequency, and the overall bandwidth is the double-sided bandwidth as given in (2.24).

In a radio system, we are normally concerned both to band-limit the transmitted signal without introducing i.s.i. and to maximize the received signal-to-noise ratio. Hence, we must implement both Nyquist and matched filtering. Here we determine what filtering is required in the transmitter and the receiver in order to achieve this.

Figure 2.26 shows the structure of a complete system, including filters in both receiver and transmitter. Note that we must eliminate i.s.i. at the input to the decision device, and hence it is the cascade of transmit and receive filters that must obey the Nyquist criterion, not the transmit filter alone. If white noise from the channel (and receiver front end) appears at the input to the receive filter, then matched filtering must be implemented by matching the receive

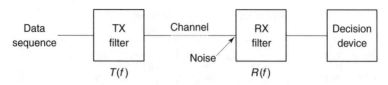

Figure 2.26 Nyquist and matched filtering in receiver and transmitter

filter to the transmitted signal. Hence we have:

$$\left.\begin{array}{ll} T(f) \times R(f) = RC(f), & \text{Nyquist criterion} \\ T(f) = R^*(f), & \text{matched filter} \end{array}\right\} \qquad (2.35)$$

where $RC(f)$ denotes a raised cosine (or other Nyquist) spectrum. Solving Equations (2.35) we have:

$$|R(f)| = |T(f)| = \sqrt{|RC(f)|} \qquad (2.36)$$

showing that both transmit and receive filters should have a square-root raised cosine response (and are known as *root-raised cosine* filters).

If the receive filter has such a response, we can define an *effective noise bandwidth* of the filter, W_{eff}. If the input noise at the receiver is white, of power spectral density N_0, then output noise p.s.d. is:

$$\eta(f) = N_0|R(f)|^2 = N_0 RC(f) \qquad (2.37)$$

Total received noise power:

$$N = \int_0^\infty \eta(f)\,df = N_0 \int_0^\infty RC(f)\,df = N_0 W_{\text{eff}} = \frac{N_0}{T} \qquad (2.38)$$

Figure 2.27 shows the same result in graphical form.

In the receiver, a demodulator recovers the in-phase and quadrature components of the baseband signal, b_p and b_q, corrupted by the noise components n_p and n_q. This is followed (in principle) by a pair of matched filters, which recovers the data estimates d_p and d_q, as shown in Fig. 2.28. The noise power spectral density at the input to the matched filter is $2N_0$, as shown in

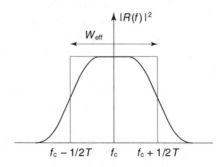

Figure 2.27 Effective noise bandwidth of a root-raised cosine filter

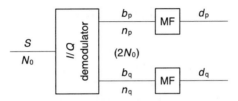

Figure 2.28   Signal and noise in demodulator (MF, matched filter)

Section 2.1.4. Hence, the signal-to-noise ratio at the output of the matched filters (using Equation (2.32)) is:

$$\left.\begin{aligned}
\frac{d_p^2}{\sigma^2} &= \frac{2E_p}{2N_0} = \frac{\overline{b_p^2}\,T}{N_0} \\[2mm]
\frac{d_q^2}{\sigma^2} &= \frac{\overline{b_q^2}\,T}{N_0}
\end{aligned}\right\} \tag{2.39}$$

where

$$\sigma^2 = P_n = W_{\text{eff}}N_0 = \frac{N_0}{T}$$

referring to Equations (2.14) and (2.38). Hence, the combined signal-to-noise ratio on the two data estimates:

$$\frac{d_p^2 + d_q^2}{\sigma^2} = \frac{A^2}{\sigma^2} = \frac{(\overline{b_p^2} + \overline{b_q^2})T}{N_0} = \frac{2E}{N_0} \tag{2.40}$$

using Equation (2.10), where E here is the energy per symbol at the input to the demodulator. In other words, the whole structure acts as a matched filter.

Thus we may represent the output of the matched filters in the form of a constellation diagram, as shown in Fig. 2.29, in which each point is surrounded by a 'region of uncertainty' whose 'spread' is indicated approximately by σ. This may be used in calculating the BER of the modulation scheme. Note that the region is circular, which implies that the 'spread', σ, is the same in all directions.

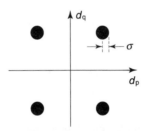

Figure 2.29   Constellation diagram of signal corrupted by noise

2.4 Basic linear modulation schemes

In this section we consider the simplest linear modulation schemes, *binary phase-shift keying* (BPSK) and *quadrature* (or *quaternary*) *phase-shift keying* (QPSK). These are the most power-efficient uncoded modulation schemes (with the exception of some multilevel FSK schemes – see Section 3.3.5), but also the least bandwidth-efficient (especially BPSK). They are nevertheless very widely used. For each we determine their bandwidth efficiency and their BER performance in AWGN, using the principles established above.

2.4.1 BPSK

The basic principle of BPSK modulation is illustrated in Fig. 2.2. Note, however, that this assumes a rectangular signalling pulse, with no filtering, whereas for practical applications filtering would be applied, probably Nyquist filtering with appropriate roll-off factor. Filtering will result in envelope variations, as shown in Fig. 2.30.

The spectrum of unfiltered BPSK is given by the Fourier transform of a rectangular pulse, and takes the well-known $\sin(x)/x$ form, with nulls at multiples of the symbol rate. This is shown in logarithmic form in Fig. 2.31. It is clear that it is unacceptable for most practical applications, since the bandwidth occupied for a realistic ACI threshold is excessive. However, if Nyquist filtering is applied, then the bandwidth is reduced to:

$$W = r_s(1 + \beta) = r_b(1 + \beta) \tag{2.41}$$

where r_b is the bit rate, since BPSK transmits one bit per symbol.

The constellation diagram of BPSK is shown in Fig. 2.32. We may use this diagram to calculate the BER performance. An error may occur if the received point is displaced because of noise on the channel, as shown. If it is displaced across the b_q axis it will then be closer to the erroneous symbol than to the

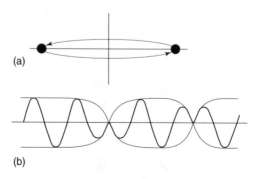

(a)

(b)

Figure 2.30 Effect of filtering on the envelope of the BPSK signal: (a) transitions in the constellation diagram, and (b) filtered modulated signal

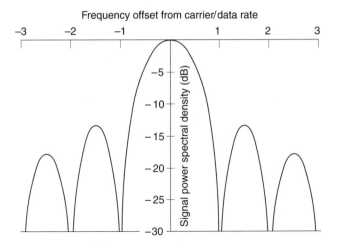

Figure 2.31 Spectrum of unfiltered BPSK

correct one. This will occur if $n_p > d/2$, regardless of n_q. The probability of error may be determined by considering the probability density function (p.d.f.) of the in-phase component of the received signal, which is shown in Fig. 2.33. The areas shown shaded represent the probabilities that one transmitted symbol will be misinterpreted as the other.

Then, the probability of error (equal to the BER) is:

$$
\left.
\begin{aligned}
P_e &= P('0')P('0' \rightarrow '1') + P('1')P('1' \rightarrow '0') \\
&= \frac{1}{2}Q\left(\frac{d/2}{\sigma}\right) + \frac{1}{2}Q\left(\frac{d/2}{\sigma}\right) = Q\left(\frac{d}{2\sigma}\right)
\end{aligned}
\right\}
\tag{2.42}
$$

where the Q-function, which is related to the complementary error function, is given by:

$$
Q(z) = \int_z^\infty \frac{1}{\sqrt{2\pi}} \exp\left(-\frac{x^2}{2}\right) dx = \frac{1}{2}\,\mathrm{erfc}\left(\frac{z}{\sqrt{2}}\right)
\tag{2.43}
$$

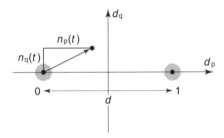

Figure 2.32 Constellation of BPSK

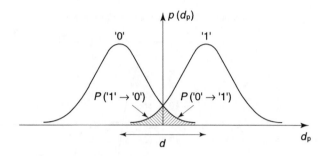

Figure 2.33   Probability density functions of in-phase component of received signal

Clearly the data amplitude $d_p = \pm d/2$ and, hence, using Equation (2.40):

$$\frac{d_p^2 + d_q^2}{\sigma^2} = \frac{d^2}{4\sigma^2} = \frac{2E}{N_0} = \frac{2E_b}{N_0} \tag{2.44}$$

$$\therefore \quad P_e = Q\left(\frac{d}{2\sigma}\right) = Q\left(\sqrt{\frac{2E_b}{N_0}}\right) \tag{2.45}$$

This is plotted in Fig. 1.10, and takes the form of the well-known 'waterfall' curve.

2.4.2   QPSK

QPSK is a simple elaboration upon BPSK in that it allows four different phases to be transmitted rather than two. The constellation diagram is shown in Fig. 2.34. Note that since there are now four possible signal states we may transmit two bits per symbol. We *label* the constellation points with unique two-bit binary words as shown.

For the same symbol rate and the same signalling pulse shape the spectrum is identical to that of BPSK, as shown by Equation (2.17). However, for the same bit rate, the symbol rate is half that of BPSK, and therefore the bandwidth is

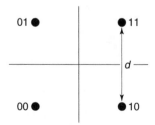

Figure 2.34   Constellation diagram of QPSK (*d*, distance between constellation points)

halved. Assuming Nyquist filtering, the bandwidth is:

$$W = r_s(1 + \beta) = \frac{r_b}{2}(1 + \beta) \tag{2.46}$$

Hence, the bandwidth efficiency is doubled.

A symbol error will occur if noise displaces the received symbol across either of the axes of the constellation diagram. The probability of displacement is the same in each direction, and hence the error probability for each axis is given by the same formula as for BPSK, but is approximately doubled overall:

$$P_e = 2Q\left(\frac{d}{2\sigma}\right) \tag{2.47}$$

where d is again the distance between constellation points. This is a slight over-estimate, since it counts the probability of displacement over both axes (into the opposite quadrant) twice. In this case, substituting into (2.40):

$$\frac{d_p^2 + d_q^2}{\sigma^2} = \frac{2(d/2)^2}{\sigma^2} = \frac{d^2}{2\sigma^2} = \frac{2E}{N_0} = \frac{4E_b}{N_0} \tag{2.48}$$

noting that $E = 2E_b$. Hence, the symbol error probability:

$$P_e = 2Q\left(\sqrt{\frac{2E_b}{N_0}}\right) \tag{2.49}$$

However, each symbol transmits two bits, and with the labelling shown in Fig. 2.34, the most probable symbol errors will corrupt only one bit. Hence, the bit error probability, or BER, is on average approximately half the symbol error probability:

$$P_b = \frac{P_e}{2} = Q\left(\sqrt{\frac{2E_b}{N_0}}\right) \tag{2.50}$$

This is identical with the BER of BPSK: thus QPSK is as power efficient as BPSK, and twice as bandwidth efficient. We can in fact view QPSK with the labelling shown, as two independent BPSK signals, modulated onto sine and cosine, respectively.

BPSK and QPSK are the most power-efficient uncoded linear modulation schemes possible, and as such find many practical applications in radio systems. They are the most common schemes used in geostationary satellite communications, since traditionally these systems are most concerned with power efficiency: they are power limited [2.1, pp. 542–75]. QPSK is probably more generally used than BPSK since it has increased bandwidth efficiency without any power penalty. However, BPSK is more simply demodulated, and carrier recovery is more straightforward (see Chapter 4). Also, while the two perform equally well in white noise, BPSK will in general perform better by 3 dB in the presence of narrowband noise.

2.5 Multilevel modulation schemes

QPSK with Nyquist filtering achieves bandwidth efficiencies between 1 and $2\,\text{bits}\,\text{s}^{-1}\,\text{Hz}^{-1}$. As we have seen, the bandwidth is determined by the symbol rate, and cannot be reduced below this rate. To achieve greater efficiencies we must increase the number of bits per symbol, by increasing further the number of signal states. In general, if there are M signal states we may transmit $k = \log_2(M)$ bits per symbol. For Nyquist filtering, bandwidth $W = r_\text{s}(1 + \beta)$ and, hence, bandwidth efficiency:

$$\eta = \frac{kr_\text{s}}{W} = \frac{\log_2(M)}{1 + \beta} \tag{2.51}$$

Normally, of course, M is chosen to be a power of 2.

2.5.1 M-PSK

The simplest means of increasing M is to generalize QPSK to more than four constellation points. This is then known as M-PSK, where M is a power of 2 greater than or equal to 8. Figure 2.35 shows the constellation diagram of 8-PSK.

The constellation points may be defined mathematically by expressing the complex data as:

$$d = A \exp\left(\frac{2\pi j i}{M}\right) = A\left[\cos\left(\frac{2\pi i}{M}\right) + j\sin\left(\frac{2\pi i}{M}\right)\right], \quad i = 0 \cdots M - 1 \tag{2.52}$$

Of course any rotation of the complete constellation has no material effect, and hence (2.52) may be expressed in other ways. A common variant is to add the angle π/M to the arguments, so that the points are placed symmetrically around the axes, rather than on them.

A symbol error again occurs if the received symbol is displaced by noise so that it lies closer to an erroneous constellation point than to the correct one. For the symbol 010 in Fig. 2.35 this will occur if it is displaced outside the

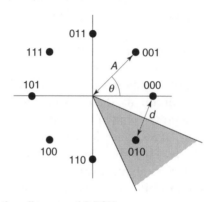

Figure 2.35 Constellation diagram of 8-PSK

region shown shaded, known as the *decision region* of the point. The boundaries of the decision region are the perpendicular bisectors of the lines joining the point to its immediate neighbours. Again, we may calculate the probability of displacement over each of these boundaries using the same formula as for BPSK and, again, the symbol error probability will be approximately twice this because there are two boundaries.

$$P_e = 2Q\left(\frac{d}{2\sigma}\right) = 2Q\left[\frac{2A\sin(\theta/2)}{2\sigma}\right] = 2Q\left[\frac{A\sin(\pi/M)}{\sigma}\right]$$

$$= 2Q\left[\sin(\pi/M)\sqrt{\frac{2E}{N_0}}\right] = 2Q\left[\sin(\pi/M)\sqrt{\frac{2kE_b}{N_0}}\right] \tag{2.53}$$

again using Equation (2.40). The labelling of Fig. 2.35 has been chosen so that any pair of adjacent points differ only in one bit (this is known as a *Gray code* labelling), and therefore a symbol error is likely to result in only one-out-of-k bit errors. Hence the BER:

$$P_b = \frac{2}{k}Q\left[\sin(\pi/M)\sqrt{\frac{2kE_b}{N_0}}\right] \tag{2.54}$$

For 8-PSK this evaluates as:

$$P_b = \frac{2}{3}Q\left(0.937\sqrt{\frac{E_b}{N_0}}\right) \tag{2.55}$$

and for 16-PSK:

$$P_b = \frac{1}{2}Q\left(0.552\sqrt{\frac{E_b}{N_0}}\right) \tag{2.56}$$

These are plotted in Fig. 2.36, compared with QPSK. Observe that the power required is increased compared with QPSK: the price of increased bandwidth efficiency is reduced power efficiency.

2.5.2 QAM

Figure 2.37(a) shows the constellation diagram for 16-PSK. Here all 16 constellation points are distributed around the circumference of a circle, and are therefore rather closely spaced. Equation (2.42) shows that the error probability depends on the distance between constellation points, and hence this is undesirable. A more even distribution would be obtained by spreading the points across the centre of the diagram. Figure 2.37(b) shows a distribution of the 16 points on a rectangular grid, which achieves this. Note that the mean square distance of points from the origin, and hence the average signal power, is the same in both cases. The minimum spacing between points, however, is increased by a factor of approximately 1.6 in the latter constellation.

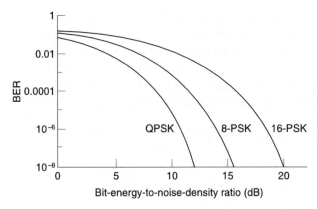

Figure 2.36 **BER versus bit-energy-to-noise-density ratio for M-PSK schemes**

This latter constellation is known as *quadrature amplitude modulation* (QAM), because it may be formed by a form of four-level amplitude modulation of the in-phase and the quadrature components of the signal separately. (Negative as well as positive amplitudes are allowed.) In general, it may be mathematically expressed as:

$$d = a(2i - K + 1) + ja(2k - K + 1), \quad i, k = 0 \cdots K - 1$$
$$K = \sqrt{M}, \quad M = 4, 16, 64, 256, \ldots \tag{2.57}$$

where the spacing between constellation points is $2a$.

Figure 2.38 shows the decision region of the point labelled 1000 in the 16-QAM constellation. This has four faces, since the point has four immediate neighbours at distance $d = 2a$. Hence, the symbol error probability for this point is now given by $4Q(d/2\sigma)$. However, for points on the periphery of the constellation, there are fewer neighbours, and hence the average symbol error probability is:

$$P_e = \overline{n_n} Q\left(\frac{d}{2\sigma}\right) = \overline{n_n} Q\left(\frac{a}{\sigma}\right) \tag{2.58}$$

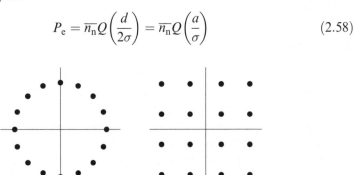

Figure 2.37 **Constellation diagrams for (a) 16-PSK and (b) 16-QAM, for the same average power**

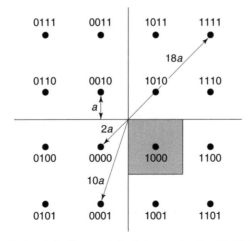

Figure 2.38   Constellation labelling and decision region for 16-QAM constellation

where the average number of immediate neighbours for 16-QAM:

$$\overline{n}_\mathrm{n} = \frac{4 \times 4 + 8 \times 3 + 4 \times 2}{16} = 3 \tag{2.59}$$

In general:

$$\overline{n}_\mathrm{n} = \frac{4(K-2)^2 + 12(K-2) + 8}{M} \tag{2.60}$$

For a QAM constellation the power is no longer a constant for all points. The average power for 16-QAM is given by:

$$\overline{A^2} = \frac{4 \times 2a^2 + 8 \times 10a^2 + 4 \times 18a^2}{16} = 10a^2 \tag{2.61}$$

In general:

$$\left.\begin{aligned}
\overline{A^2} &= \frac{\displaystyle\sum_{i=0}^{K-1}\sum_{k=0}^{K-1} a^2(2i - K + 1)^2 + a^2(2k - K + 1)^2}{M} \\[2mm]
&= \frac{\displaystyle\sum_{i=0}^{K/2-1}\sum_{k=0}^{K/2-1} a^2(2i - K + 1)^2 + a^2(2k - K + 1)^2}{M/4} \\[2mm]
&= \frac{2(K/2)\displaystyle\sum_{i=0}^{K/2-1} a^2(2i - K + 1)^2}{M/4} = \frac{4Ka^2\displaystyle\sum_{i'=0}^{K/2-1}(2i' + 1)^2}{M}
\end{aligned}\right\} \tag{2.62}$$

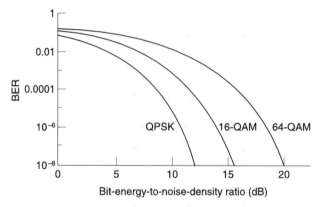

Figure 2.39   BER versus bit-energy-to-noise-density ratio for QAM constellations

Thus for 16-QAM, the symbol error probability is:

$$P_{\mathrm{e}} = 3Q\left(\frac{a}{\sigma}\right) = 3Q\left(\sqrt{\frac{\overline{A^2}}{10\sigma^2}}\right) = 3Q\left(\sqrt{\frac{2E}{10N_0}}\right) \tag{2.63}$$

Figure 2.38 shows a Gray code labelling such that neighbouring labels differ only by one bit, and therefore a symbol error will usually lead to one-bit-error out of four bits. Hence the BER:

$$P_{\mathrm{b}} = \frac{3}{4}Q\left(\sqrt{\frac{2E}{10N_0}}\right) = \frac{3}{4}Q\left(\sqrt{\frac{4E_{\mathrm{b}}}{5N_0}}\right) \tag{2.64}$$

Equations (2.60) and (2.62) may be used to find similar expressions for other values of M. The results are plotted in Fig. 2.39. Comparing with Fig. 2.36 we note that 16-QAM has an advantage of about 4 dB compared with 16-PSK, which is due to the more even distribution of points, and the resulting increased minimum distance between the points.

The disadvantage of 16-QAM compared with 16-PSK is that the signal amplitude now has an inherent variation, regardless of filtering. This may cause problems in non-linear amplifiers, and on fading channels. Also, the above analysis assumes that the average transmitted power is limited, taken over a period much longer than one symbol. In many radio systems the limitation is in fact on the peak power. In this case we must replace $\overline{A^2}$ with $\hat{A}^2$, which takes the value $18a^2$ in 16-QAM. This erodes the advantage of 16-QAM by some 2.5 dB.

2.5.3   Other constellations

A wide variety of other constellations are also possible. Note, for example, that QAM as defined above does not allow $M = 8, 32, 128$, etc. These can be achieved using the CROSS constellations, illustrated in Fig. 2.40, or by

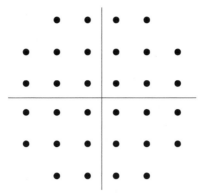

Figure 2.40   32-CROSS constellation

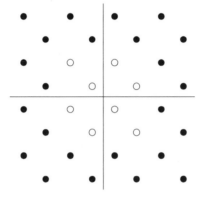

Figure 2.41   32-AMPM and 8-AMPM (in white) constellations

AMPM, as in Fig. 2.41, e.g. [2.7]. Similar techniques to those used above for QAM can be employed to calculate the BER. The results for both are similar, and are in line with the performance of the QAM constellations.

Even more complex constellations may be used, for example to achieve a lower peak-to-mean-power ratio than QAM, or to better performance on some specific channel.

2.6   System applications

As we have already pointed out, modulation as such is fundamental to radio communication systems, and therefore is used in some form in all radio systems, without exception. However, we will see in the next chapter that the effect of non-linearities in the transmitter amplifier causes degradations to the linear modulation schemes described here. Hence, the schemes described in this chapter have somewhat more restricted application. We will, however, highlight a few of these.

2.6.1 Terrestrial microwave telecommunications

In the 1960s and 1970s an extensive network of microwave telecommunications was installed to provide additional capacity for the public telecommunications network. Subsequently, with the introduction of optical fibre, these have become much less important, but they are still in use. These systems are required to transmit very high data rates in limited bandwidth, and the power budget is not restrictive. Tall towers (which may be seen at intervals across the countryside) are commonly used to provide a direct line-of-sight path, together with high gain dish antennas. Hence they are bandwidth limited, and bandwidth-efficient modulation is highly desirable. For this reason QAM modulation, up to 256-QAM, is widely used, and even higher levels have been proposed. The main difficulties experienced are due to atmospheric multipath effects, which give rise to occasional deep fades. More detail on these effects is included in Chapter 9. A useful introduction to these systems may be found in [2.1, pp. 520–42].

2.6.2 Satellite systems

Satellite communication systems, and especially geostationary satellites, have conventionally been regarded as power limited, because of the extremely long propagation paths involved and the limited power available on the spacecraft. In other respects the channel is usually very benign, only rarely being subject to multipath effects. Nevertheless linear modulation has commonly been used, although steps may be taken to reduce the effect of the non-linearity of the satellite transponder (as we will see in the next chapter). Up to now multilevel modulation has not been used because of the power limitation, but with increasing demands on spectrum, and increasing power availability on board the satellite there are now proposals to use coded 8-PSK or 16-QAM systems to improve spectral efficiency. Another example is digital audio broadcasting by satellite (see, for example, [2.8] and other articles in the same journal issue), in which multilevel modulation may be used in conjunction with orthogonal frequency division multiplexing (OFDM) – see Chapter 10.

In addition to the section on satellite systems in [2.1], there are many textbooks covering satellite systems, for example [2.9].

2.6.3 Broadcast systems

The new digital broadcast systems, both terrestrial and satellite, are, in general, bandwidth limited because of the high data rates required to supply high quality broadcast signals. Hence, the underlying modulation schemes are linear multilevel schemes up to 64-QAM. The terrestrial channel has less propagation loss than the satellite, but is subject to much more severe multipath effects. This is overcome using OFDM, as mentioned above. Digital audio broadcasting was introduced in the early 1990s [2.10] (although it has yet to reach a mass market): digital television [2.11] is at the time of writing about to launch a national service in the UK.

2.6.4   Private mobile radio

Private mobile radio (PMR) systems, as used by the emergency services and other professional groups, have rather different requirements from cellular mobile radio systems. In particular, there is often a lack of central co-ordination, which may mean that different organizations may be using adjacent channels, and thus the adjacent channel interference (ACI) threshold may be much more severe than in cellular systems. Hence, linear modulation is used in the second-generation digital standard TETRA [2.12] (now being introduced) since as we will see non-linear schemes tend to have higher 'skirts' to their spectrum so that it is difficult to guarantee very low levels of ACI. The modulation scheme used ($\pi/4$ QPSK) is described in Chapter 3.

Problems

2.1 A modulation scheme has four possible amplitude/phase states, three of which have unit amplitude and phase 0, $2\pi/3$ and $-2\pi/3$, while the fourth has zero amplitude. Draw the constellation diagram, and sketch the components of the complex baseband signal, assuming rectangular signalling pulses, for some arbitrary data sequence.

2.2 A BPSK modulation scheme uses triangular signalling pulses as shown below, where T is the bit interval. Find the power spectrum of the modulated signal. Also, sketch the components of the complex baseband signal and the modulated signal. The Fourier transform of the triangular pulse is also given below. How does the spectrum compare with that of BPSK using rectangular pulses?

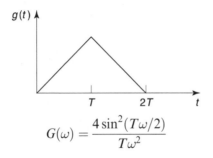

$$G(\omega) = \frac{4\sin^2(T\omega/2)}{T\omega^2}$$

2.3 Sketch the components of the baseband signal and the resultant modulated signal for FSK with difference frequency $f_c = \omega_d/(2\pi) = 1/(2T)$ for the data sequence 1100. Make appropriate assumptions regarding the phase of the signal at data symbol boundaries.

2.4 Which of the signalling pulse spectra in the figure below fulfil the Nyquist criterion?

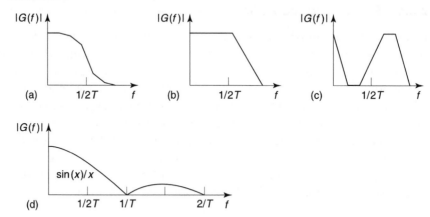

2.5 An unmodulated binary communication system uses the triangular signalling pulse of Problem 2.2. The receiver has a noise figure of 2 dB and operates at a temperature of 290 K (as in Example 1.1). If the peak amplitude of the received signal is $2\,\mu V$ in an impedance of $50\,\Omega$, and the data rate is $2\,Mbit\,s^{-1}$, find the peak signal-to-noise ratio at the output of a matched filter.

2.6 A radio communication system with a data rate of $384\,kbit\,s^{-1}$ is assigned a bandwidth of 200 kHz. Which linear modulation schemes might be used, and what would be the Nyquist roll-off factor β required in each case? Comment on which might be preferred.

2.7 Calculate the BER as a function of signal-to-noise ratio at the output of the matched filter for 8-PSK, 8-AMPM, and the eight-point constellation illustrated in the figure below. Also, calculate in each case, the peak-to-mean-power ratio (neglecting the effect of filtering).

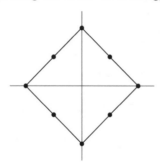

2.8 The constellation illustrated below is called STAR-16-QAM, or more precisely 8/8-STAR. It has the advantage over conventional 16-QAM that there are only eight different phase states, which may ease carrier recovery in some situations. You may assume initially that the ratio of radii of the two rings is $1:2$.

(a) Find expressions for the symbol error probability (SEP) of signals from the inner ring and the outer ring, separately. Work in terms of overall bit-energy-to-noise-density ratio (E_b/N_0). (You should consider not only the closest neighbouring points in the constellation, but also any other close points that may affect the SEP.) Hence, find the inner and outer ring SEP for $E_b/N_0 = 15\,\mathrm{dB}$.

(b) Label the constellation using the principles of the Gray code, and hence find an expression for the average BER, again in terms of E_b/N_0. Find the required E_b/N_0 for BER $= 10^{-8}$.

(c) Use the result of part (a) to suggest a simple change to the constellation (without increasing the number of different phase states) that would improve its performance. Find the effect on the required E_b/N_0.

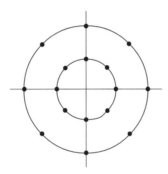

2.9 Find an expression for the symbol error probability of the 32-CROSS constellation as a function of bit-energy-to-noise-density ratio. Suggest a labelling scheme and, hence, also find the BER.

References

2.1 Glover, I.A. and Grant, P.M. (1998) *Digital Communications*, Prentice-Hall.

2.2 Lathi, B.P. (1989) *Modern Digital and Analog Communications Systems*, 2nd Edition, Holt, Rinehart and Winston.

2.3 Proakis, J.G. (1995) *Digital Communications*, 3rd Edition, McGraw-Hill.

2.4 Papoulis, A. (1962) *The Fourier Integral and its Applications*, McGraw-Hill.

2.5 Nyquist, H. (1928) Certain topics in telegraph transmission theory. *AIEE Transactions*, **47**: 617–44.

2.6 Ziemer, R.E. and Tranter, W.H. (1995) *Principles of Communications: Systems, Modulation and Noise*, 4th Edition, Wiley.

2.7 Miyauchi, K. and Igarashi, Y. (1997) Frequency–power trade-off characteristics of linear modulation systems. *Electronics and Communications in Japan, Part I, Communications*, **80**(4): 62–71.

2.8 Franchi, A., Colzi, E., Elia, C. and Harris, R.A. (1995) Performance of COFDM for satellite digital audio broadcasting. *International Journal of Satellite Communications*, **13**(4): 229–42.

2.9 Evans, B.G. (Ed.) (1999) *Satellite Communications Systems*, 3rd Edition, IEE Telecommunications Series, Institution of Electrical Engineers.

2.10 Shelswell, P. (1995) The COFDM modulation system: the heart of digital audio broadcasting. *Electronics and Communications Engineering Journal*, **7**(3): 127–36.

2.11 Reimers, U. (1999) DVB-T: The COFDM-based system for terrestrial television. *Electronics and Communications Engineering Journal*, **9**(1): 28–32.

2.12 Varrall, G. (1993) TETRA – a radio access and network technology for Europe. *Electronic Engineering*, **70**(853): 57–8.

Chapter 3

Modulation for non-linear systems

The object of this chapter is primarily to describe the class of non-linear, or exponential, modulation schemes. However, we also consider the reasons why these schemes are important, namely for use with non-linear systems such as RF power amplifiers, and accordingly we also describe the effects of these systems on linear modulation. This also leads to a study of methods for the amelioration of non-linear effects in linear modulation, and a comparison of linear and non-linear schemes. Since non-linear amplifiers are most often used where power consumption is of primary concern, and particularly in personal and cordless communication systems, the schemes described in this chapter include those that are most important in a wide range of current mobile and cordless radio standards, including GSM, DECT, the TETRA private mobile (or business) radio (PMR) standard, the North American standards IS-54 and IS-136 and PACS-UB [3.1, ch. 10], and many others.

3.1 The effect of non-linear systems

In most power-limited radio systems, the important issue is to optimize the efficiency of the RF power amplifier (commonly known as the 'high power amplifier', or HPA). This is either to minimize overall power consumption in a battery operated transmitter such as a mobile handset, or to make best use of the investment made in the HPA. This latter is especially true of satellite systems, where it is desirable to operate the HPA as near saturation as possible.

RF power amplifiers [3.2, 3.3] are classified according to the proportion of the carrier cycle for which the output device conducts, which determines both power efficiency and linearity. The most linear (and much the least efficient) are *class A*, in which the device conducts throughout the cycle. In *class B* conduction is for nominally half the cycle, which is much more efficient,

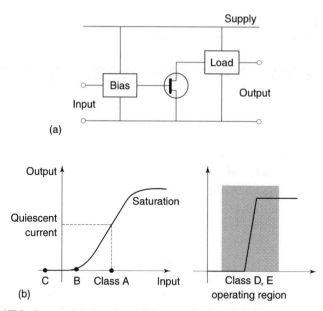

(a)

(b)

Figure 3.1   HPA classes (a) structure; (b) operating points

since it avoids large quiescent currents. ('Class AB' audio amplifiers usually have two devices in the familiar 'push–pull' configuration, each of which conducts for slightly more than half the time.) *Class C* denotes conduction for less than half the cycle. *Classes D* and *E* use the output device only as a switch, and as such may approach 100% efficiency. Figure 3.1(a) shows the general structure of these circuits, while Fig. 3.1(b) shows the device characteristics with the operating points or regions of the different configurations. Note that even the most linear class A amplifier is subject to saturation around its maximum output power.

The effect will be to distort the carrier sine wave, as shown in Fig. 3.2. Note that the amplifier will in nearly all cases be followed by a band-pass filter, which will pass only frequencies close to the fundamental. Thus the harmonic distortion that results is not in itself a severe problem. However, it will result in an amplitude-dependent phase and amplitude distortion, as shown in Fig. 3.3.

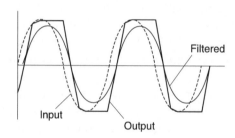

Figure 3.2   Amplitude-phase distortion in non-linear HPA: waveforms

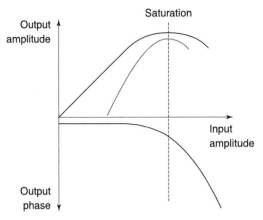

Figure 3.3 Amplitude-phase distortion in non-linear HPA: amplitude-phase characteristic

An amplitude-dependent phase delay due, for example, to the switching delay of saturated semiconductor elements, will result in the amplitude-dependent phase shift. For class B or higher, the characteristic will be more severe still, similar to the grey line shown in Fig. 3.3, and will virtually preclude any operation in the linear part. Even for more linear amplifiers, however, Fig. 3.3 shows that any amplitude variation on the input will result in unwanted modulation of both amplitude and phase of the output. These effects are known as *AM–AM* and *AM–PM conversions*. Note that if the input amplitude is constant neither of these occurs, and there is effectively no distortion.

We may express the transfer function $y(x)$ in polynomial notation:

$$y = \alpha x + \beta x^2 + \gamma x^3 + \cdots \tag{3.1}$$

Using the complex baseband representation of the modulated signal from Equation (2.8):

$$
\left.
\begin{aligned}
y(t) = {}& \frac{\alpha}{2} [b(t)\exp(j\omega_c t) + b^*(t)\exp(-j\omega_c t)] \\
& + \frac{\beta}{4} [b^2(t)\exp(2j\omega_c t) + 2b(t)b^*(t) + b^{*2}(t)\exp(-2j\omega_c t)] \\
& + \frac{\gamma}{8} [b^3(t)\exp(3j\omega_c t) + 3b^2(t)b^*(t)\exp(j\omega_c t) \\
& \quad + 3b(t)b^{*2}(t)\exp(-j\omega_c t) + b^{*3}(t)\exp(-3j\omega_c t)] \\
& + \cdots
\end{aligned}
\right\} \tag{3.2}
$$

Of these terms, the first-order term (in α) is of course undistorted. The second order (in β) has a term at twice the carrier frequency and another at baseband, neither of which will be passed by the band-pass filter. The third-order term contains a term at three times the carrier frequency, which will also be rejected, but it also contains another at the carrier frequency, which cannot be separated from the modulated signal. Expanding this term:

$$\frac{\gamma}{8}[3b^2(t)b^*(t)\exp(j\omega_c t) + 3b(t)b^{*2}(t)\exp(-j\omega_c t)]$$

$$= \frac{3\gamma[b_p^2(t) + b_q^2(t)]}{8}[b(t)\exp(j\omega_c t) + b^*(t)\exp(-j\omega_c t)] = \frac{3\gamma}{4}A^2(t)a(t)$$

$$(3.3)$$

In general, the even-order terms in the transfer function will not generate interfering products at the carrier frequency, while odd-order terms will. However, in most cases it is the third-order term that will dominate. From Equation (3.3) we note that if the amplitude $A(t)$ is constant, then there is no distortion, which agrees with the conclusion reached from our discussion of Fig. 3.3.

We may often characterize the behaviour of a non-linear system in terms of the third-order term, by considering the third-order intermodulation product of two closely spaced sine wave signals within the pass-band. For example two signals, one at ω_c and another at $\omega_c + \omega_d$, generate an intermodulation product at $\omega_c + 2\omega_d$. If the amplitude of the signal at ω_c is held constant, while that at $\omega_c + \omega_d$ is increased, we will observe a linear increase in the output term at $\omega_c + \omega_d$ (dominated by the first-order term of the transfer function), while the term at $\omega_c + 2\omega_d$ starts much smaller, but increases much more rapidly. Figure 3.4 shows a logarithmic plot of both terms. At low amplitudes (in the linear region of the characteristic), both plots are linear, although the third-order term tends to be approximately twice as steep, showing that it varies as the square of the input. At higher amplitudes both terms cease to be linear, but if we extrapolate the linear portions of the plots, the point at which they cross is called the *third-order intercept* (TOI) [3.3, p. 52; 3.4, p. 186], and gives a gauge of the non-linearity of the amplifier, which can readily be measured in practice.

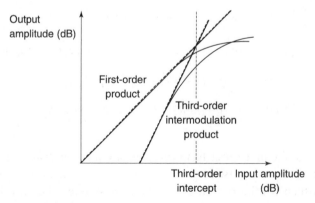

Figure 3.4   The third-order intercept

Mathematically, if the input signal:

$$x(t) = \cos(\omega_c t) + a \cos[(\omega_c + \omega_d)t] \qquad (3.4)$$

then the resultant (neglecting all but the first- and third-order terms) is:

$$y(t) = \alpha x + \gamma x^3$$

$$= \left(\alpha + \frac{3\gamma}{4} + \frac{3a^2\gamma}{2} \right) \cos(\omega_c t) + \left(a\alpha + \frac{3a\gamma}{2} + \frac{3a^3\gamma}{4} \right) \cos[(\omega_c + \omega_d)t]$$

$$+ \frac{3a^2\gamma}{4} \cos[(\omega_c + 2\omega_d)t] + \frac{3a\gamma}{4} \cos[(\omega_c - \omega_d)t] + \frac{3a\gamma}{4} \cos[(3\omega_c + \omega_d)t]$$

$$+ \frac{3a^2\gamma}{4} \cos[(3\omega_c + 2\omega_d)t] + \frac{a^3\gamma}{4} \cos[(3\omega_c + 3\omega_d)t] \qquad (3.5)$$

Of these, the last three terms are out-of-band, and the first two are the terms at the two input frequencies. The third is the third-order term of interest to us. Observe that it varies with the square of the input amplitude a. The second is the linear term in Fig. 3.4, whose magnitude is dominated by the term $a\alpha$. The third-order intercept thus occurs where:

$$\frac{3a^2\gamma}{4} = a\alpha \Rightarrow a = \frac{4\alpha}{3\gamma} \qquad (3.6)$$

where a is the relative amplitude of the second input signal.

A non-linear system also distorts the spectrum of a signal with time-varying amplitude. In general, the effect on a signal that has been filtered to reduce its bandwidth, for example by means of Nyquist filtering, is to regenerate the sidelobes, which had been eliminated. The effect is called *spectral regrowth*. Manipulating Equation (3.3) in the same way as (2.9), we obtain:

$$A(\omega) = \tfrac{1}{2}[C(\omega - \omega_c) + C^*(-\omega + \omega_c)]$$

where

$$C(\omega) = \mathbf{F}[A^2(t)b(t)] = \mathbf{F}[A^2(t)] * B(\omega) \qquad (3.7)$$

which shows that the output equivalent baseband spectrum is the convolution of the input baseband spectrum with the spectrum of the squared magnitude of the signal. Again, we note that if there is no amplitude variation, there is no distortion, and no spectral regrowth. It also shows that the smaller the variation in amplitude, the smaller the spectral regrowth, and therefore that it may be worthwhile minimizing amplitude variation, if constant amplitude is not feasible.

3.2 Linear modulation schemes for non-linear channels

In this section we describe techniques that may be applied to linear modulation to improve its performance on a channel subject to some degree of non-linearity. The basis of these was hinted at above: we should minimize the amplitude variation. First, however, we review the effects of the non-linearity on the performance of linear modulation schemes.

3.2.1 Performance of linear modulation on non-linear channels

Applying the results of the previous section, we observe that a non-linear channel will have three effects on a linear modulation scheme with Nyquist filtering:

(1) It will generate *self-interference* due to in-band intermodulation products. This can be understood in terms of a distortion of the i.s.i.-free Nyquist pulses, which will cause i.s.i. to reappear. For a third-order non-linearity, this self-interference results from the in-band third-order term in Equation (3.2). It will result in a 'spreading' of the constellation points of the recovered signal, even in the absence of noise.

(2) It will give rise to AM–AM and AM–PM conversion: that is, any variation in input amplitude will result in a non-linear variation in output amplitude, and in a phase shift. This is most noticeable where the constellation itself involves amplitude variation, as in QAM schemes.

(We distinguish *constant amplitude constellations*, such as *M*-PSK, from those inherently involving amplitude modulation, like QAM. Note that the use of a constant amplitude constellation does not imply a constant amplitude signal, since Nyquist filtering tends to introduce envelope variations, as we have seen in Chapter 2.)

(3) It will give rise to spectral regrowth. This is probably the most important effect in constant amplitude constellations.

Figure 3.5 shows a simulation block diagram to demonstrate these effects. Note how the HPA in fact lies between the two parts of the Nyquist filter: the transmit and receive halves, which are each root-raised cosines. This complicates the effects of the HPA, and implies that it is the amplitude variations in the root-raised cosine filtered signal that affect the amplifier.

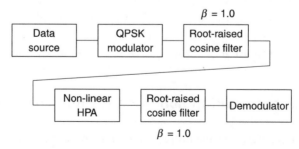

Figure 3.5 Simulation of linear modulation over a non-linear channel

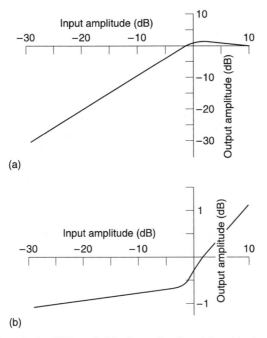

Figure 3.6 **(a) Magnitude (dB) and (b) phase (radians) input/output characteristics, plotted against input in dB, of HPA of Fig. 3.5**

The input/output amplitude and phase characteristics of the HPA are shown in Fig. 3.6. The amplifier was operated in simulation at around saturation. Note that no thermal noise was introduced in the simulation.

Figure 3.7 shows the eye diagram (a) and the constellation scatter diagram (b) for the signal at the receiver in Fig. 3.5. Note that the 'spread' of the constellation points is entirely due to self-interference resulting from the non-linear amplifier. The constellation is also phase shifted due to the amplitude-dependent phase shift of the HPA, but because all signal points have equal amplitude, this rotation can easily be compensated.

Figure 3.8 shows the spectral regrowth due to the HPA, showing the filtered spectrum before the amplifier, and that after it. The re-appearance of sidelobes is clear, and their level is only a little more than 20-dB below the carrier (−20 dBc).

Figure 3.9 explains these results, in view of the theory described above. It shows the amplitude of the input signal to the HPA, demonstrating the variation in its amplitude. The second plot shows the spectrum of this envelope variation, incorporating a sidelobe only 15–20 dB below the d.c. term, which is also visible. This, convolved with the signal spectrum, is responsible for the regrown sidelobe in the output spectrum, according to Equation (3.7).

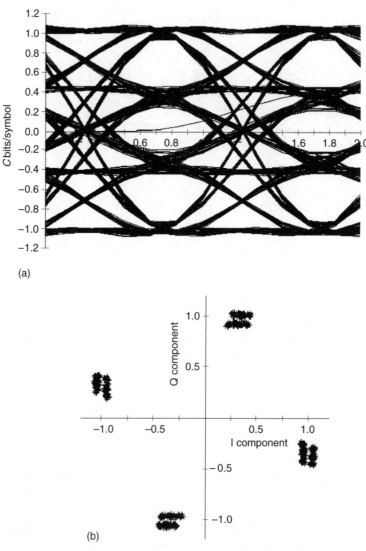

(a)

(b)

Figure 3.7 (a) Eye and (b) scatter diagram for received signal in simulation of Fig. 3.5

The simulation was repeated using a 16-QAM modulator, operating at the same average power as the QPSK system. Figure 3.10 shows the resulting scatter diagram. Here, because the constellation is not constant amplitude, the AM–AM and AM–PM conversions cause serious distortion of the constellation, resulting in performance degradation even if compensation is applied in the receiver.

Figure 3.11 shows the spectral regrowth due to the HPA for the same 16-QAM system. It is somewhat more serious than that of QPSK, because the envelope variation is greater.

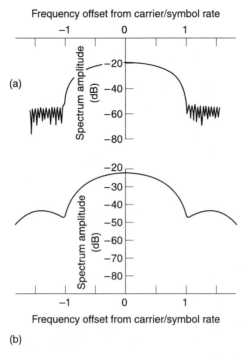

Figure 3.8 Frequency offset from carrier/symbol rate ... (a) ... Spectrum amplitude (dB) ... (b) ... Frequency offset from carrier/symbol rate

Figure 3.8   Spectrum of signal in transmitter: (a) before and (b) after HPA

3.2.2   Optimization of linear modulation for non-linear channels

We have seen that it is highly desirable when a non-linear channel is used to minimize the amplitude variation of the signal. If a transition from one symbol to the next passes through the centre of the constellation diagram, then after filtering we may expect that the envelope will drop to zero during the transition. This is demonstrated in the simulation of Fig. 3.9. Hence, it is very desirable to avoid such transitions. This can be accomplished in a number of ways, the two most important of which are:

1. Offset QPSK (OQPSK): We have noted in the previous chapter that in conventional QPSK with Gray mapping, each of the two bits per symbol are transmitted independently on one of the two channels (I and Q) of the modulator. This is also illustrated in Fig. 3.12. In offset QPSK the two bit streams are staggered, so that both channels do not change simultaneously, as shown in Fig. 3.13. The constellation diagram in Fig. 3.13 shows that transitions do not now pass through the centre of the diagram, and hence the amplitude fluctuation is much reduced. Note, however, that transitions within the constellation diagram now occur twice as frequently. This may make symbol timing more difficult to acquire. Nevertheless, because the two channels carry orthogonal signals and still have the same baud rate as conventional QPSK, the

59

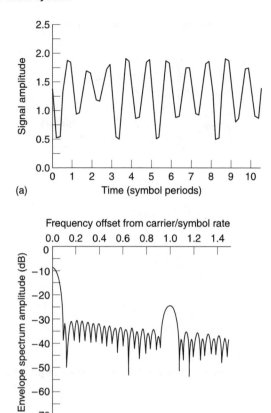

(a)

(b)

Figure 3.9 (a) Envelope of input signal and (b) its spectrum

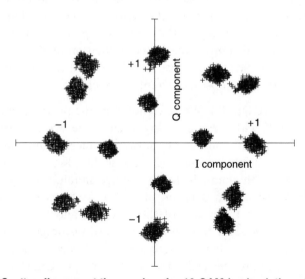

Figure 3.10 Scatter diagram at the receiver for 16-QAM in simulation of Fig. 3.5

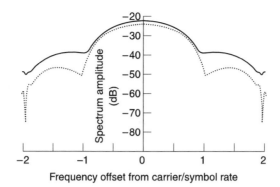

Figure 3.11   HPA output spectrum showing spectral regrowth for 16-QAM system (---), compared with QPSK (—)

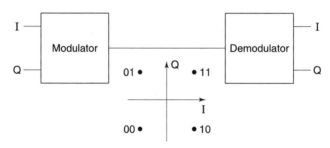

Figure 3.12   Gray coded QPSK as independent transmission on I/Q channels

bandwidth is not increased. This scheme is used in some satellite systems [3.5, ch. 19].

2. $\pi/4$ QPSK: Retains the same symbol rate as QPSK, but this time at the cost of increasing the effective constellation size. The constellation is best considered as two interleaved QPSK constellations (coloured white and

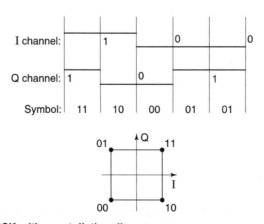

Figure 3.13   OQPSK with constellation diagram

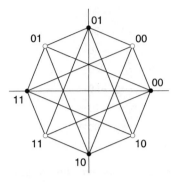

Figure 3.14 Constellation of π/4 QPSK

black in Fig. 3.14), relatively shifted by $\pi/4$ (hence the name). A point from each constellation is transmitted alternately, so once again transitions through the centre of the diagram do not occur, as Fig. 3.14 shows. Symbol timing recovery may be easier than in OQPSK, especially since some transition must occur at each symbol, but the increased constellation size may complicate carrier recovery. This scheme is of great practical importance, since it is used in the North American mobile/personal radio standards IS-54 and IS-136, and in the European TETRA standard for private business radio ([3.1; 3.6] – see also http://www.etsi.org/tetra/tetra.htm).

In practice, neither of these methods entirely remove the effects of the non-linear channel and, in particular, spectral regrowth remains a significant problem if the HPA is not highly linear. For example, Fig. 3.15 shows the output spectrum if the QPSK modulator of Fig. 3.5 is replaced by a $\pi/4$ QPSK modulator, compared with simple QPSK, in this case for 35% roll-off. The regrown sidelobes remain very close to -20 dBc: there is in fact very little improvement. If we are unable to achieve a better degree of linearity

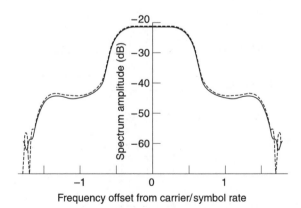

Figure 3.15 Spectral regrowth using π/4 QPSK (—), compared with QPSK (- - -), for 35% roll-off

than the amplifier simulated, non-linear modulation techniques must be used. This problem is particularly serious in PMR systems like TETRA, because to avoid near–far problems (when a transmitter on an adjacent channel is much nearer than the wanted transmitter) the standard has a very strict out-of-band radiation limit [3.7].

3.3   Non-linear modulation

Non-linear, or *exponential*, modulation effectively means frequency-shift keying (FSK – see Section 2.2). Since only the phase is (indirectly) modulated, these are inherently constant-envelope schemes, i.e. provided no post-modulation filtering is applied. The main issue, therefore, is to minimize the bandwidth or the out-of-band signal power without post-filtering. It can be shown, however, that even in principle a constant-envelope modulated signal cannot be strictly band-limited in the way a linearly modulated signal can (see, for example, spectrum plots in [3.8]).

In this section we consider first the general class of FSK modulation schemes, then the important special case of MSK (minimum-shift keying), which achieves a significant improvement in spectral characteristics. Finally, we describe the class of *continuous phase modulation* (CPM) schemes, which improve the spectrum still further. The best known and most important of these is Gaussian minimum-shift keying (GMSK), as used in the mobile radio standard GSM and in DECT digital cordless telephones [3.1].

3.3.1   FSK

In Section 2.2 we defined non-linear modulation as any scheme to which the pulse superposition model of the complex baseband signal did not apply; in other words, the signal could not be made up of the sum of time-shifted pulses weighted by the data. In the case of exponential modulation (which is probably the only significant class of non-linear modulation), we gave the complex baseband signal as (2.18):

$$b(t) = \exp(jd_i\omega_d t) \tag{3.8}$$

For the binary case this led to (2.19):

$$a(t) = \left\{ \begin{array}{l} \mathrm{Re}[\exp(j\omega_d t)\exp(j\omega_c t)] \\ \mathrm{Re}[\exp(-j\omega_d t)\exp(j\omega_c t)] \end{array} \right. = \left\{ \begin{array}{l} \mathrm{Re}\{\exp[j(\omega_c + \omega_d)t]\} \\ \mathrm{Re}\{\exp[j(\omega_c - \omega_d)t]\} \end{array} \right\}$$

$$= \left\{ \begin{array}{ll} \cos[(\omega_c + \omega_d)t], & d_i = +1 \ (\text{'1'}) \\ \cos[(\omega_c - \omega_d)t], & d_i = -1 \ (\text{'0'}) \end{array} \right\} \tag{3.9}$$

which is FSK with frequency shift $\pm\omega_d$. Equation (3.8) shows the exponential relationship between the data and the signal, which gives rise to the name.

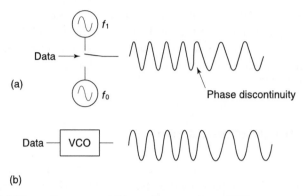

(a)

(b)

Figure 3.16   (a) Discontinuous and (b) continuous phase FSK

The most important parameter of FSK modulation is not the frequency shift itself, but rather the relationship of the frequency shift with the symbol rate r_s (or equivalently the symbol period, T). The *modulation index* is defined as:

$$h = \frac{\omega_d T}{\pi} = 2f_d T = \frac{2f_d}{r_s} \tag{3.10}$$

As we will see, this determines both the ease of demodulation of the scheme, and its spectral properties.

Another important factor is *phase continuity*. Step changes, or discontinuities, in the time domain tend to give rise to large sidelobes in the frequency domain (as is seen in the spectrum of rectangular data waveforms). Such changes will occur in FSK only if the phase of the waveform changes in the transition between symbols. This is normally avoided by ensuring that the phase is continuous across symbol boundaries, resulting in continuous phase FSK (CP-FSK). It occurs automatically if FSK is generated by feeding a data signal to a single voltage-controlled oscillator (VCO), as opposed to switching between two separate oscillators (Fig. 3.16). The mathematical model of continuous phase FSK may require the inclusion of a phase term in Equation (3.8), chosen for each symbol to ensure phase continuity:

$$b(t) = \exp(jd_i\omega_d t + \phi_i)$$

where

$$\phi_i = \phi_{i-1} + d_i\omega_d T \tag{3.11}$$

3.3.2   Optimum demodulation of FSK

The optimum demodulation of FSK involves setting up a matched filter (or equivalently a correlation detector) for each of the two possible signals, as shown in Fig. 3.17. The outputs are then compared and the greatest selected. The matched filter consists of a multiplier, multiplying by the appropriate signal frequency, followed by an 'integrate-and-dump' circuit, which integrates

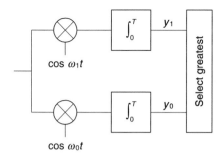

Figure 3.17   Optimum FSK demodulator

over the symbol period, then resets. (This receiver does not take into account any phase continuity of the signal, which means that other receivers may in fact perform better, as we will see.)

The output of the '1' branch 'integrate-and-dump' for inputs '1' and '0':

$$
y_1 = \begin{cases} \int_0^T \cos^2(\omega_1 t)\, dt, & \text{'1'} \\ \int_0^T \cos(\omega_0 t)\cos(\omega_1 t)\, dt, & \text{'0'} \end{cases}
$$

$$
= \begin{cases} \int_0^T \tfrac{1}{2}[1 + \cos(2\omega_1 t)\, dt], & \text{'1'} \\ \int_0^T \tfrac{1}{2}\{\cos[(\omega_1 - \omega_0)t]\cos[(\omega_1 + \omega_0)t]\}\, dt, & \text{'0'} \end{cases}
$$

$$
\approx \begin{cases} T/2, & \text{'1'} \\ \int_0^T \dfrac{T}{2(\omega_1 - \omega_0)}\sin[(\omega_1 - \omega_0)T]\, dt, & \text{'0'} \end{cases} \tag{3.12}
$$

It is clearly desirable to have zero output on the '1' branch when a '0' is transmitted (and vice versa): hence we should choose a value of shift frequency for which $\sin[(\omega_1 - \omega_0)T]$ is zero. If this is the case, we say that the '1' signal and the '0' signal are *orthogonal*, because their cross-correlation is zero. This will be the case if the modulation index:

$$
h = \frac{\omega_d T}{\pi} = \frac{(\omega_1 - \omega_0)T}{2\pi} = \frac{k\pi}{2\pi} = k \times 0.5 \tag{3.13}
$$

where k is any positive integer. Hence, we can expect optimal performance if h is some multiple of 0.5. The minimum h for which this holds is 0.5: hence the term *minimum-shift keying* (MSK). The BER performance for binary orthogonal FSK is obtained in Section 3.3.5 as a special case of *M*-FSK.

3.3.3   MSK

MSK, then is binary FSK with modulation index $h = 0.5$. We will consider the resulting spectrum in Section 3.3.4. This value of h results in an interesting

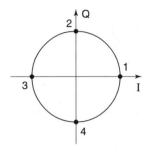

Figure 3.18 Constellation diagram of MSK

property of the effective constellation diagram, as we may see by considering the phase change $\Delta\phi$ which occurs in the course of one bit period, T:

$$\Delta\phi = \pm\omega_d T = h\pi = \frac{\pi}{2} \tag{3.14}$$

using Equation (3.10). Hence the constellation diagram, observed at the end of each symbol period, is as shown in Fig. 3.18, with $\pi/2$ between each constellation point. (The labelling of the points is arbitrary.) Note that between symbols the phase changes linearly with time, and the amplitude remains constant, so between symbols the signal moves evenly around the circle from one constellation point to another. Note also that the signal never remains on the same constellation point: it moves to one of its neighbours. For example, from point 1 it will move to point 2 (for data '1') or 4 (for '0'), then from point 2 to 3 or 1, etc.

This, of course, is identical to the constellation of QPSK, which has implications for demodulation. It also results in another interesting property. If we consider the I component amplitude as the signal moves from point 2 to 1 and then either back to 2 or to 4, we observe that it follows a half-sine function. Similarly, for the Q component in moving from 1 to 2 to 3 (or back to 1). This suggests that the signal can be decomposed into the sum of time-shifted half-sine pulses on I and Q, with amplitude ±1 depending on the data. In other words, it is effectively a linear modulation scheme with signalling pulse $g(t)$ a half-sine pulse, duration two bit periods. Figure 3.19 takes this one stage further, showing how the signal can be regarded as OQPSK with half-sine shaping. This also implies that an OQPSK modulator can be adapted to generate MSK, in place of the standard CP-FSK modulator. Note, however, that the same data will not produce identical signals in the two structures.

This also implies that an OQPSK demodulator structure (an I/Q demodulator, as used for M-PSK, but with staggered samples in the two branches), can also be used for MSK, as an alternative to the FSK demodulator. Once again, however, the same signal will not give rise to the same data in the two

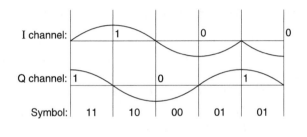

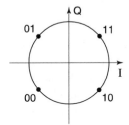

Figure 3.19   MSK as shaped OQPSK

demodulators, so a decoder may be required. Figure 3.20 shows a suitable demodulator. Note that the low-pass filters should be matched filters for the half-sine pulses.

At the end of each bit interval, this demodulator must decide between the two opposite points of the constellation diagram, i.e. it should effectively be regarded as two interleaved BPSK constellations. Hence, the BER performance is the same as that of BPSK, Equation (2.45), (or QPSK), i.e:

$$P_e = Q\left(\sqrt{\frac{2E_b}{N_0}}\right) \tag{3.15}$$

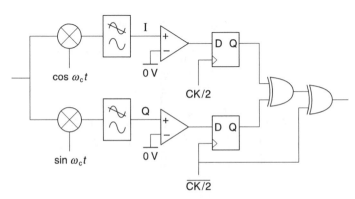

Figure 3.20   I/Q demodulator for MSK, with output decoder

3.3.4 Spectrum of MSK and other FSK schemes

The same property allows us to calculate the spectrum, $G(f)$, of MSK, and indeed all other orthogonal FSK schemes. (The calculation for the general case is extremely complex – see [3.9, pp. 209–16].) It is simply given by the Fourier transform of the half-sine pulse shape:

$$G(f) = \mathbf{F}[g(t)] = \int_{-T}^{T} \cos\left(\frac{\pi t}{2}\right) \exp(-j2\pi f t)\, dt = \frac{4T \cos(2\pi f T)}{\pi[(4fT)^2 - 1]} \qquad (3.16)$$

where T is the symbol period, and $\cos(\pi t/2)$ gives the shape of the half-sine function, shifted by T for mathematical convenience. Figure 3.21 shows this spectrum on a log scale. Note that the main lobe bandwidth is $1.5r_b$, 25% less than that of BPSK. Moreover, the sidelobes are about 24-dB below the main lobe, compared with 13 dB in BPSK.

The same approach may in fact be used to calculate the spectrum of all orthogonal FSK schemes. We distinguish between integer and half-integer modulation indices (1, 2, ..., *versus* 0.5, 1.5, ...). For integer modulation schemes the phase shift between symbols is a multiple of π. Hence, the constellation contains (at most) two points. Figure 3.22 shows the constellation, and the magnitude of the I/Q components during the course of successive symbol periods. Note that the I component is a continuous sine wave, which will generate a pair of discrete side frequencies in the modulated signal at the two signal frequencies. The Q signal consists of a series of half-sine pulses (or multiples thereof), with data-dependent amplitude, and hence gives rise to a spectrum given by the Fourier transform of the appropriate pulse shape.

Similarly, Fig. 3.23 gives the constellation and I/Q amplitudes for $h = 1.5$ (as an example of half-integer modulation). The constellation is as MSK, but this time the phase changes by $3\pi/2$ in each bit period. Both I and Q have the form of amplitude shown: there is no discrete sine-wave component. Again, the spectrum can be calculated from the Fourier transform. Figure 3.24 shows

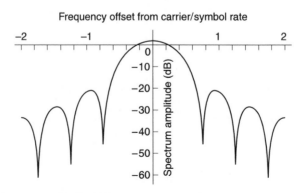

Figure 3.21 Spectrum of MSK (dB) plotted against frequency normalized to bit rate

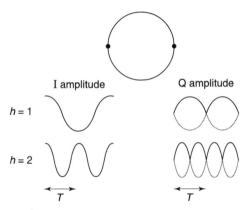

I amplitude   Q amplitude

$h = 1$

$h = 2$

T T

Figure 3.22   I/Q amplitudes for integer modulation index

the resulting spectra, on a linear scale. The impulses mark the discrete sine-wave components. This shows that as the modulation index increases, the spectrum separates into two distinct parts, around each of the signalling frequencies. The plot also gives a good guide to the spectrum for intermediate modulation indices.

3.3.5   *M*-FSK

Frequency-shift keying can be generalized from binary to M-ary, in which the data d_i is permitted to take M values, $[-(M-1), -(M-3), \ldots, -1, 1, \ldots, M-3, M-1]$. We may then transmit $\log_2(M)$ bits per M-FSK symbol. We retain the former definition of modulation index, so we now have M evenly spaced tones between $f_c \pm (M-1)f_d$. The same orthogonality condition on h still obtains. The spectrum then occupies a bandwidth of approximately $2Mf_d$, or Mhr_b, but is much more nearly flat-topped. (For orthogonal schemes, the technique of the previous section can be adapted.)

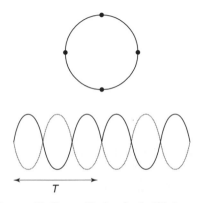

T

Figure 3.23   Constellation and I, Q amplitudes for half-integer modulation index

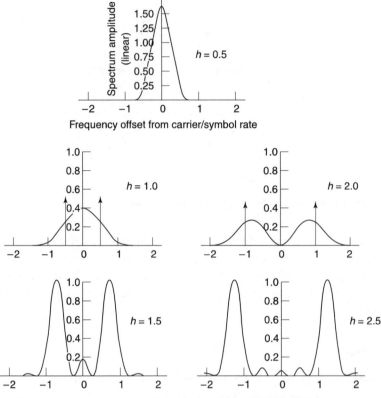

Figure 3.24 Power spectrum (on linear scale) of MSK and other orthogonal FSK schemes

The optimum demodulator structure of Fig. 3.17 can be generalized to include M branches, one for each tone. It can be shown [3.9, pp. 260–4] that for an orthogonal scheme the BER becomes:

$$P_b = \frac{2^{k-1}}{2^k - 1} \int_{-\infty}^{\infty} [1 - Q(-y)^{M-1}] \frac{1}{\sqrt{2\pi}} \exp\left[-\frac{(y - \sqrt{2kE_b/N_0})^2}{2}\right] dy$$

$$\approx \frac{M}{2} Q\left(\sqrt{2k\frac{E_b}{N_0}}\right) \tag{3.17}$$

where $k = \log_2(M)$. (The result applies to *any* scheme using M orthogonal signals, not just M-FSK.) The result is plotted in Fig. 3.25 for various values of M. It shows that M-FSK can achieve better power efficiency than any of the other schemes we have considered so far. The drawback is that it occupies a greater bandwidth for a given data rate: we have traded bandwidth efficiency for power efficiency.

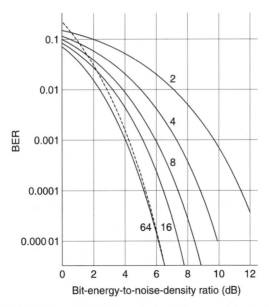

Figure 3.25   BER of _M_-FSK against bit-energy-to-noise-density ratio for various _M_ (the dashed line is the approximation for _M_ = 64)

3.3.6   Continuous phase modulation and GMSK

While MSK has a narrower bandwidth than BPSK, and is significantly better in terms of sidelobe level than any unfiltered linear scheme, it still retains side-lobes at a level that would give unacceptable adjacent channel interference in most practical systems. Any attempt to filter these out, post-modulation, would regenerate envelope variations. Hence, we require a means to improve the spectrum of MSK further.

While the continuous phase condition prevents any discontinuities in the signal, there remain discontinuities in the frequency, and hence in the signal slope. It would seem desirable to eliminate these discontinuities, which can be done by filtering the data signal _before_ modulation, as shown in Fig. 3.26. This is known as _continuous phase modulation_ (CPM): while strictly speaking the term applies to any CP-FSK scheme, it is usually only· applied to pre-filtered FSK.

A wide range of filter responses are possible [3.8, 3.9–3.12]: some impulse responses are shown in Fig. 3.27. Of those illustrated, the Gaussian, which leads to _Gaussian minimum-shift keying_ (GMSK) [3.5], is the most important: 3-RC is little used, since the others provide better spectra. 'Tamed FM' is the scheme that uses, in some sense, the optimum filter from the point of view of minimizing bandwidth; but GMSK is the most widely used, for its relative simplicity and its flexibility.

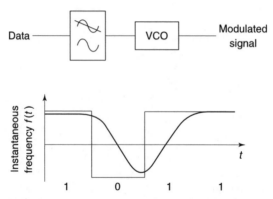

Figure 3.26 Continuous phase modulator, with plot of instantaneous signal frequency

Some resulting modulated signal spectra (plotted single-sided in dB) are shown in Fig. 3.28, compared with spectra of unfiltered (O)QPSK and MSK for the same data rate. This shows how sidelobes may be effectively eliminated by this means, although there remains some inherent out-of-band signal power. Two different values of Gaussian filter bandwidth are given for GMSK: it may be seen how choice of this parameter allows the spectrum to be tailored.

The bandwidth of the Gaussian filter is quantified in the *time-bandwidth product*, *BT*. This is the product of the 3-dB bandwidth of the filter and the symbol period (or its ratio with the bit rate). Typically values of 0.3–0.5 are used. The Gaussian response is interesting, in that the frequency response has the same shape as the impulse response. The standard deviation τ of the impulse response is related to the bandwidth B by:

$$B = \frac{\log_e(2)}{\pi\tau} = \frac{0.2206}{\tau}$$

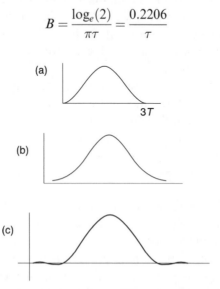

Figure 3.27 Pre-filter impulse responses for CPM: (a) raised cosine (3-RC), (b) Gaussian (GMSK) and (c) tamed FM

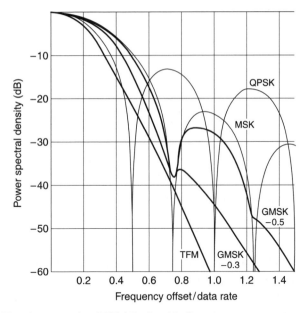

Figure 3.28   Signal spectra for CPM (single-sided)

where the impulse response

$$h(t) = \frac{1}{\tau\sqrt{2\pi}} \exp\left(-\frac{t^2}{2\tau^2}\right) \tag{3.18}$$

Hence, typically, the impulse response lasts two–three symbol periods (at the 95% level).

The price of the resulting improvement in bandwidth efficiency is, as usual, a degradation in power efficiency. However, if the time-bandwidth product is not too small (0.3 or greater), the effect is not excessive: less than 1 dB. The degradation is due to intersymbol interference in the data introduced by

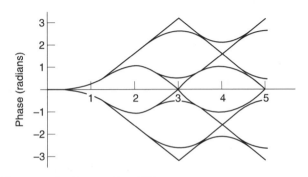

Figure 3.29   Phase trellis diagram for CPM

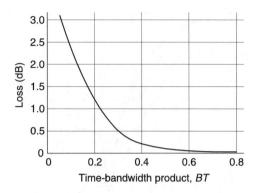

Figure 3.30   Loss factor in GMSK against time-bandwidth product

the pre-filter, which just prevents the phase from reaching its final value at the end of a symbol period. The effect can be usefully illustrated using the *phase trellis diagram*, which is a superimposed plot of all the possible phase trajectories against time for all possible data combinations, in the manner of an eye diagram, as shown in Fig. 3.29. This can be computed from the filter impulse response. (Note that the phase is in reality continuous between $+\pi$ and $-\pi$, between the top and the bottom of the diagram.) In the diagram, the underlying 'diamond' pattern would be the result for MSK; the rounding at the vertices is due to the pre-filter. The effect is to reduce the height of the eye opening, which degrades its performance in noise by a factor equal to the cosine of half the eye width. The loss factor is plotted in dB against time-bandwidth product in Fig. 3.30.

Problems

3.1 Find the in-band signal term (as in Equation (3.3)) due to a fifth-order term in the transfer function of Equation (3.1), $y(x) = \alpha x + \cdots + \varepsilon x^5 + \cdots$.

3.2 The *travelling wave tube* (TWT) is a non-linear HPA often used on board satellites. A commonly used mathematical model [3.13] of its non-linearity in amplitude response is:

$$y(x) = \frac{\alpha_r x}{1 + \beta_r x^2}$$

with $\alpha_r = 1.96$, $\beta_r = 0.99$. Expand this formula to express it as a polynomial in x and, hence, find the third-order intercept of the amplifier. Find also the input amplitude which results in saturation, defined as the point at which the output amplitude reaches a maximum.

3.3 The non-linearity in phase of the TWT may be expressed as:

$$\Phi(r) = \frac{\alpha_\phi x^2}{1 + \beta_\phi x^2}$$

with $\alpha_\phi = 2.53$, $\beta_\phi = 2.82$. A 16-QAM constellation is applied to this amplifier, with average power 3-dB below saturation (this is referred to as a 3-dB *back-off*). Find the position of the constellation points and, hence, sketch the constellation diagram, after the amplifier. Hence, also estimate the degradation in BER performance compared with the undistorted constellation, neglecting self-interference. Assume that the receiver allows for the distortion of the constellation.

3.4 Assuming that the transitions between constellation points occur along straight lines, calculate the minimum to maximum amplitude ratio (in dB) for OQPSK and $\pi/4$-QPSK.

3.5 Find expressions for the spectra of CP-FSK with modulation indices of 0.5, 1.0 and 1.5. Sketch the spectra on a logarithmic vertical scale and, hence, find the bandwidth as a function of bit rate for an out-of-band threshold 30 dB below the maximum spectral density.

3.6 Sketch the complex baseband waveforms generated by an MSK modulator in CP-FSK form and in linear form, for the same data sequence.

References

3.1 Rappaport, T.S. (1996) *Wireless Communications: Principles and Practice*, Prentice-Hall.

3.2 Cripps, S.C. (1999) *RF Power Amplifiers for Wireless Communications*, Artech House.

3.3 Pothecary, N. (1999) *Feedforward Linear Power Amplifiers*, Artech House.

3.4 Vizmuller, P. (1995) *RF Design Guide: Systems, Circuits and Equations*, Artech House.

3.5 Evans, B.G. (Ed.) (1999) *Satellite Communication Systems*, 3rd Edition, IEE Telecommunications Series, Institute of Electrical Engineers.

3.6 Varrall, G. (1998) TETRA – a radio access and network technology for Europe. *Electronic Engineering*, **70**(853): 57–8.

3.7 Kenington, P.B., Wilkinson, R.J. and Parsons, K.J. (1997) Noise performance of a Cartesian loop transmitter. *IEEE Transactions on Vehicular Technology*, **46**(2): 467–76.

3.8 Sundberg, C.-E. (1986) Continuous phase modulation. *IEEE Communications Magazine*, **24**(4): 25–38.

3.9 Proakis, J.G. (1995) *Digial Communications*, 3rd Edition, McGraw-Hill.

3.10 Aulin, T., Lindell, G. and Sundberg, C.-E. (1981) Selecting smoothing pulses for partial response digital FM. *IEE Proceedings – F*, **128**(4): 237–44.

3.11 Aulin, T., Rydbeck, N. and Sundberg, C.-E. (1981) Continuous phase modulation – Part II: partial response signalling. *IEEE Transactions on Communications*, **29**(3): 210–25.

3.12 Murota, K. and Hirade, K. (1981) GMSK modulation for digital mobile ratio telephony. *IEEE Transactions on Communications*, **COM-29**(7): 1044–50.

3.13 Saleh, A.A.M. Frequency-independent and frequency-dependent non-linear models of TWT amplifiers. *IEEE Transactions on Communications*, **29**(11): 1715–20.

Chapter 4

Modem design

Having outlined the principles of modulation, both linear and non-linear, in Chapters 1 and 2, we now consider some of the more practical details of modulators and demodulators, the combination of which in a radio terminal is commonly known as a *modem*. For reasons that will become clear, demodulation is much the more difficult task, and thus we will spend much more time on demodulation than on modulation.

Increasingly, modems for modern communication systems are fully digital in implementation: that is, as well as handling digital information, these are implemented using digital signal processing (DSP). For example, in the receiver the signal is sampled, usually at intermediate frequency (IF), and converted to digital form using an analog-to-digital converter (ADC). Thereafter, all processing is performed on this digital representation of the signal, either using a DSP processor, or in digital hardware, such as an application-specific integrated circuit (ASIC) or field programmable gate array (FPGA). This concept is also known as *software radio* [4.1]. This opens up new techniques which were not available in the older all-analog modems; wherever possible in this chapter we will describe these newer digital techniques. Increasingly, also, services of all types are implemented in digital form, from speech to high-definition video: the *multimedia* concept. This has implications for terminals [4.2] and, in turn, for the data throughput rate, BER and delay introduced by the terminal. Further, [4.3] describes the design of a state-of-the-art wireless modem, which may prove interesting as a case study.

We begin by outlining the overall structure of a modem, identifying the main elements. We then briefly review the techniques used for modulation, both linear and exponential (constant envelope). We shall see that there are two main classes of demodulator: coherent and non-coherent, each of which is then described. We note two main types of non-coherent demodulator that are most commonly used in practical communication systems: *limiter-discriminator* and *differential*. However, the main complexity of a coherent demodulator is not, in fact, in the demodulator itself, but in the sub-system required to recover the carrier reference, which is one aspect of the task of *synchronization*. Hence, in the final section we consider synchronization in general, including carrier recovery and symbol timing (or clock) recovery. We also evaluate the effect of carrier and clock timing errors on the performance of the modem.

4.1 Modem architecture

The general structure of a modem is outlined in Fig. 4.1, showing how it fits in with other elements of a radio communications transceiver. Sub-systems considered in this chapter are captioned using bold typeface. Elements which may not always be present are outlined in grey. The dashed line surrounds those elements of the receiver that are usually implemented in DSP in modern systems.

As noted in Chapter 1, the modem provides the essential link between the (digital) user interface (which we assume also to contain the FEC encoder

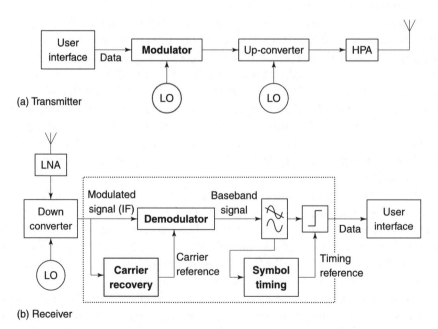

Figure 4.1 General architecture of a modem in a complete radio communication system (HPA, high power (RF) amplifier; LNA, low noise amplifier; LO, local oscillator)

and decoder) and the (analog) RF sub-systems (which interface with the antenna). At the transmitter end, the modulator generates a modulated carrier signal, either directly or by manipulating an external carrier signal. At the receiver end, the demodulator regenerates a baseband signal from the modulated signal. A *coherent* demodulator requires a regenerated carrier reference for this and, hence, requires the *carrier recovery* block: a *non-coherent* demodulator requires no external signal. In either case a *clock* signal is required, which is normally recovered from the baseband signal, to provide a symbol timing reference. This is used to drive a decision device, which estimates the transmitted symbol from a sample of the signal taken once per symbol. This is preceded by a filter, usually a *matched filter*. The theory of matched filtering and of the decision process is covered in Chapter 2.

4.2 Modulators

As we have seen in Chapter 2, for linear modulation schemes the modulator is simply a multiplier, giving the product of a sinusoidal carrier signal with the baseband data signal, usually Nyquist filtered. For BPSK it is a (four quadrant) real multiplier with a real sine wave; for other schemes it is a complex multiplier of a complex sinusoid, that is, an I/Q modulator (see Fig. 2.5). This may be implemented using an analog multiplier, usually a microwave device such as a ring modulator or an active semiconductor device, operating at relatively high frequency [4.4, ch. 17]. Alternatively, and most commonly in modern digital systems, the implementation can be entirely digital. Here all components are simply replaced by digital equivalents. The sine and cosine signals would also be generated internally.

Exponential modulation schemes like MSK and GMSK are in principle generated by frequency modulation, for example by feeding the baseband data signal (pre-filtered in the case of GMSK) directly to a voltage-controlled oscillator (VCO) – see Fig. 3.16(b). However, this is not usually the method by which the signals are generated in practice. The properties of MSK, and in particular its demodulation, depend quite critically on achieving a modulation index of precisely 0.5, and it is difficult to guarantee sufficient accuracy by this technique.

We noted in Section 3.3.3 that MSK can be treated as a linear modulation scheme: a form of OQPSK in which the signalling pulses on the I and Q branches of the modulator have a half-sine shape. This clearly provides the basis for an alternative method of generation using an I/Q modulator, as illustrated in Fig. 4.2. Note that a precoder is required for the data to obtain a signal equivalent to the conventional FSK modulator.

Unfortunately, this method cannot be used straightforwardly for GMSK (or indeed any other partial response CPM scheme). For one thing, the Gaussian

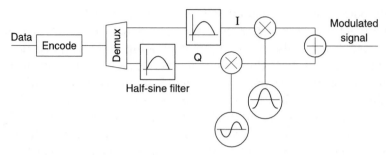

Figure 4.2 Linear modulator for MSK

prefilter changes the effective pulse shape, but more significantly it also introduces memory between symbols, so that the modulated signal for the current symbol depends on a number of previous symbols. However, an adequate approximation is possible by adding pulses of different shapes due to several successive symbols. The approach is described in detail in [4.5], and is based on the amplitude modulated pulses (AMP) decomposition of [4.6]. Figure 4.3 shows how a constant envelope GMSK signal can be approximated quite accurately as the sum of two types of Gaussian-like pulses modulating the in-phase and quadrature components in the same way as in Fig. 4.2. The errors between the exact GMSK signal and the approximation at the ends of the sequence are due to start-up transients.

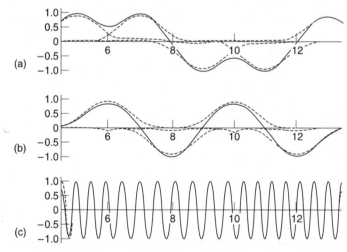

Figure 4.3 Generation of GMSK (time-bandwidth product 0.3) using AMP decomposition approach: (a) synthesis of in-phase component (solid line) from two sequences of signalling pulses (dashed lines); (b) synthesis of quadrature component; (c) resulting approximation to modulated signal (solid line) compared with exact GMSK signal (dashed line) (Note. Each graduation mark on the x-axis corresponds to two units, or one symbol period)

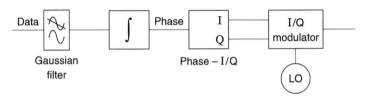

Figure 4.4   Phase modulation approach to GMSK

An alternative approach is to generate the required phase trajectory directly, as shown in Fig. 4.4. A digital filter with Gaussian impulse response is applied to the data signal, in the same way as the conventional analog implementation. This is then integrated to convert from frequency to phase. The phase is then used to generate in-phase and quadrature inputs to an I/Q demodulator, as before.

4.3   Coherent demodulators

As mentioned above, demodulators divide into two main classes: *coherent* and *non-coherent*. A coherent demodulator makes use of a *phase coherent* replica of the original carrier, identical in both frequency and phase. (In practice, of course, this must be obtained from the received signal: the techniques involved are described in Section 4.5.1). This enables it to make full use of the information available in the received signal, and thus results in optimum, or *maximum likelihood* (ML) demodulation.

Figure 4.5(a) shows the structure of a general coherent demodulator. The signal is recovered by multiplying the received signal by the replica carrier. Figure 4.5(b) shows how this results in a signal at twice the carrier frequency and in a replica of the original baseband signal (shown in grey). The former may be removed by means of a low-pass filter. A filter matched to the baseband signalling pulse then recovers the optimum signal to act as decision variable. In practice, the low-pass filter and the matched filter may be combined. As has been shown in Section 2.3.3, the whole structure then acts as a filter matched to the modulated signal.

The general demodulator contains two arms, corresponding to the two arms of the general modulator shown in Fig. 2.5. One uses a cosine wave (in phase with the original carrier) and the other a sine wave (in quadrature with it). These respond, respectively, to the in-phase and quadrature components of the modulated signal and, hence, can be used to demodulate general constellations. They are referred to as the 'I' and 'Q' branches, and the whole demodulator is called an I/Q demodulator.

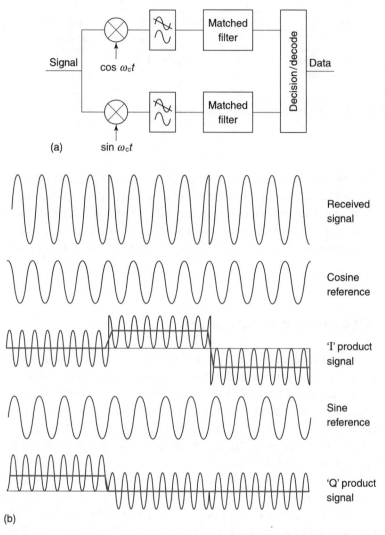

Figure 4.5   Coherent demodulation: (a) block diagram, (b) signal waveforms

Mathematically, the two product terms are (substituting for $a(t)$ from Equation (2.4)):

$$x_p(t) = a(t)\cos(\omega_c t) = b_p(t)\cos^2(\omega_c t) - b_q(t)\cos(\omega_c t)\sin(\omega_c t)$$

$$= b_p(t)\frac{1 + \cos(2\omega_c t)}{2} - b_q(t)\frac{\sin(2\omega_c t)}{2} \qquad (4.1)$$

$$x_q(t) = b_p(t)\frac{\sin(2\omega_c t)}{2} - b_q(t)\frac{1 - \cos(2\omega_c t)}{2}$$

The low-pass filter then removes the terms at $2\omega_c$, leaving $b_p/2$ on the I branch and $b_q/2$ on the Q branch.

The analysis in Chapter 2 of the performance of linear modulation schemes has in fact implicitly assumed coherent demodulation, and hence the BERs determined in Sections 2.4 and 2.5 apply to ideal coherent demodulation.

4.4 Non-coherent demodulators

A coherent demodulator is able to compare the received signal with the reference carrier, and therefore directly obtain its absolute phase. Absolute phase is not available to a non-coherent demodulator (or 'detector'), and therefore it must use other means to estimate the transmitted symbol. Only *amplitude-shift keying* (ASK) (which is not used in practice in any modern radio system, probably because of its poor power efficiency) encodes the symbol solely using signal amplitude, and hence amplitude information alone is not sufficient. Two sources of information remain which may be used in a non-coherent demodulator: instantaneous frequency and relative phase (i.e. phase change from one symbol to the next). These are used in the *limiter-discriminator* and the *differential* demodulators, respectively.

One might assume that the limiter-discriminator, which uses instantaneous frequency, is suitable for FSK schemes only, while the differential demodulator is usable for PSK schemes (and by extension other linear schemes). In fact, both techniques may be used for either type of modulation scheme, since instantaneous frequency is proportional to rate-of-change of phase. However, the limiter-discriminator is most commonly used for constant envelope modulation schemes, for reasons we will shortly note.

Because of the absence of absolute phase information, non-coherent demodulation is sub-optimum, and performs worse than coherent on the AWGN channel by 1 dB or more. However, the non-coherent detector is more robust to channel impairments such as Rayleigh fading (see Chapter 9), and phase noise in receiver local oscillators. In many radio systems, and especially in mobile radio, it is therefore preferred.

4.4.1 Envelope detector

Despite the fact that ASK is not of much practical interest, we will consider first the *envelope detector* which is used for ASK demodulation. This is primarily because it appears later as part of the FSK filter–envelope detector discussed in Section 4.4.4, and because the analysis of its performance has several interesting features which are of more general importance.

The simplest envelope detector is the diode detector used in analog AM broadcast radio receivers [4.4, p. 149 ff], one very simple form of which is shown in Fig. 4.6(a). The input and output waveforms are shown in Fig. 4.6(b). The capacitor charges through the diode during positive half-cycles of the carrier

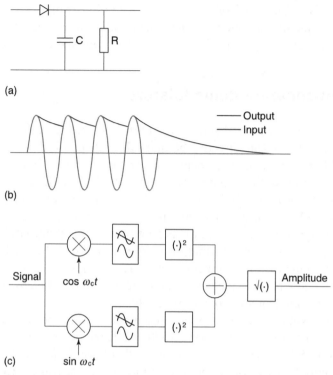

Figure 4.6 Envelope detectors: (a) simple analog circuit, (b) waveforms and (c) ideal digital implementation

for data '1', and discharges through the resistor for data '0'. Figure 4.6(c) shows an ideal envelope detector, suitable for digital implementation. It is essentially an 'I/Q' demodulator, which then obtains the amplitude as the root of the sum of the squares of the 'I' and the 'Q' components. Note that its operation does not require that the reference signals be in phase with the carrier, or even exactly the same frequency. For optimum reception the low-pass filters should be matched to the signalling pulse.

To determine the BER of this detector, we examine the statistics of the output for data '0' and '1', i.e. the statistics of the amplitude of the noisy signal. For data '0', only noise is present, and hence the output is the amplitude ν of a Gaussian noise signal, which has the Rayleigh distribution [4.7, p. 45], with probability density function:

$$p_0(\nu) = \frac{\nu}{\sigma^2} \exp\left(-\frac{\nu^2}{2\sigma^2}\right) \tag{4.2}$$

where σ is the noise standard deviation (see Equation (2.39)). For data '1', both noise and signal are present, and the output has the Rice distribution

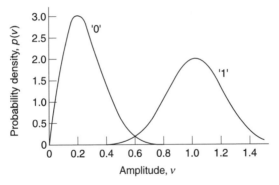

Figure 4.7   Probability density functions of envelope detector output for data '0' and data '1', assuming a unit signal and noise standard deviation of 0.2

[4.7, p. 47]:

$$p_1(\nu) = \frac{\nu}{\sigma^2} \exp\left(-\frac{\nu^2 + s^2}{2\sigma^2}\right) I_0\left(\frac{\nu s}{\sigma^2}\right) \tag{4.3}$$

where s is the signal amplitude, and I denotes the zeroth-order modified Bessel function of the first kind. These two probability distributions are illustrated in Fig. 4.7.

The optimum decision threshold is the point at which these distributions intersect. Note that in this case it is not, in general, half-way between the '0' and the '1' levels as we might expect. However, as the signal-to-noise ratio increases the threshold tends to 0.5s, so conventionally we fix the threshold at that level. The BER, or bit error probability P_{eb}, is then:

$$P_{eb} = P(1)P(1 \rightarrow 0) + P(0)P(0 \rightarrow 1) = \frac{1}{2}\int_{s/2}^{\infty} p_0(\nu)\,d\nu + \frac{1}{2}\int_0^{s/2} p_1(\nu)\,d\nu \tag{4.4}$$

Numerically, we find this is dominated by the first term, i.e.:

$$P_{eb} = \frac{1}{2}\int_{s/2}^{\infty} \frac{\nu}{\sigma^2} \exp\left(-\frac{\nu}{2\sigma^2}\right) d\nu = \frac{1}{2}\exp\left(-\frac{s^2}{8\sigma^2}\right) \tag{4.5}$$

From equation (2.40), $s^2/\sigma^2 = 2E/N_0 = 4E_b/N_0$, and hence:

$$P_{eb} = \frac{1}{2}\exp\left(-\frac{E_b}{2N_0}\right) \tag{4.6}$$

Figure 4.8 plots this BER performance, compared with that of coherently demodulated ASK. We note that it is about 1–3-dB poorer, converging as the bit-energy-to-noise-density ratio increases. It is interesting to note that with the optimum threshold chosen as indicated above, and adapted to the actual signal-to-noise ratio, non-coherent demodulation can perform better than this, significantly narrowing the gap with coherent ASK.

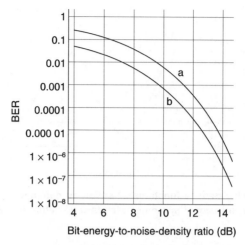

Figure 4.8   BER of non-coherent ASK (a) compared with coherent (b)

4.4.2   Limiter-discriminator

The limiter-discriminator demodulator is based on the discriminator used in analog FM demodulation [4.4, p. 361 ff]. This is a device that returns an output voltage proportional to the instantaneous frequency of the signal presented to it. Because the discriminator may also be sensitive to the signal amplitude, any amplitude variations are usually removed using an amplitude limiter. Since it is normally used with constant envelope modulation schemes, this has no effect on the signal, but under most circumstances improves the effective signal-to-noise ratio.

Figure 4.9 shows the most commonly used analog FM discriminator. It consists of two tuned circuits, tuned to frequencies a little above and a little below the carrier frequency. These are then followed by a pair of envelope detectors. The circuit then outputs the difference between the amplitudes of the two responses, which will be zero at the carrier frequency, and deviate

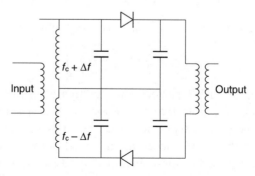

Figure 4.9   Analog FM discriminator

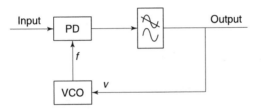

Figure 4.10   Phase-locked loop used for FM discrimination

positively and negatively either side. If the values of Δf and tuned circuit Q-factor (or quality factor) are carefully chosen, the response is approximately linear over an adequate range.

An alternative used in more modern systems is based on the *phase-locked loop* (PLL) (Fig. 4.10) [4.4, p. 361]. This contains a VCO whose output frequency f is constrained by means of a feedback control loop to follow the frequency of the input signal. The input and the VCO output are fed to a *phase detector* (PD), which gives an output proportional to the phase difference between its two inputs, and will therefore remain small only if the two inputs have the same frequency. The *loop filter*, following the PD, controls the dynamics of the loop. The VCO input voltage v must therefore be proportional to the input frequency. The PLL is much used in synchronization, both for carrier and clock recovery: a more detailed description of its operation is given in Section 4.5.2.

An all-digital implementation is also available, based on a mathematical description of an ideal limiter-discriminator. The output $y(t)$ is proportional to the rate of change of phase of the received signal $r(t)$, or:

$$y(t) = \frac{d}{dt}[\phi(t)] \tag{4.7}$$

where $\phi(t)$ is the phase of $r(t)$, which can be written as:

$$r(t) = A(t)\exp[j\phi(t)]$$
$$\therefore \; \ln[r(t)] = \ln[A(t)] + j\phi(t) \tag{4.8}$$

and hence:

$$y(t) = \frac{d}{dt}\mathrm{Im}\{\ln[r(t)]\} = \mathrm{Im}\left\{\frac{d}{dt}\ln[r(t)]\right\} = \mathrm{Im}\left[\frac{dr/dt}{r(t)}\right]$$
$$= \frac{\mathrm{Im}(dr/dt)\mathrm{Re}[r(t)] - \mathrm{Re}(dr/dt)\mathrm{Im}[r(t)]}{|r(t)|^2} \tag{4.9}$$

The block diagram in Fig. 4.11 instantiates this equation, while lending itself to direct digital implementation.

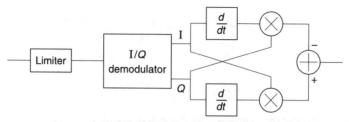

Figure 4.11   Digital implementation of limiter-discriminator demodulator

Whatever means we use to implement the discriminator, its output is proportional to the input frequency. For frequency-shift keying schemes such as GMSK, the data may be extracted directly from this demodulated signal. For linear schemes based on phase-shift keying, however, further signal processing is necessary. Signal phase is the integral of frequency, and hence the discriminator is followed by an integrator, operating over one symbol period. This then returns a signal proportional to the phase change from one symbol to the next, which can be decoded in the same way as in the differential demodulator, which we shall consider next.

4.4.3   Differential

The principle of differential demodulation [4.7, p. 274 ff] is to use the previous symbol as a phase reference for the current symbol, as shown in Fig. 4.12(a). The signal is multiplied by a copy of itself delayed by one symbol period, then filtered, as in a coherent demodulator. If the two successive symbols are in phase, the output will be positive: if out of phase, then negative. In practice, the received signal will usually be modulated down to the nominal baseband; for schemes with more than two phases (such as QPSK, 8-PSK, etc.), an I/Q

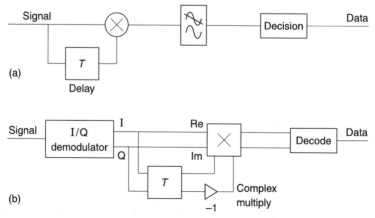

Figure 4.12   Differential demodulator: (a) for binary PSK, and (b) for general modulation

demodulator is required, as shown in Fig. 4.12(b). The multiplication is then complex conjugate, with the 'I' component as the real part, and the 'Q', inverted to implement conjugation, as imaginary, as in the complex baseband representation of Chapter 2. We then decode the phase of the product, which is equivalent to the phase difference, to find the data.

Since the demodulator responds to phase difference rather than absolute phase, the information is usually encoded at the transmitter as the difference between phases of successive symbols. Otherwise, a single symbol error might result in a long run of succeeding symbol errors. (In fact this *differential encoding* is often used with coherent demodulation, to prevent similar 'runs' of symbol errors due to carrier recovery failure.)

We may derive an approximate expression for the BER of differentially demodulated PSK (DPSK). Let the received signal (in complex form) for the kth symbol (the current symbol) be:

$$r_k = \exp[j(\phi_k + \theta)] + n_k \tag{4.10}$$

where ϕ_k is the modulated phase of the symbol, θ is the (unknown) carrier phase, relative to the local oscillator of the I/Q demodulator, and n_k is the noise in this symbol, also in complex form. Then the product, which provides the decision variable, is:

$$r_k r_{k-1}^* = \exp[j(\phi_k - \phi_{k-1})] + \exp[j(\phi_k + \theta)]n_{k-1}^* \\ + \exp[-j(\phi_{k-1} + \theta)]n_k + n_k n_{k-1}^* \tag{4.11}$$

The first term of this expression is the signal. The second and third terms are uncorrelated Gaussian noise terms of variance $|n|^2$. The fourth term is potentially correlated with the second and third, but at signal-to-noise ratios of interest it is much smaller in magnitude. Hence, for a first-order approximation we neglect it. We then note that the total noise power is twice what it would be in coherent demodulation (see Section 2.3.3), and hence we would expect the performance to be poorer by 3 dB.

In fact, for binary DPSK (DBPSK) this approximation is highly pessimistic. A very simple exact expression can be obtained:

$$P_{eb} = \frac{1}{2}\exp\left(-\frac{E_b}{N_0}\right) \tag{4.12}$$

This is plotted in Fig. 4.13, compared with the BER for coherent demodulation of BPSK, the exact expression for DQPSK (obtained from [4.7, p. 276]), and the approximation described above. The comparison between coherent and non-coherent is essentially the same as for ASK: at low BER non-coherent DBPSK has less than 1-dB poorer performance than coherent BPSK. However, DQPSK is about 2.3-dB poorer than coherent demodulation, and is quite close to the approximation. Higher order PSK modulation schemes will be still closer to the relevant approximation.

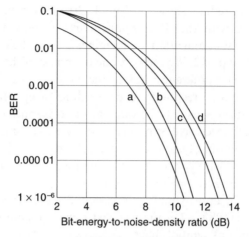

Figure 4.13 BER of (a) coherent BPSK/QPSK, (b) non-coherent DBPSK, (c) non-coherent DQPSK (exact), (d) approximation for DQPSK

As mentioned above, differential demodulation may be used for FSK schemes such as MSK and GMSK, as well as for PSK schemes, since FSK also results in a phase change between successive symbols. For MSK the phase change is $+\pi/2$ or $-\pi/2$ for data '1' and '0', respectively. In the differential demodulator of Fig. 4.12(b), this results in an output of $+j$ or $-j$, respectively, so the decision can be obtained directly by applying a threshold of zero to the imaginary (Q) part of the multiplier output.

However, if a pre-filter is applied to the modulating signal, as in GMSK, the phase change may no longer be $\pm\pi/2$ because of the intersymbol interference introduced by the pre-filter. This may reduce the output of the differential demodulator significantly, as shown by the eye diagram of Fig. 4.14(a), and

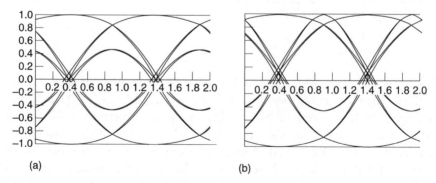

Figure 4.14 Eye diagrams for GMSK, time-bandwidth product 0.3, using a (a) one-bit differential demodulator, and (b) a two-bit differential demodulator

thus degrade the BER performance. Note that this degradation is much more serious than occurs in the coherent demodulator of GMSK described in Section 3.3.6, and may exceed 6 dB. Some improvement may be obtained by using a *two-bit differential demodulator*, in which the delay element is two bit periods long. This results in the eye diagram shown in Fig. 4.14(b). The eye opening is wider, resulting in less degradation, but it is now asymmetric, so that the optimum threshold is no longer zero, and more complex decoding is required to obtain the original data.

4.4.4 Filter–envelope detector

Some modulation schemes, especially certain FSK schemes, may use a further form of non-coherent demodulator. This consists of a pair of bandpass filters (for a binary scheme: there are m filters for an m-ary scheme), followed by envelope detectors, as shown in Fig. 4.15. The bandpass filters are centred on the nominal '1' and '0' frequencies of the modulation scheme, respectively f_1 and f_0, and implement matched filters for the '1' and the '0' signals.

Let the transmitted signals for '1' and '0' be expressed as:

$$\left. \begin{array}{l} s_1(t) = \exp j(2\pi f_1 t + \theta) \\ s_0(t) = \exp j(2\pi f_0 t + \theta) \end{array} \right\} \tag{4.13}$$

while the received signals are $r_0(t)$ and $r_1(t)$, respectively. The symbol θ is again the (unknown) transmitter phase. Then the matched filters may be implemented as correlation detectors. The outputs of the '1' matched filter for '1' and '0' signals are respectively:

$$\left. \begin{array}{l} a_{11} = \displaystyle\int_0^T r_1(t) \exp(-2j\pi f_1 t)\, dt \\[2mm] a_{10} = \displaystyle\int_0^T r_0(t) \exp(-2j\pi f_1 t)\, dt \end{array} \right\} \tag{4.14}$$

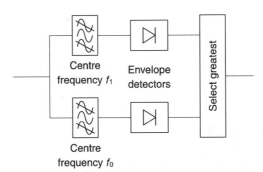

Figure 4.15 **Filter–envelope detector non-coherent demodulator**

In the absence of noise, $r_1(t) = s_1(t)$, etc. Then:

$$\left.\begin{aligned}
a_{11} &= \int_0^T \exp[j(2\pi f_1 t + \theta)]\exp[-j(2\pi f_1 t)]\,dt = T\exp(j\theta)\\
a_{10} &= \int_0^T \exp[j(2\pi f_0 t + \theta)]\exp[-j(2\pi f_1 t)]\,dt = \int_0^T \exp[2\pi j(f_0 - f_1)t + j\theta]\,dt\\
&= \exp(j\theta)\frac{\exp[2\pi j(f_0 - f_1)T] - 1}{2\pi j(f_0 - f_1)}\\
&= \exp(j\theta)\exp[\pi(f_0 - f_1)T]\frac{\sin[\pi(f_0 - f_1)T]}{\pi(f_0 - f_1)T}
\end{aligned}\right\}$$

(4.15)

and similarly for a_{00} and a_{01}. Taking the envelopes:

$$\left.\begin{aligned}
|a_{11}| = |a_{00}| &= T\\
|a_{10}| = |a_{01}| &= T\frac{\sin[\pi(f_0 - f_1)T]}{\pi(f_0 - f_1)T}
\end{aligned}\right\}$$

(4.16)

As in the case of the coherent FSK demodulator of Section 3.3.2, for optimum performance the output on the '1' branch should be zero for '0' transmitted, and vice versa, i.e. $|a_{10}|$ and $|a_{01}|$ should be zero. This occurs if:

$$(f_0 - f_1)T = 2f_d T = h = k$$

(4.17)

where k is any non-zero integer. This contrasts with the coherent demodulator, in which h need only be a multiple of 0.5 for the equivalent condition. Hence, the filter–envelope non-coherent demodulator is not as widely applicable as the other FSK demodulators we have considered, and in particular it is not suitable for MSK or GMSK.

When equation (4.17) holds, the output of the selected envelope detector, say s_1, has the Rice distribution, as in (4.3), while the non-selected output, s_0, has the Rayleigh distribution (Equation (4.2)). The probability of error is simply the probability that the latter will exceed the former (see [4.7, p. 311] for a fuller derivation):

$$P_{eb} = P(s_0 > s_1) = \int_0^\infty \int_{s_1}^\infty p_0(s_0)\,ds_0 p_1(s_1)\,ds_1 = \tfrac{1}{2}\exp\left(-\frac{E_b}{2N_0}\right)$$

(4.18)

This gives a BER performance about 3-dB poorer than that of the differential demodulator for MSK.

4.5 Synchronization

As we have seen in Fig. 4.1, the receiver requires estimates of the timing of the original signal in order to recover the information. In most systems two main timing parameters are required: carrier phase and symbol timing, although carrier phase is not required if non-coherent demodulation is used. These estimates must normally be extracted from the received signal itself. A number of textbooks include a detailed analysis of the synchronization problem, for example [4.7, ch. 6] and [4.8]. The thesis [4.9] considers a number of synchronization schemes in a practical context.

Synchronization can be approached in two ways. Either we may describe the operation of the synchronizer circuits which have been developed over the years, or we may approach the problem from first principles, giving the mathematical theory and showing how it may be implemented by certain hardware structures. It is interesting that the mathematical approach does lead to the same structures which have evolved from more *ad hoc* principles: i.e. that these structures are provably optimum or nearly optimum. Here we will begin with the mathematical approach.

This is a parameter estimation problem, which can be analyzed using statistical estimation theory. Let the received signal be:

$$r(t) = s(t; \phi, \tau) + n(t) \tag{4.19}$$

where $s(t; \phi, \tau)$ is the transmitted signal, which is a function of the phase ϕ of the original carrier and the timing delay τ of the original clock, and $n(t)$ is the noise, which we will assume to be white and Gaussian. The received signal (or rather, the vector $\mathbf{r}$ of its N samples over an *observation interval* T_0) has a probability density function which is also a function of ϕ and τ, written $p(\mathbf{r}|\phi, \tau)$. The optimum (or *maximum likelihood*, ML) estimate [4.7, p. 334] is the pair of values $\hat{\phi}$ and $\hat{\tau}$ which maximize $p(\mathbf{r}|\hat{\phi}, \hat{\tau})$ for a given received signal. If the noise is Gaussian, then $r(t) - s(t; \phi, \tau)$ has the Gaussian distribution, and hence:

$$p(\mathbf{r}|\hat{\phi}, \hat{\tau}) = \left(\frac{1}{\sigma\sqrt{2\pi}}\right)^N \exp\left[-\sum_{i=1}^{N} \frac{|r_i - s_i(\hat{\phi}, \hat{\tau})|^2}{2\sigma^2}\right]$$

$$\approx A \exp\left[-\frac{1}{N_0}\int_0^{T_0} |r(t) - s(t; \hat{\phi}, \hat{\tau})|^2 \, dt\right] \tag{4.20}$$

where A is a constant. (We have approximated the sum of the signal samples to the integral of a continuous signal.) The *log-likelihood function* (see Section 5.6.3) is then:

$$L(\hat{\phi}, \hat{\tau}) = -\frac{1}{N_0}\int_0^{T_0} |r(t) - s(t; \hat{\phi}, \hat{\tau})|^2 \, dt \tag{4.21}$$

and we choose $\hat{\phi}$ and $\hat{\tau}$ to maximize it. This is clearly equivalent to minimizing the mean square error between the received and the transmitted signal. We will show that this leads to some quite simple and intuitively comprehensible structures for carrier and clock recovery.

Equation (4.21) does, however, suggest a difficulty. To find $L(\phi, \tau)$ and to maximize it requires knowledge of $s(t)$, the transmitted signal. Since this in general depends on the data, it is not known. Synchronization techniques can be classified according to how they overcome this problem. *Data-aided* techniques require knowledge of the data, which is provided either by a set of known symbols, in the form of a *preamble* (at the beginning of a data frame) or of *pilot symbols* (interleaved within the data), or by feedback of the recovered data. *Non-data-aided* techniques do not require such knowledge: usually they calculate an average likelihood function over all the possible data symbols. Any technique that does not use a known preamble or pilot may also be referred to as *blind*.

4.5.1 Carrier recovery

We will first consider separate carrier recovery, assuming that the symbol timing is known. Under these conditions we can express $s(t; \phi)$ as $s(t) \exp(j\phi)$. Then $L(\phi, \tau)$ reduces to:

$$\left.\begin{aligned} L(\hat{\phi}) &= -\frac{1}{N_0} \int_0^{T_0} |r(t) - s(t) \exp(j\hat{\phi})|^2 \, dt \\ &= -\frac{1}{N_0} \int_0^{T_0} |r(t)|^2 \, dt + \frac{2}{N_0} \int_0^{T_0} \mathrm{Re}[r(t)s^*(t) \exp(-j\hat{\phi})] \, dt \\ &\quad - \frac{1}{N_0} \int_0^{T_0} |s(t)|^2 \, dt \end{aligned}\right\} \quad (4.22)$$

This can be maximized by finding the point at which its derivative with respect to $\hat{\phi}$ becomes zero. Note that the first term is proportional to the received signal power, and is independent of the transmitted signal phase. The last, similarly, is proportional to the transmitted signal power, and is not affected by the carrier

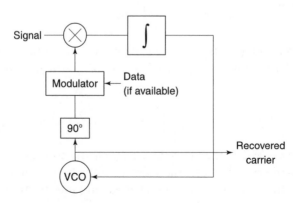

Figure 4.16 Structure of general carrier recovery loop

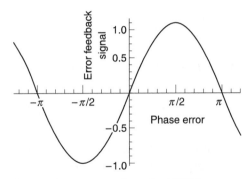

Figure 4.17 'S-curve' of carrier recovery loop (for BPSK)

phase. Then:

$$\frac{\partial L}{\partial \hat{\phi}} = \frac{2}{N_0} \int_0^{T_0} \text{Re}[-jr(t)s^*(t)\exp(-j\hat{\phi})]\, dt$$

$$= \frac{2}{N_0} \int_0^{T_0} \text{Im}[r(t)s^*(t)\exp(-j\hat{\phi})]\, dt \qquad (4.23)$$

This suggests the general structure for carrier recovery shown in Fig. 4.16. The rate of change of the voltage-controlled oscillator (VCO) phase is proportional to the input voltage. Hence, the operation of the feedback loop tends to drive the integrator input to zero, which is equivalent to finding the zero point of Equation (4.23). The 90° phase-shift block is equivalent to the multiplication by j in Equation (4.23).

We can plot the right-hand side of (4.23), or equivalently the output of the integrator in Fig. 4.16, against ϕ, resulting in a curve of the form shown in Fig. 4.17. This is known as the 'S-curve' of the recovery loop because of its general shape.

For non-data-aided carrier recovery the transmitted signal $s(t)$ is not known. We can rewrite the likelihood function to take into account the probability of the transmitted symbols. This will be illustrated in Example 4.1 by reference to the simplest possible example.

Example 4.1

Determine a suitable structure for non-data-aided carrier recovery in BPSK.

Solution For BPSK there are two possible signals, which we will write $s_0(t)$ and $s_1(t)$. The likelihood function, calculated over a single symbol period, then becomes:

$$L(\hat{\phi}) = \ln \left\{ P('0') \exp\left[-\frac{1}{N_0} \int_0^T |r(t) - s_0(t)\exp(j\hat{\phi})|^2\, dt \right] \right.$$

$$\left. + P('1') \exp\left[-\frac{1}{N_0} \int_0^T |r(t) - s_1(t)\exp(j\hat{\phi})|^2\, dt \right] \right\}$$

Averaging over the observation interval of length $T_0 = NT$, and assuming equiprobable symbols $(P('0') = P('1') = 1/2)$:

$$L(\hat{\phi}) = \frac{1}{N} \sum_{i=1}^{N} \ln \left\{ \tfrac{1}{2} \exp \left[-\frac{1}{N_0} \int_0^T |r_i(t) - s_0(t) \exp(j\hat{\phi})|^2 \, dt \right] \right.$$
$$\left. + \tfrac{1}{2} \exp \left[-\frac{1}{N_0} \int_0^T |r_i(t) - s_1(t) \exp(j\hat{\phi})|^2 \, dt \right] \right\}$$

where $r_i(t)$ denotes the received signal during the ith symbol period. Neglecting the constant terms in the argument of the exponential, as in Equation (4.22),

$$L'(\hat{\phi}) = \frac{1}{N} \sum_{i=1}^{N} \ln \left[\tfrac{1}{2} \exp \left\{ -\frac{1}{N_0} \int_0^T \mathrm{Re}[r_i(t) s_0^*(t) \exp(-j\hat{\phi})] \, dt \right\} \right.$$
$$\left. + \tfrac{1}{2} \exp \left\{ -\frac{1}{N_0} \int_0^T \mathrm{Re}[r_i(t) s_1^*(t) \exp(-j\hat{\phi})] \, dt \right\} \right]$$

$$= \frac{1}{N} \sum_{i=1}^{N} \ln \left[\tfrac{1}{2} \exp \left\{ -\frac{A}{N_0} \int_0^T \mathrm{Re}[r_i(t) \exp(-j\hat{\phi})] \, dt \right\} \right.$$
$$\left. + \tfrac{1}{2} \exp \left\{ \frac{A}{N_0} \int_0^T \mathrm{Re}[r_i(t) \exp(-j\hat{\phi})] \, dt \right\} \right]$$

$$= \frac{1}{N} \sum_{i=1}^{N} \ln \cosh \left\{ \frac{A}{N_0} \int_0^T \mathrm{Re}[r_i(t) \exp(-j\phi)] \, dt \right\}$$

putting $s_0(t) = +A$ and $s_1(t) = -A$. Then:

$$\frac{\partial L}{\partial \hat{\phi}} = \frac{1}{N} \sum_{i=1}^{N} \tanh \left\{ \frac{A}{N_0} \int_0^T \mathrm{Re}[r_i(t) \exp(-j\hat{\phi})] \, dt \right\} \frac{A}{N_0} \int_0^T \mathrm{Im}[r_i(t) \exp(-j\hat{\phi})] \, dt$$

$$\approx \frac{1}{N} \sum_{i=1}^{N} \frac{A^2}{N_0^2} \int_0^T \mathrm{Re}[r_i(t) \exp(-j\hat{\phi})] \, dt \int_0^T \mathrm{Im}[r_i(t) \exp(-j\hat{\phi})] \, dt$$

where the approximation holds for small arguments of tanh. This leads to the carrier recovery loop shown in Fig. 4.18, which is known as the Costas loop [4.4, p. 314]. Here the integrator in each branch implements the two integrals, while the loop filter preceding the VCO implements the averaging process.

The operation of this loop can be understood intuitively, and indeed it was first devised on this basis. If the VCO is in phase with the carrier, then the upper branch has zero output, regardless of the data, and hence the correction signal to the VCO is also zero. If it is advanced in phase, then for data '1' the upper branch will yield a small negative output, which will reduce the VCO input voltage, and correct its phase. Conversely, for data '0' the upper branch output will be positive, but the lower will be negative, again resulting in a negative correction; and vice versa if the VCO is advanced in phase.

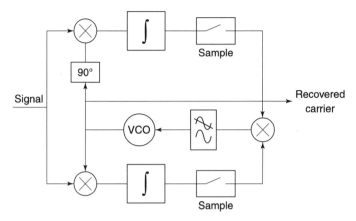

Figure 4.18   Costas loop for non-data-aided carrier recovery in BPSK

Note that for small x the function $\ln \cosh(x) \approx x^2$. This suggests an alternative approach: the *squaring loop*. Here the received signal is fed to a square-law device:

$$y(t) = x^2(t) = \{\mathrm{Re}[s(t)\exp(j\omega_c t + \phi)]\}^2$$
$$= \mathrm{Re}\{\tfrac{1}{2}[|s(t)|^2 + s^2(t)\exp[2j\omega_c t + 2\phi)]\}$$

Since $s_0^2(t) = s_1^2(t) = 1$, this is an unmodulated sine wave at twice the original carrier frequency (plus a d.c. term). A phase-locked loop (see below) can then lock to this signal, and we may recover the original carrier frequency using a divide-by-two circuit such as a flip-flop.

The squaring loop may readily be generalized for other modulation schemes. For example, in QPSK the four possible symbols may be written as $s(t) = (\pm 1 \pm j)/\sqrt{2}$. If these are raised to the fourth power, all four symbols become $s^4(t) = -1$, and again the modulation is removed. In general, a constellation with M-fold rotational symmetry can be raised to the Mth power, resulting in a component at M times the original carrier frequency. Thus 8-PSK should be raised to the eighth power. QAM, for any size constellation, has four-fold symmetry, and therefore a carrier can be recovered from a fourth power loop, but in this case the modulation is not completely removed. In all cases the power law device enhances the noise, and significantly degrades the accuracy of phase estimation in the presence of noise.

The Cramer–Rao bound [4.10, 4.11] gives a limit on the accuracy of carrier recovery in the presence of noise, giving a lower bound on the variance of the phase error for a given observation interval, T_0. In fact the Cramer–Rao bound is simply the expected variance of the phase of a noisy carrier, averaged over the observation interval. Figure 4.19 shows a phasor diagram.

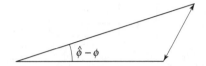

Figure 4.19 Phasor diagram showing effect of noise on phase estimate

It may then be shown that the variance of the phase error:

$$\text{var}(\hat{\phi} - \phi) \geq \frac{N_0}{A^2 T_0} = \frac{1}{N(E_s/N_0)} \qquad (4.24)$$

where N is the number of symbols within the observation interval, and E_s/N_0 is the symbol-energy-to-noise-density ratio. The performance of the non-data-aided BPSK carrier synchronizer of Example 4.1 is compared with the Cramer–Rao bound in Fig. 4.20. A thorough analysis of the performance of such synchronizers is given in [4.8, Section 6.3].

4.5.2 The phase-locked loop

The phase-locked loop [4.4, ch. 10; 4.12] may be regarded as the solution to an even simpler problem than non-data-aided carrier recovery for BPSK: recovering an unmodulated carrier. We may put $s(t) = 1$ in Equations (4.22) and (4.23), resulting in a structure identical to Fig. 4.18, but without the modulator. This, essentially, is the *phase-locked loop* (PLL). However, it is frequently generalized by replacing the integrator with a low-pass filter, known as the *loop filter*, as shown in Fig. 4.21. For small phase error, the multiplier in fact functions as a *phase detector* (PD), whose output is proportional to the phase difference between the inputs (less 90°). The VCO phase is given by $\hat{\phi}(t) = K \int v(t) \, dt$, which using the Fourier transform yields the

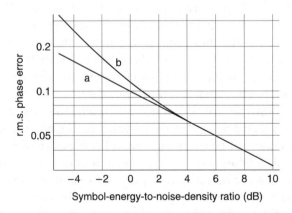

Figure 4.20 Cramer–Rao bound on r.m.s. phase error (a), compared with ideal non-data-aided recovery of BPSK (b), for observation length of $N = 100$ symbols

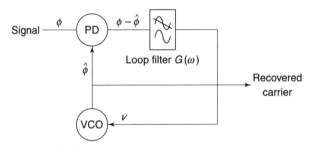

Figure 4.21 Phase-locked loop

relationship:

$$\hat{\Phi}(\omega) = \frac{K}{j\omega} V(\omega) \qquad (4.25)$$

where V and Φ denote Fourier transforms, K is the gain constant of the VCO, expressed in $\text{rad s}^{-1}\,\text{V}^{-1}$.

The resulting loop then functions as a feedback control loop, with transfer function:

$$H(\omega) = \frac{KG(\omega)/j\omega}{1 + KG(\omega)/j\omega} = \frac{KG(\omega)}{j\omega + KG(\omega)} \qquad (4.26)$$

This allows us to calculate the error in the phase estimate due to noise. The variance of the error:

$$\text{var}(\phi - \hat{\phi}) = \frac{1}{A^2} \int_{-\infty}^{\infty} N_0 |H(2\pi f)|^2 \, df = \frac{N_0 W_{\text{eff}}}{A^2} \qquad (4.27)$$

where W_{eff} is the (double-sided) equivalent noise bandwidth of the loop and A is the received signal amplitude. Again we are assuming that the noise is small.

The equivalent noise bandwidth of a PLL is related to the *loop bandwidth*, which is a very important parameter of the loop. The term normally refers to the single-sided 3-dB bandwidth. As we have seen, the equivalent noise bandwidth determines the effect of noise on the phase error. The loop bandwidth (in general terms) determines the ability of the loop to track variations in carrier phase or frequency. Such variations occur in practical radio systems due to Doppler shifts, or to phase noise in local oscillators [4.13, 4.14]. The loop bandwidth is also related to the *lock-in range* of the loop: the range of input frequencies over which it will acquire phase lock. This is, however, related to the non-linear behaviour of the loop, and is complex to analyze. More detail is given in [4.12]. The wider the loop bandwidth, the smaller the phase error due to carrier variations, and the greater the lock-in range, but the wider also the equivalent noise bandwidth, and hence the greater the phase error due to noise. Hence, it is important to choose the optimum loop bandwidth.

Example 4.2

Find the frequency response of the simplest possible (first-order) PLL.

Solution   The very simplest PLL has no loop filter at all, i.e. $G(\omega) = 1$. Then:

$$H(\omega) = \frac{K}{K + j\omega} = \frac{1}{1 + j\omega/K}$$

This is a first-order response (although the loop filter is zero order), and so the loop is called a first-order loop. Its frequency response is plotted in the form of a Bode plot in Fig. 4.22: we note that the cut-off frequency (i.e. the loop bandwidth) is $K/2\pi$. The equivalent noise bandwidth:

$$W_{\text{eff}} = \int_{-\infty}^{\infty} |H(2\pi f)|^2 \, df = \int_{-\infty}^{\infty} \frac{K^2}{K^2 + (2\pi f)^2} \, df = \frac{K}{2}$$

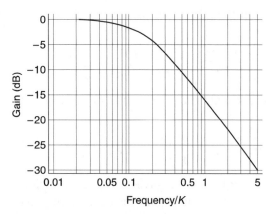

Figure 4.22   Bode plot of first-order loop frequency response normalized to VCO constant, K

Clearly, with this simple first-order response the equivalent noise bandwidth is large compared with the loop bandwidth: a higher-order response is required for most applications. In general, the loop order is one greater than the order of the loop filter. Thus a first-order loop filter results in a second-order response. However, a variation on the first-order filter is usually used, with the response:

$$G(\omega) = \frac{1 + j\omega\tau_1}{1 + j\omega\tau_2} \tag{4.28}$$

By careful choice of τ_1 and τ_2, as well as the VCO constant K, this allows the loop response to be tailored as required.

4.5.3 Symbol timing recovery

We now proceed to symbol timing recovery, again considered separately. This is a similar estimation problem, and as we shall see it results in quite similar structures, operating this time on the demodulated signal at the output of the matched filter (see Fig. 4.1).

As for carrier recovery, we first show how the ML timing estimator is derived. Starting with Equation (4.21), this time we assume that carrier phase is known. We can then write:

$$s(t; \phi, \tau) = s(t; \tau) = \sum_{i=1}^{N} d_i g(t - iT - \tau) \tag{4.29}$$

where $g(t)$ is the signalling pulse shape (see Section 2.1.5), and d_i is the data value.

Then:

$$
\begin{aligned}
L(\hat{\tau}) &= -\frac{1}{N_0} \int_0^{T_0} |r(t) - s(t; \hat{\tau})|^2 \, dt \\
&= -\frac{1}{N_0} \int_0^{T_0} |r(t)|^2 - 2\,\mathrm{Re}[r(t)s^*(t; \hat{\tau})] + |s(t; \hat{\tau})|^2 \, dt
\end{aligned}
\tag{4.30}
$$

This is similar to Equation (4.22), and once again we note that the first term is independent of τ. Likewise, the integral of the last term over a long observation interval is also nearly independent of τ. Hence, as before:

$$
\left.
\begin{aligned}
L'(\hat{\tau}) &= \frac{2}{N_0} \int_0^{T_0} \mathrm{Re}[r(t)s^*(t; \hat{\tau})] \, dt \\
&= \frac{2}{N_0} \int_0^{T_0} \mathrm{Re}\left[r(t) \sum_{i=1}^{N} d_i^* g(t - iT - \hat{\tau})\right] dt \\
\frac{\partial L'}{\partial \hat{\tau}} &= \frac{2}{N_0} \sum_{i=1}^{N} \mathrm{Re}\left\{d_i^* \frac{\partial}{\partial t}\left[\int_0^{T_0} r(t)g(t - iT - \hat{\tau}) \, dt\right]\right\} = 0
\end{aligned}
\right\}
\tag{4.31}
$$

The integral is the output of a matched filter sampled at an offset τ from the optimum sample instant. Again we can implement this in the form of a feedback loop which attempts to drive $\partial L'/\partial \tau$ to zero, as shown in Fig. 4.23. Here the summation is implemented in the form of a low-pass filter, which fulfils the function of the loop filter. Waveforms from this synchronizer are shown in Fig. 4.24, showing the effect of a small timing error, which means that the derivative is sampled at a point at which it is non-zero. When multiplied by the recovered data this results in a consistently negative signal, which changes the clock frequency until it is brought into synchronism. At this point the error signal goes to zero.

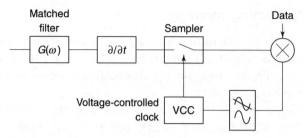

Figure 4.23   Data-aided symbol synchronizer

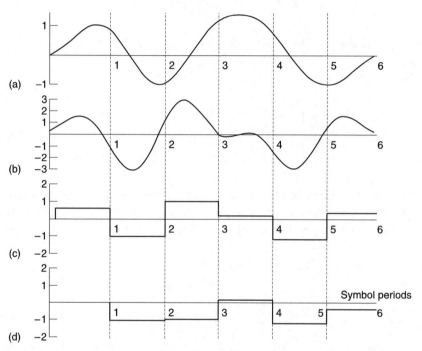

Figure 4.24   Waveforms in data-aided symbol synchronizer: (a) after matched filter, (b) after differentiator, (c) after sampler (sampling points indicated by dotted lines), (d) before loop filter

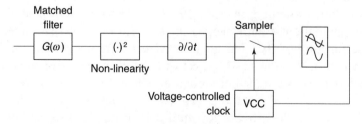

Figure 4.25   Non-data-aided symbol synchronizer

This is of course a data-aided synchronizer, requiring as it does knowledge of the transmitted data. A non-data-aided synchronizer can be obtained in the same way as in Example 4.1. Assuming BPSK is used, we can write:

$$L'(\hat{\tau}) = \frac{1}{N}\sum_{i=1}^{N}\ln\left[\tfrac{1}{2}\exp\left\{-\frac{1}{N_0}\int_0^T \mathrm{Re}[r(t)s_0^*(t;\hat{\tau})]\,dt\right\}\right.$$

$$\left. +\tfrac{1}{2}\exp\left\{-\frac{1}{N_0}\int_0^T \mathrm{Re}[r(t)s_1^*(t;\hat{\tau})]\,dt\right\}\right]$$

$$= \frac{1}{N}\sum_{i=1}^{N}\ln\cosh\left\{\frac{1}{N_0}\int_0^T \mathrm{Re}[r(t)g(t - iT - \hat{\tau})]\,dt\right\}$$

$$\approx \frac{1}{N}\sum_{i=1}^{N}\left\{\frac{1}{N_0}\int_0^T \mathrm{Re}[r(t)g(t - iT - \hat{\tau})]\,dt\right\}^2$$

$$= \frac{1}{N}\sum_{i=1}^{N}y^2(\hat{\tau})$$

$$\frac{\partial L'(\tau)}{\partial \tau} \approx \frac{2}{N}\sum_{i=1}^{N}y(\tau)\frac{\partial y(\tau)}{\partial \tau} \quad \text{or} \quad \frac{1}{N}\sum_{i=1}^{N}\frac{\partial y^2(\tau)}{\partial \tau} \tag{4.32}$$

Figure 4.25 shows a synchronizer that implements this equation by adjusting the sample clock until an averaged $\partial y^2(\tau)/\partial \tau$ goes to zero. The resulting waveforms are shown in Fig. 4.26. Observe that whenever a data transition occurs, a pulse is generated at the output of the differentiator. Thus this part of the circuit can be regarded as a transition detector, tending to generate a signal component at the clock frequency. The sampler and voltage-controlled clock oscillator then behave like a phase-locked loop, which locks to this component.

The grey line in Fig. 4.26(d) shows the output of the sampler for zero timing error. This shows that the output is not identically zero, but rather is zero on average over a sequence of data. This may result in random variations in the sample point due to the data pattern alone, even in the absence of noise, in this type of synchronizer. This is known as *pattern jitter*.

The above equations and block diagrams apparently assume analog continuous-time signals. In practice, of course, in most modern communication systems they will be implemented digitally using discrete time processors. However, according to the sampling theorem any band-limited signal can be perfectly represented by a sequence of samples taken at a rate equal to twice its bandwidth. Thus these synchronizers can be implemented digitally provided sufficient samples are taken. If raised-cosine Nyquist filtering is used (see Section 2.3.1), the bandwidth will be between one and two times the symbol rate. All the information in the signal can, therefore, be recovered by sampling

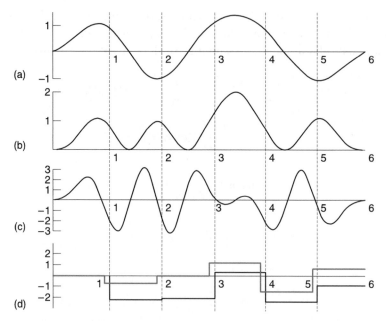

Figure 4.26 Waveforms in non-data-aided synchronizer: (a) after matched filter, (b) after non-linearity, (c) after differentiator, and (d) after sampler

at twice the symbol rate. A synchronizer based on this sampled representation is described as *two samples per symbol*. (Other modulation schemes, such as GMSK, may not be strictly band-limited in this way, but two samples per symbol are usually still adequate.)

This is in contrast to carrier synchronization, in which only one sample per symbol is required to extract all the information concerning the carrier phase. It is also possible to perform symbol timing recovery using one sample per symbol (for example by detecting non-zero intersymbol interference), but because such synchronizers cannot make use of all the information in the received signal they generally have poorer performance. Section 6.3 of [4.8] again gives details of the performance of various symbol synchronizers, including a Cramer–Rao bound for this problem.

It might appear that because the optimum symbol timing may need to be continuously variable, a large number of samples per symbol is required to allow the required timing precision. However, it is possible to provide continuously variable timing even with as small a number as two, by interpolating between samples. This can be done using an FIR digital filter, called an *interpolation filter*. Then the sample clock used in the analog-to-digital converter (ADC) may be fully asynchronous to the received data. Figure 4.27 [4.9, p. 97] shows an asynchronous timing recovery loop in a digital receiver.

In many such systems the synchronizer may not be implemented as a feedback loop at all, but rather as a *feedforward* system, in which the optimum

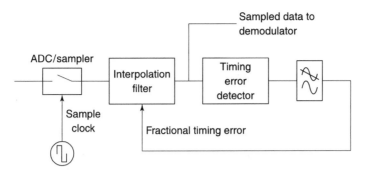

Figure 4.27   Digital asynchronous timing recovery loop

timing is estimated in a single pass from the received signal, then applied in order to recover the data. For example in most TDMA receivers (such as in the GSM mobile radio standard) a complete data burst is read into memory, then processed in the time between bursts. Among other functions, the symbol timing is extracted and then applied in order to demodulate the data.

Note that when FEC coding (see Chapter 5) is applied to a communication system the task of a synchronizer, in both symbol timing and carrier recovery, generally becomes more difficult. FEC coding has the effect that systems can operate at lower bit-energy-to-noise-density ratio (because of the coding gain they provide – see Section 5.1). Moreover, because of the redundancy introduced by the code, they operate at a still lower signal-to-noise ratio, which may be less than 0 dB in some systems. This may make it difficult for a synchronizer placed before the decoder to operate, and this, rather than the performance of the code, may limit the performance of the overall system. To overcome this problem requires a joint decoding and synchronization technique. This is an area of current research, and only a few examples, such as [4.15], have appeared in the literature.

We have also assumed in the foregoing that when carrier phase is estimated, symbol timing is known, and vice versa. Of course, in practice, this will not be the case: one of the parameters must be estimated first! In this case it is usually easier to perform symbol timing recovery first, since non-data-aided timing recovery is largely unaffected by carrier phase. However, if data-aided timing recovery is required, using feedback of data symbol decisions, joint recovery of carrier phase and symbol timing is required. Some consideration of this problem, including a block diagram of a synchronization loop, is given in [4.7, Section 6.4].

4.5.4   Effect of synchronization error

An error in synchronization, whether carrier phase or symbol timing, will degrade the BER performance of the modem. The Cramer–Rao bound shows that even under ideal conditions such errors are inevitable, so it is important to evaluate their effect. First, we illustrate the effect of carrier phase error by reference to an example.

Example 4.3

What is the effect of carrier phase error in QPSK?

Solution   Figure 4.28 shows how a carrier phase error ϕ affects the coherent demodulation of a QPSK symbol. The black circles indicate the original positions of the constellation points, and the dashed lines the decision region boundaries. The white circle shows the relative position of a symbol received with phase error ϕ and amplitude A.

The distances d_0 and d_1 from the decision region boundaries become:

$$d_0 = A \sin\left(\frac{\pi}{4} - \phi\right), \quad d_1 = A \sin\left(\frac{\pi}{4} + \phi\right)$$

Assuming Gray code constellation labelling (as shown), the BER becomes:

$$P_{eb} = \tfrac{1}{2}Q\left(\frac{d_0}{\sigma}\right) + \tfrac{1}{2}Q\left(\frac{d_1}{\sigma}\right) = \tfrac{1}{2}Q\left[\frac{A}{\sigma}\sin\left(\frac{\pi}{4} - \phi\right)\right] + \tfrac{1}{2}Q\left[\frac{A}{\sigma}\sin\left(\frac{\pi}{4} + \phi\right)\right]$$

For moderate phase error the first term dominates, and the effect approximates to a degradation of signal-to-noise ratio of $10\log_{10}(\sin(\pi/4 - \phi))$ dB.

However, in practice, the phase error is a random variable, rather than a fixed offset. Figure 4.29 shows the average BER of QPSK for a random phase error with Gaussian distribution of various values of standard deviation (in radians). We observe that not only is there an effective signal-to-noise ratio degradation, but there is also an irreducible BER floor due to phase errors of

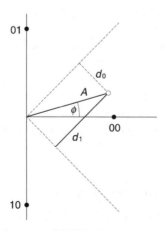

Figure 4.28   Constellation diagram of QPSK with carrier phase error ϕ

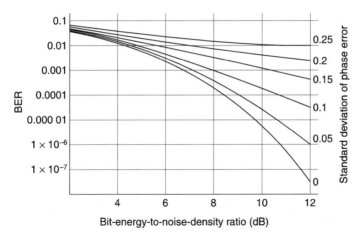

Figure 4.29 Effect of various values of random phase jitter (radians) on BER performance of QPSK

greater than $\pi/4$. Note, however, that this is a comparatively long-term average BER: in practice, the errors may occur in bursts, because the phase error will normally change relatively slowly.

The above equation may readily be generalized for M-PSK:

$$P_{eb} = \frac{1}{\log_2(M)} \left\{ Q\left[\frac{A}{\sigma}\sin\left(\frac{\pi}{M} - \phi\right)\right] + \tfrac{1}{2}Q\left[\frac{A}{\sigma}\sin\left(\frac{\pi}{M} + \phi\right)\right] \right\}$$

$$\approx \frac{1}{\log_2(M)} Q\left[\frac{A}{\sigma}\sin\left(\frac{\pi}{M} - \phi\right)\right] \tag{4.33}$$

and similar calculations may be performed for QAM.

The effect of symbol timing error is a little different, assuming that raised-cosine Nyquist filtering is used. The objective of Nyquist filtering (see Section 2.3.1) is to restrict the signal bandwidth while removing intersymbol interference (i.s.i.) at the sampling instant for each symbol. However, if there is a timing error in the symbol sampling, the i.s.i. returns, causing performance degradation or, potentially, irreducible errors. Figure 4.30 shows how this may arise. The waveform of the symbol sampled nominally at $t = 0$ is shown in bold; that for other symbols in grey. The actual sample instants are shown as dotted lines leading to i.s.i. in the centre symbol given by the values of the grey waveforms at the appropriate sample point. The i.s.i. clearly depends on the actual data, and is thus a random variable. (Because of the central limit theorem, this distribution of the i.s.i. is approximately Gaussian for small roll-off factors, since in this case a large number of data symbols affect the i.s.i.)

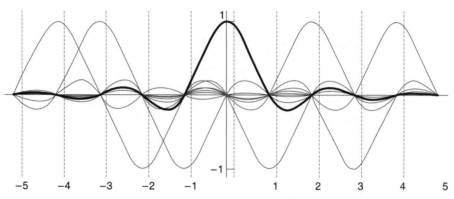

Figure 4.30   Re-introduction of intersymbol interference in Nyquist-filtered signal with symbol timing error

The i.s.i. may, in fact, be modelled as an additional noise source, of power:

$$N_{\text{i.s.i.}} = \sum_{i=-\infty, i\neq 0}^{\infty} g^2(iT + \tau) \approx a(\beta)\tau^2$$

where

$$a(\beta) = \sum_{i=-\infty, i\neq 0}^{\infty} [g'(iT + \tau)]^2 \tag{4.34}$$

and where $g(t)$ is the signalling pulse (see Section 2.1.5).

Values of a for various roll-off factors, β, are tabulated in Table 4.1. This shows how the sensitivity of the receiver to timing error decreases with increasing roll-off factor (and hence bandwidth). For this reason (if no other) it is easier to design a system with a looser Nyquist roll-off factor.

If τ is a random variable, $N_{\text{i.s.i.}}$ is directly related to its variance σ_τ^2 as $N_{\text{i.s.i.}} = a(\beta)\sigma_\tau^2$. This effective noise may be added to the thermal noise in the receiver to estimate the effect of timing jitter, giving the family of curves shown in Figs 4.31 and 4.32 (for 40 and 100% roll-off, respectively). As in the case of phase error, the BER shown is an average over a number of symbols, and on a shorter time-scale the BER may be bursty. Again, we note that in addition to a significant degradation in effective signal-to-noise ratio an error floor may appear, such that for 40% roll-off performance is

β	0.1	0.2	0.3	0.4	0.5	0.6	0.7	0.8	0.9	1.0
$a(\beta)$	2.77	2.38	1.98	1.62	1.29	1.0	0.75	0.54	0.37	0.22

Table 4.1   Values of constant a in Equation (4.33) for various roll-off factors, β

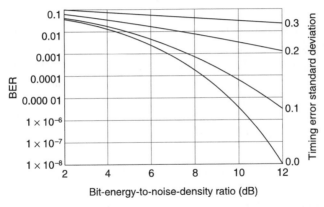

Figure 4.31 Effect of timing jitter of various standard deviations (fraction of symbol period) on BER for QPSK with 40% roll-off

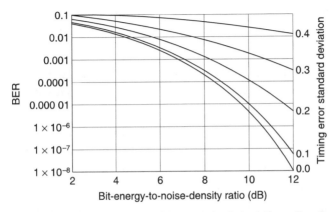

Figure 4.32 Effect of timing jitter of various standard deviations (fraction of symbol period) on BER for QPSK with 100% roll-off

extremely poor for any timing error greater than 0.1 radians r.m.s. Figure 4.32 shows how increased roll-off factor improves robustness: at 100% roll-off a reasonable performance is obtained for a timing error standard deviation 0.2 radians.

Problems

4.1 Sketch the waveforms in a coherent demodulator when a QPSK signal with constellation points at $\pm\pi/4$, $\pm3\pi/4$ is received. If the constellation labelling is Gray coded, suggest a decision circuit to output the data.

4.2 For bit-energy-to-noise-density ratios of 10, 12 and 14 dB, find the optimum threshold in the decision device of an ideal ASK envelope detector demodulator. In each case also find the BER if this threshold is used, and compare with the default threshold assumed in Section 4.4.1. This problem will be much simplified by the use of a mathematical analysis package like *Mathematica*. In the absence of such a package, or other means of evaluating Bessel functions, it may be useful to note that the Rician distribution of Equation (4.3) is quite well approximated by the Gaussian distribution with mean s and standard deviation σ. Also the integral of the Rayleigh distribution:

$$\int_t^\infty \frac{\nu}{\sigma^2} \exp\left(-\frac{\nu^2}{2\sigma^2}\right) d\nu = \exp\left(-\frac{t^2}{2\sigma^2}\right)$$

4.3 In the envelope detector of Fig. 4.6(a) ripple occurs with data '1' while intersymbol interference occurs following a '1'–'0' transition, as shown in Fig. 4.6(b). If both of these effects are to be kept to less than 10% of the signal amplitude, what is the minimum ratio of IF carrier frequency to symbol rate, and what is the optimum RC time constant for this minimum ratio?

4.4 Sketch waveforms within the digital ASK demodulator of Fig. 4.6(c), assuming a small frequency error between the reference and the received signal carrier.

4.5 By examining the eye diagrams of Fig. 4.14, estimate the degradation of a one-bit and a two-bit differential detector for GMSK with time-bandwidth product 0.3, compared with MSK. Also show how the output data may be decoded in the two-bit detector.

4.6 How should the *M*-FSK modulation scheme of Section 3.3.5 be adapted for use with a filter–envelope non-coherent detector? What other non-coherent detectors might be used with *M*-FSK?

4.7 Derive the shape of the S-curve for BPSK in the absence of noise, assuming ideal data-aided carrier recovery. Repeat for QPSK.

4.8 Find and plot the exact shape of the S-curve for ideal non-data-aided BPSK carrier recovery (from the equation for $\partial L/\partial \phi$ in Example 4.1), assuming a rectangular signalling pulse. Repeat the derivation also for QPSK. Assume a signal-to-noise ratio of 10 dB. (This requires access to a mathematical analysis software package.)

4.9 Find the response of a second-order PLL using the loop filter of Equation (4.28). Choose values for K, τ_1 and τ_2 to give a critically damped second-order response with a cut-off frequency of 100 Hz.

4.10 Determine and plot the effect of a fixed carrier phase error on the BER of 16-QAM.

4.11 A QPSK system is required to operate with a bit-energy-to-noise-density ratio of 12 dB at a BER of 10^{-6} at worst. Find the maximum allowable clock timing jitter if Nyquist filtering is used with a roll-off factor between 20 and 100%.

References

4.1 Software radio. (1999) *IEEE Personal Communications Magazine*, special issue, **6**(4).

4.2 Lettieri, P. and Srivastava, M.B. (1999) Advances in wireless terminals. *IEEE Personal Communications Magazine*, **6**(1): 6–19.

4.3 Grimm, J., Fitz, M.P., Krogmeier, J.V., Che, T.A., Magnusen, T., Gansman, J. and Kuo, W.Y. (1997) High efficiency narrowband wireless modems for ITS applications. *ITS Journal*, **3**(4): 333–52.

4.4 Young, P.H. (1994) *Electronic Communications Techniques*, 3rd Edition, Merrill (Macmillan).

4.5 Jung, P. and Baier, P.W. (1992) On the representation of CPM signals by linear superposition of impulses in the bandpass domain. *IEEE Journal Selected Areas in Communications*, **10**(8): 1236–42.

4.6 Laurent, P.A. Exact and approximate construction of digital phase modulations by superposition of amplitude modulated pulses (AMP). *IEEE Transactions on Communications*, **34**(2): 150–60.

4.7 Proakis, J.G. (1995) *Digital Communications*, 3rd Edition, McGraw-Hill.

4.8 Meyr, H., Moeneclaey, M. and Fechtel, S.A. (1998) *Digital Communications Receivers: Synchronisation, Channel Estimation and Signal Processing*, Wiley.

4.9 Verdin, D. (1996) Synchronisation in sampled receivers for narrowband digital modulation schemes, D.Phil thesis, University of York.

4.10 Van Trees, H.L. (1968) *Detection, Estimation and Modulation Theory*, Wiley.

4.11 Cramer, H. (1946) *Mathematical Methods of Statistics*, Princeton University Press.

4.12 Gardner, F.M. (1979) *Phaselock Techniques*, Wiley.

4.13 Jakes, W.C. (1974) *Microwave Mobile Communications*, Wiley.

4.14 Robins, W.P. (1982) *Phase Noise in Signal Sources: Theory and Applications*, Peregrinus (IEE).

4.15 Coulton, P., Hannaford, C. and Honary, B. (1995) Coding for both protection and synchronisation. *IEE Proceedings – Communications*, **142**(6): 352–6.

Chapter 5

Principles of FEC Coding

Coding is a general term covering a wide range of techniques, widely used in digital communication systems for a variety of purposes. It is a technique that applies naturally to digital systems, and is one of the main advantages of digital over the older analog systems. It is perhaps the main reason why digital television systems, for example, will be able to offer many times the number of channels available in the current analog broadcast systems.

A working definition of coding might be:

> a systematic scheme for the replacement of the original information symbol sequence by a sequence of code symbols, in such a way as to permit its reconstruction

Figure 5.1 shows a sort of taxonomy of coding schemes, showing the main categories, in which the divisions of interest here are shown in bold. Other areas are also of great interest, but are covered elsewhere. For example *cryptography* [5.1] is growing in importance from such considerations as Internet security, electronic funds transfer, and the security of mobile radio. *Source coding* [5.2, p. 316 ff], such as speech coding [5.3] and MPEG video coding [5.4], is largely responsible for the increase in efficiency of digital systems like digital television, where it allows much of the redundancy of the original picture to be removed. *Line coding* [5.2, p. 223] is widely used to eliminate d.c. components from data transmitted over long-haul optical fiber systems.

In this course we are concerned with error control, or more generally with increasing the robustness of data transmission in the presence of channel

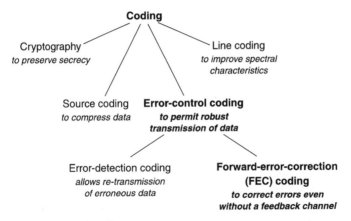

Figure 5.1　A taxonomy of coding

perturbations such as noise. One approach is the use of *error-detection coding* [5.5, ch. 9], in which errors are detected and a re-transmission requested via some return, or feedback, channel. This is the technique widely used in computer networks, and incorporated into the data link layer of the OSI protocol stack [5.6]. However, here we focus on *forward-error-correction* (FEC) coding, which is able to correct transmission errors even without a feedback channel.

5.1　Rationale of error-control coding

The basic function of error-control coding, as the name suggests, is to reduce the number of reception errors in a digital communications system. This is quantified as the *bit error ratio* (BER), sometimes loosely referred to as the 'error rate', which is defined as the ratio of the number of bits received in error to the total number of bits received. For example, FEC coding is used in this way in current cellular systems, such as GSM, to protect those bits of coded speech that are more important in terms of their effect on the quality of reproduction.

However, coding has another function, which is in fact more important in most applications. Clearly, the BER may normally be reduced simply by increasing the signal-to-noise ratio (SNR) at the input to the demodulator. The advantage of coding then is that the same BER may be achieved for a lower SNR in a coded system than in a comparable uncoded system. This may allow the power budget to be relaxed, giving a number of potential system advantages. The advantage given by a coded system can then be measured as *coding gain*.

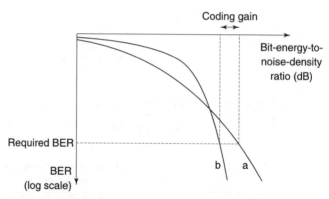

Figure 5.2   Curves of BER versus bit-energy-to-noise-density ratio for uncoded (a) and coded (b) systems

The coding gain of a coding scheme may be defined, cf. [5.7] as:

the reduction in bit-energy-to-noise-density ratio E_b/N_0 in the coded system compared with the uncoded for a given BER and for the same data rate.

Note the use of E_b/N_0 rather than SNR: this ensures that any differences in the bandwidth required are automatically allowed for. Figure 5.2 gives 'waterfall' curves for a coded and an uncoded system, showing the coding gain. Note the importance of quoting the BER at which the coding gain is measured: the coding gain varies very significantly with BER, and above a certain level may even be negative.

In fact, most coding schemes give a lower coding gain at higher BERs. Hence, the usefulness of coding depends strongly on the required BER for the service being provided. Data services commonly require very low BERs, 10^{-8} or below, and at these levels coding has long been recognized as very important. Since speech services, on the other hand, can generally operate adequately with quite high BERs, it has often been perceived that there is little to gain by FEC coding in mobile telephony systems. However, the potential of coding, particularly integrated with modulation, even in this application, has recently begun to be realized.

Another motivation for the development and the application of coding has been the fundamental work of Claude Shannon on information theory in the late 1940s [5.8, 5.9]. Shannon showed that for any given channel it was possible to transmit information at a rate known as the *capacity* of the channel, with arbitrarily small error rate. Since the capacity is typically much greater than the rate achieved by conventional methods, even with moderate error rates, this opens the possibility of making much more efficient use of communications resources by the use of coding. For example, a channel with bandwidth of

1 MHz, operating at a signal-to-noise ratio of 10 dB, has a Shannon capacity of nearly 3.5 Mbit s^{-1}; whereas a rate of about 700 kbit s^{-1}, with a significant error rate, is the best that would be expected without coding.

5.2   Principles of FEC coding

Shannon showed that the method by which this capacity increase can be achieved, paradoxically, is by the addition of redundant information to the transmitted data. This is done in such a way that the wanted information can be reconstructed from the received data, despite the corruption introduced by the channel. For a binary system this is done by inserting additional bits, called *check* or *parity bits*, into the transmitted data. These check bits are obtained from the information bits by an appropriate algorithm.

Example 5.1

Illustration of a code for a 2 bit message.

Consider, for example, a 2 bit message, to which three check bits are added.

There are four possible messages, giving rise to four possible 5 bit encoded blocks, called *codewords*.

$$
\begin{array}{c}
00:000\\
01:110\\
10:011\\
11:101
\end{array}
$$

Information bits   Check bits

Suppose the second of these is transmitted, but an error occurs in the second bit, so that it is received as 00110. This error can be detected, because the resulting word is not one of the permitted codewords. It can also be corrected, by comparing the received word with each of the codewords in turn. It differs in one place from the second codeword, but in two or more from each of the others, and thus the decoder can correctly select the codeword 01110 as the intended one.

The number of places in which two words differ is characterized as a 'distance' between them, called the *Hamming distance* (named in honour of Richard Hamming, who invented the first practical FEC codes [5.10]). In these terms the operation of the decoder is to select the codeword closest in Hamming distance to the received word, as shown in Fig 5.3.

The distance between codewords is also a useful measure of the error correcting power of the code. Errors in a transmitted word will 'move' the

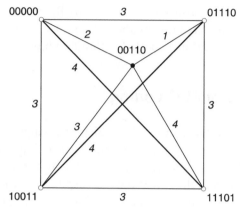

Figure 5.3   Hamming distances for code of Example 5.1

received word a Hamming distance d equal to the number of errors, as shown in Fig. 5.4. Provided this distance is less than halfway to the nearest alternative codeword, the decoder will still select the correct codeword. Thus the code will always correct a maximum number of errors:

$$t < \frac{d_{min}}{2} \tag{5.1}$$

where d_{min} is the minimum Hamming distance between any pair of codewords. In Example 5.1, d_{min} is 3, so the code will indeed always correct single errors. Note that the inequality is *strictly* less than, since if the received word is exactly halfway between two codewords, the receiver will not be able to select the correct word reliably.

The cost of this error-correction capability, apart from the increased complexity of the receiver, is the need to transmit additional check bits in addition to the information bits. These additional bits constitute *redundancy*. Clearly, because of this redundancy a code can transmit information only at a rate somewhat lower than would be possible over the uncoded channel. This appears to contradict Shannon's result that capacity may be increased through the use of coding. This paradox will be resolved in Chapter 8.

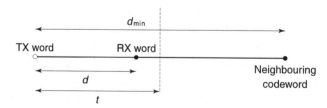

Figure 5.4   Hamming distances

5.3 Types of code

Codes can be classified according to a number of different bases. For example, the code of Example 5.1 is a *systematic binary block code*. It is also a *linear code*, and hence a *group code*. It may also be referred to as a (5, 2) or a (5, 2, 3) code.

5.3.1 Radix

The first classification is according to the *radix* of the code symbols (i.e. how many different code symbols are generated by the encoder). Most of the codes we will consider are binary, with radix 2, and code symbols $\{0, 1\}$. Other possible radices include:

> 3 (*ternary*), symbols $\{-1, 0, +1\}$;
> 4 (*quaternary*), symbols $\{0, 1, 2, 3\}$
> 8 (*octal*), symbols $\{0, 1, \ldots, 7\}$
> 16 (*hexadecimal*), symbols $\{0, 1, \ldots, 9, A, \ldots, F\}$

etc. The set of permitted code symbols is known as the *alphabet*.

Ternary codes are sometimes used in line coding, in which the objective is to eliminate the d.c. component of the signal. Other codes whose symbols are actually non-binary are sometimes transmitted in binary form by mapping each symbol to a different pattern of bits, for example the symbols of a hexadecimal code might be transmitted as blocks of four bits. (Reed–Solomon codes are an example of non-binary codes of this sort: see Section 6.3.6.) Non-binary codes may also be transmitted directly as the symbols of a multilevel modulation scheme.

Note that the geometric model introduced in Section 5.5 does not inherently restrict the code symbols to any finite alphabet: it allows the signal sample values (equivalent to code symbols) to take any of a continuous range of values.

5.3.2 Block and convolutional codes

The main division, however, is between *block* and *convolutional* codes. The code used in Example 5.1 was a block code: the data were split into fixed length blocks, each of which was mapped independently onto a code block. Chapter 6 deals with the most important classes of block code. In a convolutional code, in contrast, a code block depends not only on the current information block, but also on one or more previous blocks. This will be described in more detail in Chapter 7. The convolutional code results in a rather more complex code structure, and means that the concept of an independent codeword of fixed length must be replaced by the more general idea of a *code sequence* which may, in principle, be semi-infinite.

Block codes are frequently classified according to the number of information bits and the total number of bits, including check bits. Thus an (n, k) code has k data bits and $n-k$ check bits, giving a total length of n. The *rate*, defined as the proportion of information bits in the transmitted code sequence, is then k/n. Thus the code in Example 5.1 is a $(5, 2)$ code, having a rate of 0.4. A third number may be added, usually denoting the minimum Hamming distance (although sometimes, confusingly, it is the number of bits correctable). Thus in Example 5.1 the code is $(5, 2, 3)$. Convolutional codes are described in a similar way, except that the third number is usually the number of input blocks that affect the current output code block, known as the *constraint length*.

5.3.3 Systematic and non-systematic codes

In Example 5.1 it was possible to make a clear distinction in the transmitted codeword between the original information bits and the added parity check bits. Thus it is called a *systematic* code. This need not be the case, however. We might have chosen the following codewords:

$$00000$$
$$11101$$
$$00111$$
$$11010$$

to correspond to the data 00, 01, 10, 11, respectively. It is now no longer possible to identify this data in the codeword. Such a code is *non-systematic*.

Clearly, systematicity imposes a constraint on the code which is not present if the code does not have to be systematic, and this may affect its performance. Thus it is known, for example, that for some classes of convolutional code, systematic codes are inferior to non-systematic. However, for most block codes it is always possible to re-arrange the code into systematic form without affecting its minimum Hamming distance. Systematic codes have the advantage that the data are available within the received word even before decoding is performed, which can greatly simplify decoder design. Thus most practical block codes are used in systematic form.

5.3.4 Group codes

The code in Example 5.1 is known as a *linear* code, because each codeword can be expressed as a linear combination of two or more other codewords. In other words, the sum of any pair of codewords results in another codeword. The form of addition specified here is symbol-by-symbol *modulo-2 addition*. 'Addition modulo some radix M' means that if the result of the addition is outside the range $\{0 \cdots M - 1\}$, then we must subtract (or add) M as necessary to bring it back into the range. Modulo-2 addition is simply binary addition neglecting the carry, i.e:

$$0 + 0 = 0$$
$$0 + 1 = 1$$
$$1 + 0 = 1$$
$$1 + 1 = 0$$

This also happens to be identical to the exclusive-OR (XOR) logic function. The reader may check that the sum of any pair of codewords of the example code on this basis results in another codeword.

The code is then said to be *closed* under symbol-by-symbol modulo-2 addition. This is one condition of linearity: another is that it must also contain the all-zeros codeword. The definition may be extended to non-binary codes by replacing modulo-2 addition with 'addition modulo the code radix'. In this case one further condition must be applied: the code must also contain the *additive inverse* of each codeword: i.e. that word which when added to the original codeword will give the all-zeros word. For example, if a quaternary code contains the codeword 0123, then it must also contain 0321. (Note that for a binary code, each codeword is its own additive inverse.)

Although there may be some non-linear codes that perform better than equivalent linear ones, this property is so mathematically convenient that nearly all practical binary codes are linear. The linearity property greatly simplifies encoding and decoding, as we will see when we look at practical codes. It also makes it much simpler to find the minimum Hamming distance. Since the whole code may be generated by adding each of the non-zero codewords to any given codeword, the set of Hamming distances to all other codewords must be the same for all codewords, and the same as the distances from the all-zeros codeword. Thus the set of Hamming distances is given by the set of Hamming weights: the number of '1's in the words. In the example this is 3, 3, 4, and hence we see immediately that the minimum distance is 3, without having to compare all pairs of words.

The property of linearity may be generalized to codes defined on the geometric model described below. The equivalent codes are known as *group codes*, having the property of *geometrical uniformity* [5.11]. This means that the coded signals form a mathematical group, closed under some definition of addition. Such codes have properties equivalent to those described above.

5.4 Bounds on the performance of a digital communication system

As mentioned above, Claude Shannon in the late 1940s derived a series of bounds on the capacity of any digital communication system in the presence of channel noise or errors [5.8, 5.9]. These have until very recently been theoretical limits that could not be approached in practice, but they have provided a useful yardstick against which to assess practical coding schemes. To describe these bounds, we need first to describe the quantitative measure of information introduced by Shannon [5.8, 5.12].

5.4.1 Information content

The most obvious quantitative measure of information content is the number of bits required to store or transmit the information. However, not all bits carry the same amount of 'real' information. For example, if a source is known to produce many more '0's than '1's, then the '1's, being more unexpected, convey more than the '0's. Shannon encapsulated this concept of information content in the definition:

> *Information* is the resolution of uncertainty

Uncertainty is measured using probability, and hence we may say that the information conveyed by a symbol A:

$$I(A) = f(P(A)) \tag{5.2}$$

where $P(A)$ denotes the *a priori probability* of A; and $f(\cdot)$ denotes some appropriate function. Consider a message made up of two independent symbols A and B. Then:

$$I(AB) = f(P(A, B)) = f(P(A)P(B)) \tag{5.3}$$

We would expect the information conveyed by two symbols to be the sum of the information of each separately:

$$I(AB) = I(A) + I(B)$$
$$\therefore \quad f(P(A)P(B)) = f(P(A)) + f(P(B)) \tag{5.4}$$

This is clearly satisfied if we use the logarithm for $f(\cdot)$ – but the information content would then be negative. Hence we let:

$$I(A) = -\log[P(A)] = \log\left[\frac{1}{P(A)}\right] \tag{5.5}$$

Now consider a binary source giving a message of length n, so that there are 2^n possible messages, of probability $P = 1/2^n$, and information content:

$$I = \log\left(\frac{1}{P}\right) = \log(2^n) = n\log(2) \tag{5.6}$$

If the base of the logarithm is 2, then $I = n$, and information content is measured in *bits*, which agrees with our expected measure of information. It is important, however, to distinguish between the number of 'physical' bits in a message, and the information content in bits, which in general may be less.

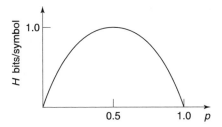

Figure 5.5 Entropy of a binary source

The average information rate, or *entropy*, H, of a source is given by weighting the information content of the symbols by their probability:

$$H = \sum_{i=0}^{m-1} P(A_i) \log_2 \left[\frac{1}{P(A_i)} \right] \tag{5.7}$$

In the binary case:

$$H = P('1')I(1) + P('0')I(0) = p \log_2 \left(\frac{1}{p} \right) + (1-p) \log_2 \left(\frac{1}{1-p} \right) \tag{5.8}$$

where p is the probability of '1'. This function is plotted in Fig. 5.5.

Example 5.2

A data source produces quaternary symbols 0–3 with the following probabilities. Find the entropy of the source. Find also the entropy if the symbols are equiprobable.

$$0 : 0.8 \qquad 1 : 0.1 \qquad 2 : 0.05 \qquad 3 : 0.05$$

Solution From Equation (5.7), the entropy:

$$H = 0.8 \log_2(1/0.8) + 0.1 \log_2(1/0.1) + 0.05 \log_2(1/0.05)$$
$$+ 0.05 \log_2(1/0.05)$$
$$= 0.257 + 0.332 + 2 \times 0.216$$
$$= 1.021 \text{ bits/symbol}$$

If the symbols were equiprobable (i.e. all had a probability of $1/4$), then the entropy would be

$$4 \times \tfrac{1}{4} \times \log_2 \left(\frac{1}{\frac{1}{4}} \right) = \log_2(4) = 2$$

Note that this is the information rate that can be represented by mapping each quaternary symbol into a pair of bits, and thus is clearly the maximum entropy the source can generate.

121

5.4.2 Shannon bound for the discrete channel

A *discrete channel* is treated as a simple 'symbol pipe' – one symbol is transmitted at one end, and some symbol (usually the same one, we hope) is received at the other end of the channel. We may define a set of *transition probabilities* for the channel, giving the probabilities of receiving one symbol given another was transmitted. The simplest example is the *binary symmetric channel*, in which the transition probabilities are given by the error probabilities, as illustrated in Fig. 5.6.

In the general case, suppose a symbol Y_j is received. The information transferred by this event is the 'uncertainty of the receiver before' minus 'the uncertainty after':

$$I = H_{\text{prior}} - H_{\text{post}} \tag{5.9}$$

A priori uncertainty is just the entropy of the source:

$$H_{\text{prior}} = H(X) = \sum_{i=0}^{m-1} P(X_i) \log_2 \left[\frac{1}{P(X_i)} \right] \tag{5.10}$$

A posteriori uncertainty is obtained from the set of probabilities of the X_is given that Y_j was received:

$$H_{\text{post}} = H(X|Y_j) = \sum_{i=0}^{m-1} P(X_i|Y_j) \log_2 \left[\frac{1}{P(X_i|Y_j)} \right] \tag{5.11}$$

Then, average information transfer (or *mutual information*):

$$I(X;Y) = \sum_{j=0}^{m-1} P(Y_j)[H(X) - H(X|Y_j)] = H(X) - H(X|Y)$$

where

$$H(X|Y) = \sum_{i,j=0}^{m-1} P(X_i, Y_j) \log_2 \left[\frac{1}{P(X_i|Y_j)} \right] \tag{5.12}$$

Alternatively:

$$I(X;Y) = H(Y) - H(Y|X)$$

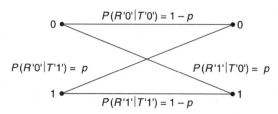

Figure 5.6 Binary symmetric channel with error probability p

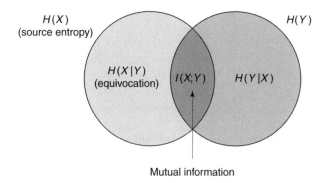

$H(X)$
(source entropy)

$H(Y)$

$H(X|Y)$
(equivocation)

$I(X;Y)$

$H(Y|X)$

Mutual information

Figure 5.7   Illustration of information transfer

where

$$H(Y|X) = \sum_{i,j=0}^{m-1} P(Y_i, X_j) \log_2 \left[\frac{1}{P(Y_i|X_j)} \right] \tag{5.13}$$

Figure 5.7 provides a useful illustration of the relationship between the quantities involved in Equations (5.12) and [(5.13), some of which have special names, as shown.

Shannon then defined:

The capacity (in bits/symbol) of a channel is the maximum mutual information, maximised over all possible sets of transmitter symbol probabilities

Usually (for a symmetric channel) the maximum is attained for equiprobable symbols. Shannon [5.8] then proved that:

A channel can transmit information at any rate lower than its capacity with arbitrarily small error rate

For the binary symmetric channel:

$$C = \max_{P(0),P(1)} [H(X) - H(X|Y)]$$

$$= \max_{P(0),P(1)} \left[H(X) - p \log_2 \left(\frac{1}{p} \right) - (1-p) \log_2 \left(\frac{1}{1-p} \right) \right] \tag{5.14}$$

$H(X)$ has a maximum of unity when $P('0') = P('1') = 1/2$. Then:

$$C = 1 - p \log_2 \left(\frac{1}{p} \right) - (1-p) \log_2 \left(\frac{1}{1-p} \right) \tag{5.15}$$

This is plotted in Fig. 5.8, and on a logarithmic scale of error probability in Fig. 5.9 to give more detail. The bound can be used to evaluate binary error-correcting codes, as we will see.

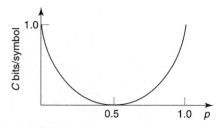

Figure 5.8   Capacity of the binary symmetric channel versus error probability

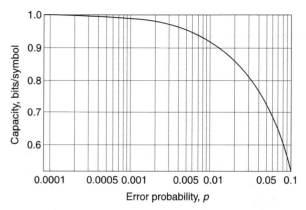

Figure 5.9   Capacity of the binary symmetric channel versus error probability (logarithmic scale)

Physically, however, communication channels are not ultimately discrete 'symbol pipes' subject to errors, but are continuous, analog systems subject to disturbances such as noise. Shannon also introduced a bound on the capacity of such channels which is more generally applicable than the one described above. However, it requires us first to introduce a very useful general model of a digital communication system using a continuous channel [5.9].

5.5   Geometric model

In any communication system the information is transferred in the form of some time-varying quantity or *signal*. In a radio system, the signal is ultimately the electromagnetic field strength. Usually our communication signal must be for practical purposes of restricted bandwidth. Consider a general signal of bandwidth W and duration T. According to the sampling theorem, this can be represented unambiguously by a set of $n = 2WT$ samples. (Note that even if the signal is at RF, the number of samples is determined by the bandwidth, and not the maximum frequency: we assume that bandpass sampling is used.) In a conventional digital signalling system the samples can represent the

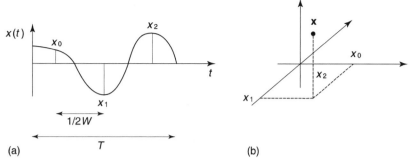

Figure 5.10   Geometric model: (a) sampled signal, (b) geometric representation

symbol values. In the geometric model, we use these n samples as coordinates of an n-dimensional Euclidean space. The signal is then represented by a single point in that space. Figure 5.10 illustrates the principle in three dimensions: the largest number we can readily draw! Of course, in practice, we are interested in much longer signals, and therefore much larger numbers of dimensions, which will require us to use the principles of higher-dimensional Euclidean geometry.

There are a number of useful analogies to be drawn between the characteristics of a signal and its geometric representation. For example, by Pythagoras's theorem extended into n dimensions, the distance from the origin of $\mathbf{x}$ is given by:

$$d^2 = \sum_{i=0}^{n-1} x_i^2 = \|\mathbf{x}\|^2 = E = ST \tag{5.16}$$

In other words, squared distance from origin $\Leftrightarrow$ signal energy. Now, suppose $\mathbf{x}$ represents a transmitted signal and $\mathbf{y} = \mathbf{x} + \mathbf{n}$ is the same signal corrupted by noise $\mathbf{n}$ of power N:

$$y(t) = x(t) + n(t)$$

$$\mathbf{y} = \mathbf{x} + \mathbf{n} = \{x_0 + n_0, x_1 + n_1, \ldots, x_{n-1} + n_{n-1}\} \tag{5.17}$$

Then, the squared distance between transmitted and received signals, as illustrated in Fig. 5.11:

$$d^2 = \|\mathbf{y} - \mathbf{x}\|^2 = \|\mathbf{n}\|^2 = \sum_{i=0}^{n-1} n_i^2 = NT \tag{5.18}$$

Hence, the squared distance between the received and transmitted signals points $\Leftrightarrow$ noise energy. Because of this model based on n-dimensional Euclidean space, the quantity:

$$d^2 = (y_0 - x_0)^2 + (y_1 - x_1)^2 + \cdots (y_{n-1} - x_{n-1})^2$$

$$= \|\mathbf{y} - \mathbf{x}\|^2 = \sum_{i=0}^{n-1} (y_i - x_i)^2 \tag{5.19}$$

125

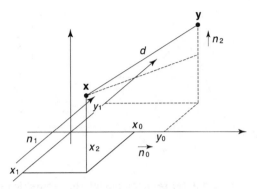

Figure 5.11   Distance between received and transmitted signals

which has the form of a mean squared error between the signals, is known as the squared *Euclidean distance* between them. It has great significance for assessing codes, as we shall see.

Equation (5.18) implies that if a signal **x** is transmitted over a noisy channel, then the received point **y** will lie on an n-dimensional 'hypersphere of uncertainty' centred on **x** (of radius $\propto NT$). For correct reception, the receiver must be able to distinguish between possible transmitted signals, which implies that these hyperspheres must not overlap. Shannon used this to derive an upper bound on the capacity of a noisy, band-limited channel [5.9].

5.5.1   Geometric model of a code

In Section 5.2 we described a code as a set of permitted codewords that were to be transmitted across a channel which was then treated as a 'symbol pipe'. In the geometric model we are concerned with the signals that are transmitted across the physical channel corresponding to the codewords. Each codeword of length n is represented by a point in n-dimensional space, and hence the code is modelled as a set of points in space. A binary code, such as that in example 5.1 of Section 5.2, has by definition only two possible sample values for each symbol. In geometric terms, the codewords correspond to vertices of an n-dimensional *hypercube*. The code then consists of a sub-set of these vertices.

Figure 5.12 shows a very simple length 3 binary code (it is assumed that polar transmission is used, '1' $\rightarrow +1$, '0' $\rightarrow -1$). The codewords are shown in black, and labelled in bold type:

$$
\begin{array}{l}
000 \\
011 \\
110 \\
101
\end{array}
$$

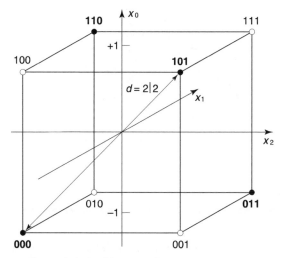

Figure 5.12   Geometric model of a binary code

The minimum Hamming distance of this code is 2: Fig. 5.12 shows (by Pythagoras) that the minimum Euclidean distance between any pair of codewords in the geometric model is $2\sqrt{2}$. In general, the Euclidean distance between two binary codewords of Hamming distance d_H (with polar transmission, unit amplitude) is $2\sqrt{d_H}$.

In general, however, the signals need not be restricted to those corresponding to binary codes. A code may be any set of signals of given duration and bandwidth, corresponding to any set of points in n-dimensional space. As we shall see, Shannon makes use of a wholly random code, represented by a random distribution of points, in determining the maximum capacity of a channel.

5.5.2   Shannon bound for the continuous channel

Consider a communication system that can transmit one of a set of M equiprobable signals of bandwidth W in time T. Each signal thus represents $k = \log_2(M)$ bits. According to the sampling theorem, each signal can be represented by $n = 2WT$ samples. We assume that the maximum average signal power is S and that the signal is subject to noise of power N.

In the geometric representation, all the transmitted signals must be restricted to an n-dimensional hypersphere of radius $\sqrt{(ST)}$ around the origin (since this radius corresponds to their maximum energy). Similarly, all the received signals (whose power is at most $S + N$) are restricted to an overall signal space of radius $\sqrt{(S + N)T}$. As mentioned above, the transmitted signals are surrounded by 'hyperspheres of uncertainty' of radius $\sqrt{NT}$. Provided these do not overlap, it should always be possible for the receiver to distinguish between two transmitted signals, and hence to receive the message with no

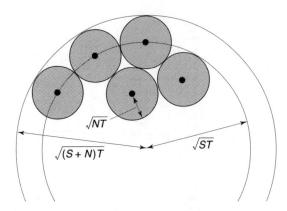

Figure 5.13 Signal space for calculating capacity of noisy channel

error. The capacity of the channel is then determined by the number M of 'hyperspheres of uncertainty' that can be accommodated within the overall signal space without overlap. This is illustrated in Fig. 5.13.

Clearly, an upper limit on this number is given by the volume of the signal space divided by the volume of the 'hyperspheres of uncertainty'. We would expect the actual number to be less than this, since spheres cannot be packed together without either overlapping or spaces being left between. The volume of an n-dimensional hypersphere is given [5.13, p. 167] by:

$$V_n(r) = C_n r^n \tag{5.20}$$

where $C_n = \pi^{n/2}/\Gamma(n/2 + 1)$: the volume of a unit radius n-sphere. (Note that this reduces to π for $n = 2$, and $4\pi/3$ for $n = 3$.) Hence:

$$M \le \frac{C_n[(S+N)T]^{n/2}}{C_n(NT)^{n/2}} = \left(1 + \frac{S}{N}\right)^{n/2} \tag{5.21}$$

Hence, the information per signal period I, and the capacity C can be obtained:

$$\left. \begin{array}{l} I = \log_2(M) \le \log_2\left[\left(1 + \dfrac{S}{N}\right)^{n/2}\right] = \dfrac{n}{2}\log_2\left(1 + \dfrac{S}{N}\right) \\[12pt] C = \dfrac{I}{T} \le \dfrac{n}{2T}\log_2\left(1 + \dfrac{S}{N}\right) = W\log_2\left(1 + \dfrac{S}{N}\right) \end{array} \right\} \tag{5.22}$$

This is plotted in Fig. 5.14, and is clearly an upper bound on the capacity. However, Shannon also showed [5.9], remarkably, that it could be achieved in the limit as $n \to \infty$, and achieved, moreover, using random codes (i.e. a completely random assignment of signals to transmitted messages). Formally, he showed that provided the rate of a random code was less than the capacity (by some arbitrarily small amount), that the expected error probability, averaged over all possible codes, would tend to zero as $n \to \infty$. Since the average over all codes achieves this capacity, there must be at least one code which is

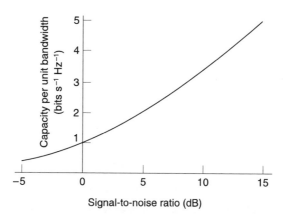

Figure 5.14 Shannon bound on capacity versus signal-to-noise ratio

at least this good. Thus, (5.22) is not only an upper bound, it is achievable with as low a BER as we may wish, provided we use a sufficiently long code (and thus a sufficiently complex decoder). In practice it has proved very difficult to approach this bound within an even remotely achievable decoder complexity. However, in 1993 codes and decoding algorithms (known as *turbo-codes*) were discovered, which can approach the bound within a fraction of 1 dB with a practical decoder. We will describe these in Chapter 11.

For a channel subject to white Gaussian noise of given power spectral density, N_0, it is more useful to express the bound in terms of bit-energy-to-noise-density ratio, E_b/N_0. We may re-arrange the bound to give a lower bound on required E_b/N_0:

$$\left.\begin{array}{c} C \leq W \log_2\left(1 + \dfrac{E_b/T_b}{N_0 W}\right) = W \log_2\left(1 + \dfrac{E_b}{N_0}\dfrac{C}{W}\right) \\[3mm] \therefore \quad \dfrac{E_b}{N_0} \geq \dfrac{2^{C/W} - 1}{C/W} \quad \text{or} \quad \dfrac{2^\eta - 1}{\eta} \end{array}\right\} \qquad (5.23)$$

where η is the spectral efficiency (see Section 1.2). The bound is plotted in Fig. 5.15. Note that unlike Fig. 5.14, this shows that there is an absolute lower limit on E_b/N_0 below which communication is impossible. This is given by:

$$\underset{\eta \to 0}{Lt}\left\{\frac{2^\eta - 1}{\eta}\right\} = \log_e(2) = 0.693 \text{ or } -1.59\,\text{dB} \qquad (5.24)$$

These bounds can be used more widely than those of Section 5.4.2, which apply only (in the form given) to binary codes on a discrete binary channel. (This is equivalent to what is described below in Section 5.6.1 as *hard decision decoding*.) The bounds of this section, in contrast, apply to any coded signal (including the coded modulation schemes of Chapter 8), with the optimum possible decoding techniques.

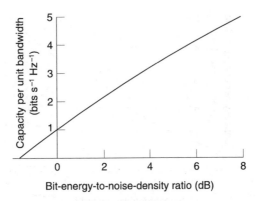

Figure 5.15   Shannon bound in terms of bit-energy-to-noise-density ratio

5.6   Decoding

The task of the decoder is to recover the original transmitted codeword from the received noisy signal, or errored received word. More accurately (since the original codeword can never be recovered with certainty) it is to find the codeword which is most likely to be the one transmitted. We consider now the two main types of decoding, and show that they correspond to the selection of the 'closest' permitted codeword according to two different *metrics*. This agrees with the intuitive approach to decoding illustrated by Example 5.1.

5.6.1   Hard decision decoding

Example 5.1 illustrates the case when the channel is treated as a 'symbol pipe', and the decoder has only a (possibly errored) received word $\mathbf{Y} = \{y_0, y_1, \ldots, y_{n-1}\}$ (in which the ys are symbols of the codeword) to work on. This is known as *hard decision decoding*, because it assumes that the demodulator has made 'hard and fast' decisions on the received symbols. The decoder must then select the most likely transmitted codeword $\mathbf{C}_m$, given that received word. Mathematically, it is the codeword which maximizes the conditional probability $P(\mathbf{C}_m|\mathbf{Y})$. (This is known as the *maximum a posteriori*, or MAP, criterion.) Now:

$$P(\mathbf{C}_m|\mathbf{Y}) = \frac{P(\mathbf{C}_m, \mathbf{Y})}{P(\mathbf{Y})} = \frac{P(\mathbf{Y}|\mathbf{C}_m)P(\mathbf{C}_m)}{P(\mathbf{Y})} \tag{5.25}$$

$P(\mathbf{Y})$ is the same for all $\mathbf{C}_m$. We assume also that all codewords are equiprobable, and hence $P(\mathbf{C}_m)$ is also constant. Hence maximizing $P(\mathbf{C}_m|\mathbf{Y})$ is equivalent to maximizing $P(\mathbf{Y}|\mathbf{C}_m)$, which is known as the *maximum likelihood* (ML) criterion [5.14, p. 245; 5.15, pp. 177–8]. If $\mathbf{Y}$ is at a Hamming distance d from $\mathbf{C}_m$, this is simply the probability of d errors occurring in the received word:

$$P(\mathbf{Y}|\mathbf{C}_m) = p^d(1-p)^{n-d} \tag{5.26}$$

where p (which lies between 0 and 1) is the error probability on the channel. $P(\mathbf{Y}|\mathbf{C}_m)$ obviously decreases with increasing d, and hence the most likely codeword is the closest to the received word in Hamming distance. We say that Hamming distance is the optimum *metric* for hard decision decoding. We have thus justified, mathematically, the straightforward approach to decoding of Section 5.2 – perhaps at excessive length, but we have in the process introduced some concepts that we will find useful later.

5.6.2 Soft decision decoding

Hard decision decoding neglects some of the information available at the receiver, which could be used to improve the efficiency of decoding. In *soft decision decoding* information on the reliability of the decisions taken by the demodulator is passed to the decoder. The decoder may then change those bits that are least reliable in its search for a valid codeword, and is therefore more likely to arrive at the correct codeword.

The reliability information can be obtained from the received analog signal, upon which the '1' or '0' decision is taken according to whether it is above or below a certain threshold. Decisions taken on signals close to the threshold are clearly less reliable than those where the signal is a long way above or below it. This is illustrated in Fig. 5.16, which shows how hard decision decoding may lead to decoding error. If reliability information is used to change the least reliable decision, correct decoding results.

Figure 5.17 shows a different approach to the same decoding problem. Here we compute the (squared) Euclidean distance to each codeword, and select the closest. The Euclidean distance encapsulates the reliability information used in Fig. 5.16. It is equivalent to selecting the codeword with the least squared error.

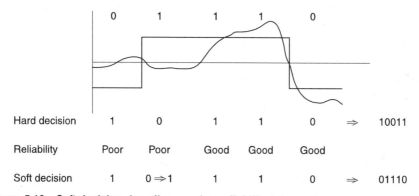

Figure 5.16   Soft decision decoding – using reliability information

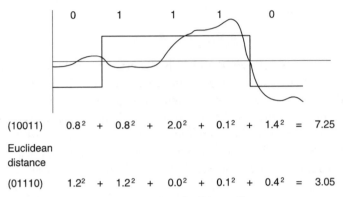

$$(10011) \quad 0.8^2 \; + \; 0.8^2 \; + \; 2.0^2 \; + \; 0.1^2 \; + \; 1.4^2 \; = \; 7.25$$

Euclidean
distance

$$(01110) \quad 1.2^2 \; + \; 1.2^2 \; + \; 0.0^2 \; + \; 0.1^2 \; + \; 0.4^2 \; = \; 3.05$$

Figure 5.17   Soft decision decoding – using Euclidean distance

We can justify this mathematically in the same way as for hard decision decoding. Equation (5.25) still applies, except that $\mathbf{Y}$ becomes a vector of 'soft' signal sample values $y_0 \cdots y_{n-1}$. Hence, strictly, the discrete probabilities $P(\mathbf{Y}|\mathbf{C}_m)$ and $P(\mathbf{Y})$ in equations (5.25) and (5.26) become probability density functions $p(\mathbf{Y}|\mathbf{C}_m)$ and $p(\mathbf{Y})$. If the noise is Gaussian, then $p(\mathbf{Y}|\mathbf{C}_m)$ is given by an n-dimensional Gaussian distribution, with mean $\mathbf{C}_m$:

$$p(\mathbf{Y}|\mathbf{C}_m) = \frac{1}{(\sigma\sqrt{2\pi})^n} \exp\left[-\frac{\sum_{i=0}^{n-1}(y_i - c_{mi})^2}{2\sigma^2} \right] = \frac{1}{(\sigma\sqrt{2\pi})^n} \exp\left(-\frac{d^2}{2\sigma^2} \right) \quad (5.27)$$

where d is the Euclidean distance between $\mathbf{Y}$ and $\mathbf{C}_m$ according to Equation (5.19). Since this is also a decreasing function of d, the most likely codeword is that closest in Euclidean distance, again agreeing with our intuitive notion of optimum decoding. This is therefore known as *maximum likelihood* (ML) decoding.

Thus, optimum decoding involves selecting the codeword closest to the received signal in Euclidean distance. This is equivalent to dividing the signal space into contiguous regions, each containing all points closer to one codeword than any other. These are known as the *decision regions* (or sometimes the *Voronoi regions* [5.16]) of the corresponding codewords, and are illustrated (in two dimensions) in Fig. 5.18. We may note that this is identical in concept to the decision regions encountered in Chapter 2 in demodulating multilevel modulation schemes (Figs 2.35 and 2.38). The boundaries of the decision regions are formed by the perpendicular bisectors of the lines joining neighbouring codeword points (in general these boundaries will be $(n-1)$-dimensional sub-spaces, the equivalent of faces in n-dimensions).

5.6.3   Log likelihood ratios

In the previous sections we have shown how optimum decoding can be performed by looking at the likelihood of the various possible transmitted

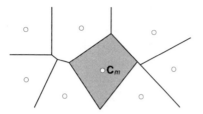

Figure 5.18 Decision regions for ML decoding

codewords, and how this relates to the metrics of Euclidean and Hamming distances. It is useful to be able to quantify the concept of likelihood, and this can be done using *log likelihood ratios* (LLR). In this section we describe these, and show their relationship with the distance metrics.

The *likelihood ratio* of two possible codewords given a received signal vector is simply the ratio of the conditional probabilities of the two:

$$L(\mathbf{C}_p, \mathbf{C}_q|\mathbf{Y}) = \frac{P(\mathbf{C}_p|\mathbf{Y})}{P(\mathbf{C}_q|\mathbf{Y})} = \frac{P(\mathbf{Y}|\mathbf{C}_p)P(\mathbf{Y})P(\mathbf{C}_p)}{P(\mathbf{Y}|\mathbf{C}_q)P(\mathbf{Y})P(\mathbf{C}_q)} = \frac{P(\mathbf{Y}|\mathbf{C}_p)}{P(\mathbf{Y}|\mathbf{C}_q)} \qquad (5.28)$$

again assuming that the codewords are equiprobable. This can take a very wide range of possible values, and can become very large if the probability of $\mathbf{C}_q$ is very small. The LLR [5.15, p. 99] is then the logarithm of this, which has the advantage of compressing the range of the LLR somewhat. Since the probabilities of joint events multiply together, the LLR has the additional advantage that LLR values will add under such circumstances. The LLR is in fact the true metric for which Hamming and Euclidean distances are only proxies.

For hard decision decoding, the LLR:

$$\begin{aligned} \Lambda(\mathbf{C}_p, \mathbf{C}_q|\mathbf{Y}) &= \log_e(\mathbf{C}_p, \mathbf{C}_q|\mathbf{Y}) = \log_e[P(\mathbf{Y}|\mathbf{C}_p)] - \log_e[P(\mathbf{Y}|\mathbf{C}_q)] \\ &= \log_e[p^{d_p}(1-p)^{n-d_p}] - \log_e[p^{d_q}(1-p)^{n-d_q}] \\ &= d_p \log_e(p) + (n-d_p)\log_e(1-p) - d_q \log_e(p) \\ &\quad - (n-d_q)\log_e(1-p) \\ &= (d_p - d_q)\log_e\left(\frac{p}{1-p}\right) \end{aligned} \right\} \qquad (5.29)$$

where d_p and d_q are the Hamming distances between $\mathbf{Y}$ and $\mathbf{C}_p$ and $\mathbf{C}_q$, respectively, and provided p is small, and hence $\log_e(1-p) \simeq 0$. For soft decision decoding:

$$\begin{aligned} \Lambda(\mathbf{C}_p, \mathbf{C}_q|\mathbf{Y}) &= \log_e\left[\frac{1}{(\sigma\sqrt{2\pi})^n}\exp\left(-\frac{d_p^2}{2\sigma^2}\right)\right] - \log_e\left[\frac{1}{(\sigma\sqrt{2\pi})^n}\exp\left(-\frac{d_q^2}{2\sigma^2}\right)\right] \\ &= \frac{d_q^2 - d_p^2}{2\sigma^2} \end{aligned} \qquad (5.30)$$

where d_p and d_q are now the Euclidean distances between $\mathbf{Y}$ and $\mathbf{C}_p$ and $\mathbf{C}_q$. Equations (5.29) and (5.30) show how Hamming and Euclidean distances do in fact relate in a very simple way to the LLR. For binary codes we can expand and simplify (5.30) still further, using (5.19):

$$d_p^2 = \sum_{i=0}^{n-1} (y_i - c_{pi})^2 = \sum_{i=0}^{n-1} (y_i^2 + c_{pi}^2 - 2y_i c_{pi})$$

$$= \|\mathbf{Y}\|^2 + \|\mathbf{C}_p\|^2 - 2\sum_{i=0}^{n-1} y_i c_{pi} = \|\mathbf{Y}\|^2 + \|\mathbf{C}_p\|^2 - 2\mathbf{Y} \cdot \mathbf{C}_p \qquad (5.31)$$

where $\cdot$ denotes the vector-dot or inner product, which is also the sample-by-sample correlation of the two signals. Now if $\|\mathbf{C}_p\| = \|\mathbf{C}_q\|, \forall p, q$, which is the case for a broad class of code called *spherical codes* [5.17, 5.18] including all binary codes, then we may simplify (5.30):

$$\Lambda(\mathbf{C}_p, \mathbf{C}_q | \mathbf{Y}) = \frac{d_q^2 - d_p^2}{2\sigma^2} = \frac{\displaystyle\sum_{i=0}^{n-1} y_i c_{qi} - \sum_{i=0}^{n-1} y_i c_{pi}}{\sigma^2} = \frac{\mathbf{Y} \cdot \mathbf{C}_q - \mathbf{Y} \cdot \mathbf{C}_p}{\sigma^2} \qquad (5.32)$$

and hence LLRs may be generated simply by multiplying received signal samples by codeword samples, a simpler operation than calculating Euclidean distances. This corresponds to calculating the correlation between the received word and the possible codewords, and returning the codeword with the greatest correlation.

The LLR may also be used to calculate the degree of certainty of decoded bits at the output of a decoder. This is used in iterative decoding, as in the decoding of turbo-codes (see Chapter 11). Let $\mathbf{P}$ denote the set of codewords in which the bit of interest is '1', and $\mathbf{Q}$ the set in which it is '0'. Then the LLR of this bit, which is the logarithmic ratio of the probabilities of these events, is:

$$\Lambda('1', '0'|\mathbf{Y}) = \log_e \left[\sum_{p \in \mathbf{P}} p(\mathbf{C}_p|\mathbf{Y}) \right] - \log_e \left[\sum_{q \in \mathbf{Q}} p(\mathbf{C}_q|\mathbf{Y}) \right]$$

$$= \log_e \left[\sum_{p \in \mathbf{P}} \exp\left(-\frac{d_p^2}{2\sigma^2} \right) \right] - \log_e \left[\sum_{q \in \mathbf{Q}} \exp\left(-\frac{d_q^2}{2\sigma^2} \right) \right] \qquad (5.33)$$

The summations will be dominated by the term with the smallest value of d, and hence:

$$\Lambda('1', '0'|\mathbf{Y}) \approx \log_e \left\{ \exp\left[-\frac{d_p^2(\min)}{2\sigma^2} \right] \right\} - \log_e \left\{ \exp\left[-\frac{d_q^2(\min)}{2\sigma^2} \right] \right\}$$

$$= \frac{d_q^2(\min) - d_p^2(\min)}{2\sigma^2} \qquad (5.34)$$

5.7 Performance of coded systems

In general, it is very difficult to make accurate predictions of the performance, for example the BER, of coded systems. Accurate closed-form analytical expressions, such as those used for the BER of linear modulation schemes in Chapter 2, are not in general available. In many cases computer simulation is the most accurate and computationally efficient technique, which accounts for the popularity of simulation as a means of evaluating coding schemes. However, a number of bounds and estimates exist, which are accurate under certain conditions, and these are frequently useful where simulation is impractical (such as when the BER is very low), or as an independent validation of simulation results [5.18].

The geometric model provides the basis for such estimates. Consider one codeword surrounded by a number of neighbours, as shown in schematic form in Fig. 5.19, which only shows two dimensions. (We need only be concerned with *neighbours*, defined as those codewords whose decision regions border that of the codeword in question [5.17]. Thus in the diagram words 1–6 are neighbours of 0; 7 is not.)

An error occurs if received word R is displaced out of the decision region of the transmitted signal (assumed in Fig 5.19 to be point 0); for example, point 1 is chosen in error if R is displaced over line D1. This occurs if the component of d in the direction $0 \to 1 > d_{min}/2$, or equivalently if the noise component in this direction $n_0 > d_{min}/2$.

Assuming Gaussian noise, the probability of this error:

$$P(0 \to 1) = Q\left(\frac{d_{min}}{2\sigma}\right) \tag{5.35}$$

But the probability of displacement in any direction is the same:

$$\therefore P(0 \to q) = Q\left(\frac{d_{min}}{2\sigma}\right) \tag{5.36}$$

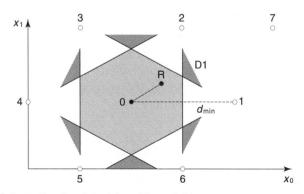

Figure 5.19   Schematic of codeword and its neighbours

for all points q which are neighbours of 0, lying at a distance d_{min}. Hence, the probability of any error:

$$P_e = P\left(\bigcup_{q \in N_n} (0 \to q) \right) \le \sum_{q \in N_n} P(0 \to q) = n_n Q\left(\frac{d_{min}}{2\sigma} \right) \qquad (5.37)$$

where N_n denotes the set of nearest neighbours, and n_n is its size. Note that this is an upper bound [5.19, p. 155], known as the *union bound*, on P_e because it counts some regions of the signal space twice (or more), such as the regions shaded in darker grey in Fig. 5.19.

Note that the expression is nearly identical to that for the error probability of a multilevel constellation, such as Equation (2.58). It is simply a generalization to n-dimensions of this expression. The bound is, however, not always such a good estimate (so *tight*) as it is for multilevel modulation. (A bound is said to be *tight* if the quantity it bounds is very close to the bound under some conditions.) It is usually tight for high signal-to-noise ratios (or low error probabilities), but may be much less so for some schemes at relatively high error rate. Especially if n_n is very large, the bound may be inaccurate even at error rates of practical interest.

If the neighbours do not all lie at the same distance, then the bound becomes:

$$P_e \le \sum_j n_{nj} Q\left(\frac{d_j}{2\sigma} \right) \qquad (5.38)$$

where d_j is a measure of the distances of the neighbours, and n_{nj} reflects the numbers at each distance. However, in many cases the term with the smallest d dominates this summation, and hence Equation (5.37) remains a good approximation (and possibly a better one than the full bound of (5.38)). However, it then ceases to be a strict upper bound. It also assumes that the set of distances to its neighbours is the same for all codewords, which may not be the case in general. However, group codes have the same property in respect of their Euclidean distances as linear codes have for their Hamming distances, and hence for these codes the assumption does apply.

Equations (5.37) and (5.38) give estimates of the probability of error in decoding a complete word, and hence the *word error ratio* (WER). In most cases we are interested rather in the probability of bit error, the BER. This can also be estimated by considering the number of bit errors associated with each erroneous codeword. We may write:

$$P_b \le \sum_j e_j Q\left(\frac{d_j}{2\sigma} \right) \qquad (5.39)$$

where e_j is the sum of the number of bit errors corresponding to all erroneous codewords at distance d_j from the correct word, divided by the number of data bits per word. For many codes the values of e_j are available, and will be given later. However, for systematic binary block codes it is possible to estimate e_j from n_{nj}. For binary codes, we may relate the Euclidean distance d_j to the Hamming distance d_{Hj}, i.e. to the number of code bit errors that occur. It is reasonable to assume that these will, on average, be evenly distributed through the codeword, among the k data bits and $(n-k)$ parity bits. Hence, the average number of data bit errors will be $d_{Hj}k/n$, out of the k bits transmitted on the codeword, and thus:

$$e_j = \frac{1}{k} n_{nj} \frac{d_{Hj}k}{n} = \frac{n_{nj} d_{Hj}}{n} \tag{5.40}$$

It is useful to relate the above expressions, where the BER is given in terms of the standard deviation σ of the noise, to the bit-energy-to-noise-density ratio, E_b/N_0. We have assumed that the noise on each signal sample is independent, which implies that the noise is white up to half the sampling frequency, $f_s/2 = n/2T$. The noise power on each sample $N = \sigma^2$, and hence the noise power spectral density:

$$N_0 = \frac{N}{W} = \frac{2N}{f_s} = \frac{2NT}{n} \tag{5.41}$$

Since the r.m.s. radius of codewords from the origin is $\propto S$, the signal power, S, scales as the square of the Euclidean distances of the code. We may then relate S to E_b as:

$$E_b = \frac{ST}{k} \tag{5.42}$$

Usually we take a convenient value for this mean radius, such as unity, and calculate the Euclidean distances accordingly. For example, for a binary code $S = 1$ corresponds to symbol values $\{-1, +1\}$. We have shown above in Section 5.5.1 that the Euclidean distances in such a code are given by $2\sqrt{d_H}$. Then:

$$\frac{d_j}{\sigma} = 2\sqrt{d_{Hj}}\sqrt{\frac{S}{N}} = 2\sqrt{d_{Hj}}\sqrt{\frac{kE_b/T}{nN_0/2T}} = 2\sqrt{\frac{k}{n}\frac{2E_b}{N_0}} \tag{5.43}$$

This expression may then be substituted into Equations (5.37)–(5.39) above.

The same type of bound may readily be applied to hard decision decoding. Equation (5.37) becomes

$$P_e = P\left(\bigcup_{q \in \mathbf{N}_n} (0 \to q)\right) \leq \sum_{q \in \mathbf{N}_n} P(0 \to q) = n_n \, p^{d_{min}} (1-p)^{n-d_{min}} \tag{5.44}$$

and the subsequent equations may be adapted accordingly, although as we will see in Chapter 6 this does not apply to all decoders.

Problems

5.1 (a) A *single parity check* (SPC) code of length n contains $(n-1)$ data bits and one *parity check* bit, which is added so that the total number of '1's in the codeword is even.

   (b) A *repetition code* of length n consists of two codewords: all '1's and all '0's.

   For each of these codes, write down their description in the nomenclature (n, k, d_{min}), find the number of errors they will correct, and show that they are linear.

5.2 Write down a possible set of codewords for a $(5, 3)$ systematic binary linear code. Find the minimum distance of your code.

5.3 A ternary data source generates the symbols '+' and '−' with equal probability, and the symbol '0' with probability p. Find the entropy of this source as a function of p.

5.4 Find the capacity of a quaternary channel with transition probabilities as illustrated in the following figure.

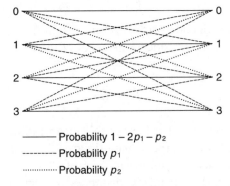

——— Probability $1 - 2p_1 - p_2$

- - - - - - Probability p_1

·············· Probability p_2

5.5 A length 3 ternary code on the alphabet '0', '−', '+' consists of the codewords +00, −00, 0+0, 0−0, 00+, 00−. If the symbols amplitudes are 0, −1 and +1, respectively, sketch the geometric representation of the code and find the minimum Euclidean distance as a function of the energy of the codewords.

   How could this code be generalized to length 4? What would be the rate (in bits per symbol) of the length 4 code, and its minimum Euclidean distance as a function of signal energy? Compare this with the binary code (using polar mapping) with the following codewords:

0000	1111
0011	1100
0110	1001
0101	1010

5.6 Calculate the spectral efficiency and required bit-energy-to-noise-density ratio of BPSK, QPSK, 8-PSK, 16-QAM and 64-QAM, assuming ideal Nyquist filtering with zero roll-off, and a required BER of 10^{-6}. Mark these as points on a plot of the Shannon bound and, hence, estimate the mean difference in dB between uncoded modulation schemes and the bound.

5.7 Find the proportion of the volume which lies closer than 0.1 from the surface of a 16-dimensional sphere.

5.8 For the code illustrated in Fig. 5.12, the received symbol amplitudes are -0.11, -0.21, 1.34. Find the log likelihood ratios between the codeword 000 and each of the other three codewords, for both hard and soft decision decoding (the latter assuming a Gaussian noise channel with no attenuation). Find, also, for soft decision decoding the log likelihood ratio of each bit.

5.9 For the code you defined in Problem 5.2, find the distance spectrum: i.e. the number of words at each Hamming distance from a given reference codeword. Hence, write down the union bound on the word error probability in terms of signal-to-noise ratio, assuming soft decision decoding. Estimate also the union bound on BER as a function of bit-energy-to-noise-density and, hence, the coding gain of this code for a required BER of 10^{-6}.

References

5.1 Menezes, A.J., Van Oorschot, P.C. and Vanstone, S.A. (1997) *Handbook of Applied Cryptography*, CRC Press.

5.2 Glover, I.A. and Grant, P.M. (1998) *Digital Communications*, Prentice-Hall.

5.3 Salami, R.A., Hanzo, L., *et al.* (1992) Speech coding. In R. Steele (Ed.) *Mobile Radio Communications*, IEEE Press–Pentech Press.

5.4 Sikora, T. (1997) MPEG digital video coding standards. *IEEE Signal Processing Magazine*, **14**(5): 82–100.

5.5 Sweeney, P. (1991) *Error Control Coding: an Introduction*, Prentice-Hall.

5.6 Tanenbaum, A. (1981) *Computer Networks*, Prentice-Hall.

5.7 Farrell, P.G. (1990) Coding as a cure for communications calamities – the successes and failures of error control. *Electronics and Communications Engineering Journal*, **2**(6): 213–20.

5.8 Shannon, C.E. (1948) A mathematical theory of communication. *Bell System Technical Journal*, **27**: 379–423 and 623–56. (Obtainable at: http://galaxy.ucsd.edu/new/external/shannon.pdf)

5.9 Shannon, C.E. (1949) Communication in the presence of noise. *Proceedings IRE*, **37**: 10–21.

5.10 Hamming, R.W. (1950) Error detecting and correcting codes. *Bell System Technical Journal*, **29**: 147–60.

5.11 Forney, G.D. (1991) Geometrically uniform codes. *IEEE Transactions on Information Theory*, **37**(5): 1241–60.

5.12 Usher, M.J. and Guy, C.G. (1997) *Information and Communication for Engineers*, Macmillan.

5.13 Hamming, R.W. (1980) *Coding and Information Theory*, Prentice-Hall.

5.14 Proakis, J.G. (1995) *Digital Communications*, 3rd Edition, McGraw-Hill.

5.15 Blahut, R.E. (1987) *Principles and Practice of Information Theory*, Addison Wesley.

5.16 Conway, J.H. and Sloane, N.J.A. (1982) Voronoi regions of lattices, second moments of polytopes and quantisation. *IEEE Transactions on Information Theory*, **28**: 211–26.

5.17 Sloane, N.J.A. (1981) Tables of spherical codes and sphere-packings. *IEEE Transactions on Information Theory*, **27**: 504–22.

5.18 Aldis, J.P. (1992) The application of many dimensional Euclidean geometry to the study of spherical codes. D.Phil thesis, University of York.

5.19 Blahut, R.E. (1990) *Digital Transmission of Information*, Addison Wesley.

Chapter 6

Cyclic block codes

As mentioned in Section 5.3, the main division of FEC codes is between block and convolutional codes. In this chapter we consider block codes, and in particular the most important sub-class of these, the *cyclic* block codes. As we shall see, the cyclic property results in very useful features of the code, which allow the use of simple hardware structures for encoding and decoding. In this chapter we introduce these features, and describe the main types of block code used in practical systems, the most important of which are the Bose–Chaudhuri–Hocquenghem (BCH) and the Reed–Solomon codes. In addition to the 'conventional' hard decision decoding techniques, we also consider soft decision decoding techniques for block codes, and in particular the more recently introduced trellis decoding technique (cf. Section 5.6).

Cyclic codes, such as BCH and Reed–Solomon, are based on the mathematical theory of *finite fields*, or *Galois fields*. In the main part of this chapter we will, however, avoid this theory wherever possible. It is given in more detail in Appendix 1, which gives the background theory required to obtain BCH and Reed–Solomon codes, and an introduction to the algorithms used for hard decision decoding.

An excellent and readable introduction to cyclic block codes (among others) is given in [6.1], although this is now out-of-print. The classic text is probably [6.2], but a slightly less mathematical, though still very thorough, treatment is given by [6.3], which also covers convolutional codes.

6.1 Description of cyclic codes

6.1.1 Definition

In the classification of Section 5.3, cyclic codes are linear block codes. Many, but not all, are binary codes: Reed–Solomon is an example of an important class of code which is non-binary. Most are systematic, or at least can be obtained in systematic form, as we shall see. The cyclic property itself is defined [6.3, p. 85] as:

> A code is cyclic if any cyclic shift of any codeword is also a codeword.

Hence, if $\mathbf{c} = \{c_0, c_1, \ldots, c_{n-1}\}$ is a codeword of a cyclic code, then so is its cyclic shift $\mathbf{c}^1 = \{c_{n-1}, c_0, c_1, \ldots, c_{n-2}\}$ and, of course (by induction), so are all distinct cyclic shifts of that codeword. Note, however, that this does not imply that all codewords are cyclic shifts of one another. Note also that since it is linear, a cyclic code must contain the all-zeros codeword: the all-zeros word is its own cyclic shift.

Example 6.1

Show that the (3, 2, 2) code (see Section 5.3 for the numbering) containing the codewords:

$$000 \qquad 110 \qquad 011 \qquad 101$$

is linear and cyclic.

Solution We may observe that each codeword as listed, except the all zeros, in a cyclic shift, one place to the right, of the one on its left. We also observe that the modulo-2 sum of any pair forms another codeword. (This is a single parity check, SPC code.)

Example 6.2

Show that the following linear (7, 4) code (called a Hamming code) is cyclic:

0000000	1111111
1101000	1011100
0110100	0101110
0011010	0010111
0001101	1001011
1000110	1100101
0100011	1110010
1010001	0111001

Solution Note the two groups of codewords, which are cyclic shifts of one another, in addition to the all-zeros (which must be present) and all-ones codewords. Starting from the codeword 1101000, which we will call the *generator* codeword, we can generate all the first group of codewords as its cyclic shifts. We can also generate the codeword 1011100 and hence all its cyclic shifts, as the modulo-2 sum of the first two cyclic shifts of the generator: $1101000 + 0110100 = 1011100$. Finally, the all-ones word can be obtained as the sum: $1101000 + 0010111 = 1111111$. (Note that the generator is not unique: we could equally have started from the word 1011100.) We will build on this observation in Sections 6.1.2 and 6.1.3 to show how cyclic codes may be defined and represented.

Since this is a linear code, the minimum Hamming distance is equal to the minimum weight (number of non-zero symbols) of any codeword (Section 5.3.4), which in this case is 3 (the weight of all the first group of words above). Hence, this is a single error correcting code – the defining property of all Hamming codes.

6.1.2 Matrix representation

A consequence of linearity is that every codeword may be formed as the modulo-2 sum of two or more other codewords. Hence we can choose a sub-set of the codewords, which may or may not include the generator, called the *basis*, which may be added together in various combinations to form all other codewords. Again the basis is not unique: there are a number of possible choices. However, the basis codewords must be *linearly independent*, which is to say that none can be formed as the modulo-2 sum of any combination of the others.

For instance, in Example 6.2 above, the following four codewords may be chosen as the basis:

$$1000110$$
$$0100011$$
$$0010111$$
$$0001101$$

It can be seen that these four are linearly independent. Then all 16 codewords can be obtained as a weighted sum of these four, where the weights can take the values 0 or 1. For example $1101000 = 1 \times 1000110 + 1 \times 0100011 + 0 \times 0010111 + 1 \times 0001101$.

This may be formalized by writing the basis codewords symbol-by-symbol as the rows of a matrix, called the *generator matrix*, **G** [6.3, pp. 51–5]. In the example:

$$\mathbf{G} = \begin{bmatrix} 1 & 0 & 0 & 0 & 1 & 1 & 0 \\ 0 & 1 & 0 & 0 & 0 & 1 & 1 \\ 0 & 0 & 1 & 0 & 1 & 1 & 1 \\ 0 & 0 & 0 & 1 & 1 & 0 & 1 \end{bmatrix} \tag{6.1}$$

Then each codeword may be obtained by multiplying this matrix by a different length 4 binary vector $\mathbf{d}$:

$$\mathbf{c} = \mathbf{dG} \qquad (6.2)$$

For example, if $\mathbf{d} = 1101$, then $\mathbf{c} = 1101000$.

You will note that $\mathbf{c}$ contains $\mathbf{d}$ in its first four positions: this will be the case for any vector $\mathbf{d}$, and is a consequence of the choice of the basis codewords. If $\mathbf{d}$ contains the data being encoded, then $\mathbf{c}$ will contain this data in addition to a number of parity bits: i.e. the code is systematic. This is because the basis has been chosen such that the generator matrix may be partitioned into an identity matrix and a *parity* matrix:

$$\mathbf{G} = [\mathbf{I}|\mathbf{P}]$$

$$\therefore \mathbf{c} = \mathbf{dG} = \mathbf{d}[\mathbf{I}|\mathbf{P}] = \mathbf{d}|\mathbf{p} \qquad (6.3)$$

Note that this choice of basis also guarantees that the basis codewords are linearly independent.

In this way any cyclic code (or indeed any linear code) can be represented in terms of a generator matrix, which can be chosen so as to give a systematic form of the code. The approach may also be extended to non-binary codes.

6.1.3 Polynomial representation

We may also represent a codeword as a polynomial in a dummy variable x, using the code symbols as coefficients, such that the codeword $\mathbf{c} = \{c_0, c_1, \ldots, c_{n-1}\}$ is represented [6.3, p. 86] as:

$$c(x) = c_0 + c_1 x + c_2 x^2 + \cdots + c_{n-1} x^{n-1} \qquad (6.4)$$

The advantage of this apparently cumbersome representation is that cyclic shifts may be expressed as multiplication by x:

$$c^1(x) = c_{n-1} + xc_0 + c_1 x^2 + c_2 x^3 + \cdots + c_{n-2} x^{n-1}$$

$$xc(x) = xc_0 + c_1 x^2 + c_2 x^3 + \cdots + c_{n-2} x^{n-1} + c_{n-1} x^n$$

$$= c^1(x) - c_{n-1} + x^n c_{n-1} = c^1(x) + c_{n-1}(x^n - 1) \qquad (6.5)$$

where n is the code length. Hence the remainder on dividing $xc(x)$ by $x^n - 1$:

$$xc(x) \bmod (x^n - 1) = c^1(x) \qquad (6.6)$$

and, by induction, any cyclic shift:

$$c^{(i)}(x) = x^i c(x) \bmod (x^n - 1) \qquad (6.7)$$

Of course if the code is binary, and modulo-2 addition applies, $x^n - 1 \equiv x^n + 1$.

In the code of Example 6.1 the codeword 101 can be written $1 + x^2$. Multiplying by x we have $x + x^3$ but, of course, since this is a length 3 code the term x^3 is not allowed. Hence we take the remainder modulo $(x^3 + 1)$, using long division of polynomials:

$$
\begin{array}{r}
1 \\
x^3 + 1 \overline{\smash{\big)}\, x^3 + x} \\
x^3 + 1 \\
\hline
x + 1
\end{array}
$$

which yields $x + 1$, or 110.

Since the code is linear, the modulo-2 sum of any combination of cyclic shifts of a codeword is also in the code. Indeed, we have seen in the Example 6.2 code that all codewords may be generated in this way from one codeword. This can be expressed in polynomial form as:

$$c(x) = [d_0 g(x) + d_1 x g(x) + \cdots + d_{k-1} x^{k-1} g(x)] \bmod (x^n - 1)$$

$$= d(x)g(x) \bmod (x^n - 1) \tag{6.8}$$

where $g(x)$ is the polynomial form of one of the non-zero codewords. (It is also clear that the all-ones codeword cannot be used for this purpose, either.)

If $g(x)$ has order not greater than $n - k$, and $d(x)$ has order $k - 1$, then their product will have order not greater than $n - 1$, and hence the modulo $x^n - 1$ operation is redundant. Then the polynomial $d(x)$ can be taken to be the polynomial representation of the k-bit data word. There will always be one codeword in a cyclic code that yields a polynomial of the required order, which is then called the *generator polynomial* of the code. In Example 6.2 $k = 4$, and hence $g(x)$ must have order not greater than 3. The only usable codeword is 1101000, which has already been identified as the generator codeword for the code, and which leads to the generator polynomial $1 + x + x^3$.

Thus we see that by taking advantage of the cyclic properties of the code we may replace the generator matrix representation of the code with the much more compact generator polynomial. Note, however, that not all possible generator polynomials correspond to cyclic codes, as we shall now see.

Example 6.3

List the codewords of the (7, 4) code with the generator polynomial $1 + x + x^2 + x^3$. Is this code cyclic?

Solution Using Equation (6.8) we can obtain the codewords of this code from all the possible length 4 (order 3) data polynomials. Again, because the order of the generator is 3, the modulo operation is redundant. The 16 codewords are:

0000000	1001011
1111000	1100110
0111100	0110011
0011110	1011010
0001111	0101101
1000100	1010101
0100010	1101001
0010001	1110111

An attempt has been made here to list these words as shifts of one another, but it can be seen that not all cyclic shifts of all codewords are in the code: that is, it is not cyclic. In fact it will be observed that whenever a '1' is shifted from the right-hand end of the codeword to the left, the cyclic pattern is lost.

Looking more closely at Equation (6.5) we can see the reason why the code of Example 6.3 is not cyclic. Rearranging this, we have that the cyclically shifted word $c^1(x) = xc(x) - c_{n-1}(x^n - 1)$. If $c(x)$ is a codeword of a code with generator polynomial $g(x)$, then $c(x) \bmod g(x)$ must be zero. However, $c^1(x)$ is then a codeword (i.e. the code is cyclic) if and only if either $c_{n-1} = 0$ or:

$$(x^n - 1) \bmod g(x) = 0 \qquad (6.9)$$

Long division of polynomials shows that $(x^7 + 1) \bmod (1 + x + x^2 + x^3) = x \neq 0$, and hence the code is not cyclic. Equation (6.9) can thus be used as a test to determine whether a code with given generator polynomial, and given length n, is cyclic.

6.2 Encoding and decoding

In this section we consider basic encoding and decoding methods for cyclic block codes. In particular, we show how the cyclic structure of the codes results in a simple encoding/decoding structure using shift registers. Our consideration of decoding, however, includes only the basic principles of hard decision decoding. We leave till later soft decision decoding, and specific algorithms for specific codes.

6.2.1 Systematic and non-systematic encoding

We have already given above two different descriptions of the encoding process, in terms of the generator matrix and, for cyclic codes, in terms of the generator polynomial. In the case of the generator matrix we have shown that the form given in Equation (6.3) results in a systematic form of the code. However, using the polynomial representation (in Example 6.2):

$$\mathbf{d} = 1000 \Rightarrow d(x) = 1 \Rightarrow c(x) = g(x) = 1 + x + x^3 \Rightarrow \mathbf{c} = 1101000$$

and so on. The codeword does not contain the data explicitly, and hence the code is not systematic. There are usually significant advantages in a systematic form of a block code (it allows the data to be extracted directly from an error-free codeword), and thus it would be desirable to perform systematic encoding using the polynomial representation [6.3, pp. 90–1]. This can be obtained thus:

(1) Express the data $\mathbf{d}$ in polynomial form, as $d(x)$.
(2) Multiply $d(x)$ by x^{n-k} (equivalent to shifting the data bits to the right-hand end of the codeword.
(3) Divide the result by $g(x)$, and take the remainder $r(x)$.
(4) Form the codeword polynomial as:

$$c(x) = r(x) + x^{n-k} d(x) \tag{6.10}$$

Example 6.4

Encode 1011 in systematic form in the (7, 4) code of Example 6.2

Solution

(1) $d(x) = 1 + x^2 + x^3$
(2) $x^{n-k} d(x) = x^3 + x^5 + x^6$
(3)

$$
\begin{array}{r}
x^3 + x^2 + x + 1 \\
x^3 + x + 1\overline{)x^6 + x^5 + x^3} \\
\underline{x^6 + x^4 + x^3} \\
x^5 + x^4 \\
\underline{x^5 + x^3 + x^2} \\
x^4 + x^3 + x^2 \\
\underline{x^4 + x^2 + x} \\
x^3 + x \\
\underline{x^3 + x + 1} \\
1
\end{array}
$$

$$\Rightarrow r(x) = 1 \text{ or } \mathbf{r} = 100$$

(4) $c(x) = r(x) + x^{n-k} d(x) = 1 + x^3 + x^5 + x^6 \Rightarrow \mathbf{c} = \mathbf{rd} = 1001011$

which is systematic, although the data word is found at the end of the codeword, rather than at the beginning. The same data, encoded using the generator matrix of (6.1), would yield the codeword 1011100.

Note that the remainder polynomial must always have order less than that of the generator polynomial (i.e. at most $n - k - 1$), and the minimum power in $x^{n-k}d(x)$ is of course x^{n-k}. Hence these two parts of the codeword will not overlap, and therefore the code must always be systematic. Further:

$$c(x) \bmod g(x) = [r(x) + x^{n-k}d(x)] \bmod g(x)$$

$$= r(x) + r(x) = 0 \text{ modulo-2} \qquad (6.11)$$

Hence, $c(x)$ is always a codeword of the code generated by $g(x)$.

6.2.2 Shift register implementation of encoder

Since a right shift is equivalent to multiplication of the codeword polynomial by x, it is easy to see that polynomial multiplication can be performed using a shift register [6.3, pp. 95–8]. However, if a sequence is fed to a single-stage shift register right-most bit first, the output sequence is in fact left-shifted, i.e. multiplied by x^{-1}. Two sequences can then be modulo-2 added using an exclusive-OR (XOR) gate, as shown in Fig. 6.1.

Hence the structure of Fig. 6.1 performs the multiplication $1 + x^{-2} + x^{-3}$. We may normalize this by dividing by the operator equivalent to the delay through the whole structure, i.e. x^{-3}. The multiplication is then by $x^3 + x + 1$, the generator polynomial of Example 6.2. The output is in fact a codeword of Example 6.2.

This structure may be used, in general, to multiply a data sequence by a generator polynomial. A connection to the shift register corresponds to a term in the generator polynomial (coefficient '1'); no connection corresponds

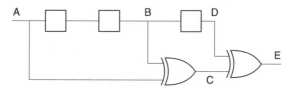

Figure 6.1   Polynomial multiplication using a shift register

A	0001011	$a(x) = x^3 + x^5 + x^6$
B	0101100	$b(x) = x^{-2}a(x) = x + x^3 + x^4$
C	0100111	$c(x) = a(x) + x^{-2}a(x) = x + x^4 + x^5 + x^6$
D	1011000	$d(x) = x^{-3}a(x) = 1 + x^2 + x^3$
E	1111111	$e(x) = a(x) + x^{-2}a(x) + x^{-3}a(x) = 1 + x + x^2 + x^3 + x^4 + x^5 + x^6$

Table 6.1   Code sequences and polynomial representations in Fig. 6.1

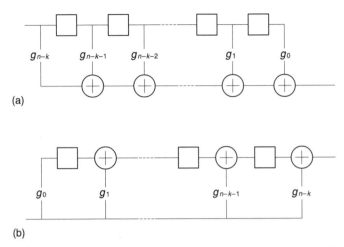

(a)

(b)

Figure 6.2   General structure for multiplication by a generator polynomial

to no term (coefficient '0'). Two equivalent structures are shown in Fig. 6.2. In Fig. 6.2(a), which is the form used in Fig. 6.1, the right-most connection represents the unit coefficient; the left-most, the highest power of the generator polynomial $(n - k)$. In Fig. 6.2(b) the order is reversed. Note that the XOR gates of Fig. 6.1 have been drawn here as modulo-2 adders. This equivalent representation will be used hereafter.

This structure will implement non-systematic encoding of a cyclic code; a similar structure will perform the modulo-$g(x)$ operation required for systematic encoding (Fig. 6.3).

Note that at the end of this process the shift register contains the parity bits $\mathbf{r} = 100$, corresponding to $r(x) = 1$, as obtained by the systematic encoding procedure of the previous section. Note also that the vector $\mathbf{q} = 1111$ corresponds to the quotient polynomial obtained in the polynomial division, $1 + x + x^2 + x^3$. You will observe that the shifting-and-adding process within the shift register mirrors the operations carried out during the polynomial long division operation.

Figure 6.3(b) shows a shift register structure which in effect performs the same operation as the generator, except that the sequence $\mathbf{d}$ now appears as the output, and $\mathbf{q}$ is the input. After $\mathbf{q}$ has been entered, the same parity bits $\mathbf{r}$ appear in the shift register. If a further $n - k = 3$ zeros are now clocked into the register, $\mathbf{r}$ will appear as a sequence at the output, and the sequence $\mathbf{d}$ will be further right-shifted (i.e. multiplied by x^{n-k}). Then we may write:

$$q(x)g(x) = d(x)x^{n-k} + r(x) \quad \text{or} \quad d(x)x^{n-k} = q(x)g(x) + r(x)$$

remembering that this is modulo-2 arithmetic. This confirms that $r(x)$ is indeed the remainder sequence we want.

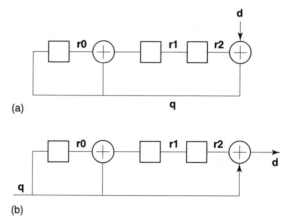

Figure 6.3 (a) Shift register structure to perform modulo-$g(x)$ operation (for $g(x) = 1 + x + x^3$); (b) equivalent form showing operation

d	q	r0	r1	r2
–	–	0	0	0
1	1	1	1	0
1	1	1	0	1
0	1	1	0	0
1	1	1	0	0

Table 6.2   Data in shift register of Fig. 6.3

6.2.3   Syndrome decoding

The linearity property in general, and the cyclic property in particular, also simplifies the (hard decision) decoding of these codes. A similar approach is used in both the matrix [6.3, pp. 55–62] and the polynomial representation [6.3, pp. 98–110] of a code.

In matrix representation, we first choose a *parity check matrix* **H** such that:

$$\mathbf{GH}^T = \mathbf{0} \tag{6.12}$$

(**H** is an $(n - k) \times k$ matrix). Then we obtain the *syndrome*, **s**, by post-multiplying the received word **r** by $\mathbf{H}^T$. Now the received word can be expressed as the sum (modulo-2 for a binary code) of the transmitted codeword **c** and an error pattern **e**. Hence:

$$\mathbf{s} = \mathbf{rH}^T = (\mathbf{c} + \mathbf{e})\mathbf{H}^T = \mathbf{cH}^T + \mathbf{eH}^T = \mathbf{dGH}^T + \mathbf{eH}^T = \mathbf{eH}^T \tag{6.13}$$

using Equations (6.2) and (6.12). Thus the syndrome depends only on the error pattern, not on the transmitted codeword. The error pattern can therefore be obtained from the syndrome, for example by using a look-up table for which the syndrome provides the index. Other methods exist: see Section 6.2.4, and

Appendix 1. The look-up table would require an entry for each syndrome, i.e. 2^{n-k} entries. Once the error pattern is known, it can be corrected. Of course a look-up table could be provided for each received word giving the correct word, but this would require a table of size 2^n.

For a systematic code, in which the generator matrix is given by $\mathbf{G} = [\mathbf{I}_k | \mathbf{P}]$, we may use the parity check matrix (where the subscript denotes the size of the identity matrix):

$$\mathbf{H} = [\mathbf{P}^{\mathrm{T}} | \mathbf{I}_{n-k}]$$

Then

$$\mathbf{GH}^{\mathrm{T}} = [\mathbf{I} | \mathbf{P}]\left[\frac{\mathbf{P}}{\mathbf{I}}\right] = \mathbf{P} + \mathbf{P} = 0 \tag{6.14}$$

Example 6.5(a)
Form the parity check matrix for the Hamming (7, 4) code (Example 6.2), in matrix formulation.

Solution

$$\mathbf{G} = [\mathbf{I} | \mathbf{P}] = \begin{bmatrix} 1 & 0 & 0 & 0 & 1 & 1 & 0 \\ 0 & 1 & 0 & 0 & 0 & 1 & 1 \\ 0 & 0 & 1 & 0 & 1 & 1 & 1 \\ 0 & 0 & 0 & 1 & 1 & 0 & 1 \end{bmatrix}$$

$$\mathbf{H} = [\mathbf{P}^{\mathrm{T}} | \mathbf{I}] = \begin{bmatrix} 1 & 0 & 1 & 1 & 1 & 0 & 0 \\ 1 & 1 & 1 & 0 & 0 & 1 & 0 \\ 0 & 1 & 1 & 1 & 0 & 0 & 1 \end{bmatrix}$$

$$\mathbf{GH}^{\mathrm{T}} = \begin{bmatrix} 1 & 0 & 0 & 0 & 1 & 1 & 0 \\ 0 & 1 & 0 & 0 & 0 & 1 & 1 \\ 0 & 0 & 1 & 0 & 1 & 1 & 1 \\ 0 & 0 & 0 & 1 & 1 & 0 & 1 \end{bmatrix} \begin{bmatrix} 1 & 1 & 0 \\ 0 & 1 & 1 \\ 1 & 1 & 1 \\ 1 & 0 & 1 \\ 1 & 0 & 0 \\ 0 & 1 & 0 \\ 0 & 0 & 1 \end{bmatrix} = \begin{bmatrix} 0 & 0 & 0 \\ 0 & 0 & 0 \\ 0 & 0 & 0 \\ 0 & 0 & 0 \end{bmatrix}$$

Form the syndromes for 1100101, 1011101 and 1001101:

$$\begin{matrix} [1100101] \\ [1011101] \\ [1001101] \end{matrix} \begin{bmatrix} 1 & 1 & 0 \\ 0 & 1 & 1 \\ 1 & 1 & 1 \\ 1 & 0 & 1 \\ 1 & 0 & 0 \\ 0 & 1 & 0 \\ 0 & 0 & 1 \end{bmatrix} = \begin{matrix} [000] \\ [001] \\ [110] \end{matrix}$$

We observe that the syndrome of the first word is zero, and hence the word is a codeword: no error has occurred. The other syndromes may be used as the index to a look-up table giving the error pattern: we will complete the decoding process when we consider Hamming codes in the next section.

For cyclic codes the syndrome may also be computed in polynomial notation. Here we compute the syndrome (for both systematic and non-systematic forms of the code) by performing the modulo-$g(x)$ operation at the receiver. Clearly if the word is a codeword, the syndrome will again be zero. Repeat Equation (6.13) in polynomial notation:

$$r(x) = c(x) + e(x)$$

$$s(x) = r(x) \bmod g(x) = c(x) \bmod g(x) + e(x) \bmod g(x)$$

$$= e(x) \bmod g(x) \tag{6.15}$$

Hence once again the syndrome depends only on the error pattern, and we may obtain the error pattern from the syndrome. The syndrome can be formed using the shift register structure of Fig. 6.3, remembering that in the polynomial form the order of the data and parity bits is reversed.

We will return to this worked example in Example 6.5(b).

6.2.4 Error probability of hard decision syndrome decoding

For linear block codes subject to syndrome decoding we can obtain a more accurate and straightforward estimate of the error probability than the union bound approach described in Section 5.7 (which is likely to be a substantial over-estimate, since it counts many error patterns twice). We note that each syndrome corresponds to a different correctable error pattern. We assign the minimum weight error patterns (which are most probable) to the syndromes, thus minimizing the error probability. Now there are $2^{n-k} - 1$ distinct non-zero syndromes, and hence $2^{n-k} - 1$ correctable error patterns. There are a total of $\sum_{i=1}^{t} {}^{n}C_i$ patterns of t or fewer errors, which of course our t-error-correcting code must correct. Hence, in general, there will also be:

$$n_c(t+1) = 2^{n-k} - 1 - \sum_{i=1}^{t} {}^{n}C_i \tag{6.16}$$

correctable patterns of $t+1$ errors. The probability of each pattern of i errors is $p^i(1-p)^{n-i}$, where p is the channel symbol error probability. The word error probability is then given by:

$$P_{\text{ew}} = 1 - \left[\sum_{i=0}^{t} {}^{n}C_i p^i (1-p)^{n-i} + n_c(t+1)p^{t+1}(1-p)^{n-t-1} \right] \tag{6.17}$$

We use the estimate in Section 5.7 for the number of bit errors per symbol error for a systematic code, assuming that the dominant uncorrected error pattern contains $d_H(min) = 2t + 1$ errors. Then the bit error probability:

$$P_b \approx \frac{2t + 1}{n} P_{ew} \tag{6.18}$$

In practice, we find that we may neglect the correctable error patterns of weight $t + 1$ for code lengths above 31, and at low error probabilities we may further use the very simple approximation:

$$P_b \approx \frac{2t + 1}{n} {}^nC_{t+1} p^{t+1} \tag{6.19}$$

6.3 Types of block code

We now consider the most important types of cyclic block code, describing their characteristics, how they are generated, and outlining the (hard decision) decoding techniques available. We also determine their coding gain using hard decision decoding.

6.3.1 Single parity check codes

Together with repetition codes, single parity check (SPC) codes are probably the simplest possible non-trivial codes, although they cannot be used for forward error correction with hard decision decoding. The principle is to add a single bit to a data word in such a way that the total Hamming weight (number of '1's) is either even (for an even parity code) or odd (for an odd parity). Even parity is most commonly used, and will be assumed hereafter. Thus a length n codeword contains $k = n - 1$ information bits, and therefore the rate $R = (n - 1)/n$.

The codes are linear, since the modulo-2 sum of any two codewords must also have even weight, and thus must also be a codeword, and the all-zeros word is also a permitted codeword. The minimum Hamming weight is obviously 2, and thus this must be the code's minimum distance d_{min}. The codes may therefore be described as $(n, n - 1, 2)$ codes. Hard decision decoding will not guarantee to correct even single errors, since from Equation (5.1) the number of errors corrected $t = 0$. The codes are used primarily (and very widely) for error detection, most notably in the standard 8-bit ASCII codes.

Note that the codes are also cyclic, since any cyclic shift of a codeword will still have even weight, and therefore will be a codeword. The generator matrix has the form:

$$\begin{bmatrix} 1 & 0 & \cdots & 0 & 1 \\ 0 & 1 & & 0 & 1 \\ \vdots & & \ddots & \vdots & \vdots \\ 0 & 0 & \cdots & 1 & 1 \end{bmatrix}$$

and the generator polynomial is simply $1 + x$.

6.3.2 Repetition codes

Repetition codes are formed simply by repeating a single information bit n times. The codes have two codewords, all '0's and all '1's, and the Hamming distance is n. The repetition codes will therefore correct $t = \lfloor n/2 \rfloor$ errors. The code is linear (since $111 \cdots + 111 \cdots = 000 \cdots$), and trivially cyclic, since each codeword is its own cyclic shift. Its generator matrix is a single all '1's row, and its generator polynomial is $1 + x + x^2 + \cdots + x^{n-1}$.

6.3.3 Hamming codes

Hamming codes were in fact the first class of FEC code discovered, by Richard Hamming [6.4] soon after Shannon's paper on information theory, which demonstrated the gains possible using coding. They are usually formulated in terms of the matrix representation although, as we will see, they are also cyclic codes and admit of a polynomial representation.

We saw when considering syndrome decoding using the matrix representation that the syndrome of a word with error pattern e is given by $e\mathbf{H}^T$ (Equation (6.13)). Now consider each of the n single error patterns: $1000\ldots$, $0100\ldots$, etc. Clearly, the syndrome for the single error pattern with '1' in the ith position is simply the ith row of $\mathbf{H}^T$. Thus if we ensure that each row of $\mathbf{H}^T$ is distinct and non-zero, the code will be able to distinguish, and hence correct, all single error patterns. If the code is systematic, we fill in the bottom $(n - k)$ rows of $\mathbf{H}^T$ with the rows of the identity matrix (according to Equation (6.14)). Then we complete the construction by filling the remaining rows with the other possible distinct rows. We omit, of course, the all-zeros row, which is the syndrome for no error. We may then construct $\mathbf{G}$.

This is called a Hamming code, and it is evidently single error correcting. In fact it is called a *perfect* single error correcting code, since it will correct all single errors and no patterns of two or more. Its minimum Hamming distance is thus 3. The length of the syndrome is $(n - k)$, and hence there are $2^{n-k} - 1$ non-zero syndromes, which must correspond to the n single error patterns. Hence for a Hamming code:

$$n = 2^{n-k} - 1 \tag{6.20}$$

which has solutions for (n, k) of $(3, 2), (7, 4), (15, 11), (31, 26), (63, 57) \cdots - n$ always one less than a power of 2.

Example 6.5(b)

Complete the decoding of Example 6.5(a).

Solution   Observe that in the parity check matrix constructed in Example 6.5 above, all the columns of **H** (and hence the rows of $\mathbf{H}^T$) are distinct. This confirms that this code is indeed a Hamming code. We have already noted that it is a cyclic code, and in fact this is true in general. We can construct the generator polynomial by taking the codeword polynomial of lowest order, as we have already seen.

With this observation we can complete the decoding from Example 6.5. Word 1011101 has syndrome 001, which is the last row of $\mathbf{H}^T$, and hence the error is in the last position: the corrected word is 1011100. 1001101 has syndrome 110, which is the first row, and hence the error is in the first position: the corrected word is 0001101.

The BER performance of the first few Hamming codes on a BPSK/QPSK channel, with hard decision decoding, is shown in Fig. 6.4, compared with uncoded transmission. Note that the coding gain is not large (less than 1 dB at 10^{-3} for all codes), and that it does not increase greatly with code length: there appears to be very little improvement above length 31.

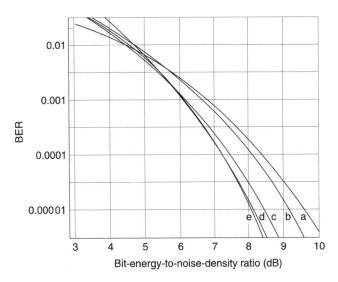

Figure 6.4   BER performance of Hamming codes with hard decision decoding: (a) uncoded; (b) (7, 4); (c) (15, 11); (d) (31, 26); (e) (63, 57)

6.3.4 Finite fields

As mentioned above, the most important types of cyclic block code, namely the BCH and the Reed–Solomon codes, are based on the theory of finite, or Galois, fields [6.3, pp. 24–40]. We shall, however, relegate the detailed field theory to Appendix 1. In the case of BCH codes the fields are important only as a means of constructing the generator polynomials: once constructed (or obtained from a suitable table), the polynomials may be used as described above. They are also relevant to the decoding algorithms. For Reed–Solomon codes, however, the case is more complicated: the code symbols themselves are elements of the field.

Finite fields are groups in which two operations are defined, which for convenience are referred to as 'addition' and 'multiplication', although they behave differently from addition and multiplication of the natural numbers. The field is said to be *closed* under these two operations, which means that any such operation results in another member of the group. Thus the number of elements is finite (hence the name), unlike the set of natural numbers. Here, however, in order to introduce the principles of Reed–Solomon coding we will simply define the two operations by means of a pair of look-up tables, for addition and multiplication.

6.3.5 BCH codes

Hamming codes, being only single error correcting, have significant limitations. Figure 6.4 shows that their coding gain is rather limited. As their length increases (which might be expected to increase their power), the probability of an uncorrectable error in fact increases, leading to the limit on coding gain that we have noted above. Clearly, a multiple error correcting code is required to provide increased gain. Bose–Chaudhuri–Hocquenghem codes (universally known as BCH codes) [6.3, pp. 141–83; 6.5; 6.6] provide a solution: a family of cyclic codes that can be designed to correct almost any required number of errors.

The construction of BCH codes is described in Appendix 1. An algorithm is described that, given a desired number t of errors corrected, will construct a generator polynomial for a code which corrects at least t errors. Although finite fields are used in this algorithm, the resulting generator polynomial always has coefficients 0 or 1. Here, we give a selection of these codes in Table 6.3 (taken from the comprehensive tables given in [6.2] and [6.3, p. 583]), showing n, k and d_{min}, as well as their generator polynomials and an estimate of their coding gain. Thus d_{min} as given is derived from the designed error correcting power. As mentioned above, the algorithm produces a code that will correct at least the designed number of errors. Some codes will in principle correct more; however, most decoding algorithms will only correct

n	k	d_{min}	Generator polynomial	Coding gain (dB)
7	4	3	$x^3 + x + 1 = 1011 = 13_8$	0.5
	1	7	$x^6 + x^5 + x^4 + x^3 + x^2 + x + 1 = 177_8$	–
15	11	3	$x^4 + x + 1 = 10011 = 23_8$	1.3
	7	5	721	1.0
	5	7	2467	0.8
	1	15	77777	–
31	26	3	45	1.6
	16	7	107657	2.0
	11	11	5423325	2.0
	6	15	313365047	0.7
63	57	3	103	1.7
	51	5	12471	2.5
	45	7	1701317	2.9
	39	9	166623567	3.0
	36	11	1033500423	3.2
	30	13	157464165547	3.0
127	120	3	211	1.7
	71	19	6255010713253127753	3.8
	57	23	3352652525705053517721	3.4
255	247	3	435	1.6
	187	19	5275531354000132236351	4.2
	131	37	21571333147151015126125027744214202416547 1	4.1

Table 6.3   Minimum distance, generator polynomials and coding gains (for word error rate 10^{-6}) of a selection of BCH codes

the designed number of errors. The coding gains given are calculated using Equation (6.19) solved for a required BER of 10^{-6}, using the designed error correcting power of the code. The generator polynomials are given in octal form: to obtain the polynomial form, convert to binary. The binary digits then give the coefficients in the generator polynomial, the least significant bit corresponding to the lowest power, as shown for some of the shortest codes.

As for the Hamming codes, the length n of BCH codes (at least for their most common, or *primitive*, form) is always one less than a power of 2. Note that the first code for each length in Table 6.3 corresponds to the Hamming code: the Hamming codes are in fact a special case of the BCH codes, putting $t = 1$. The last code (lowest k – not included for all n) under each length is the $(n, 1, n)$ repetition code, which also is a special case of the BCH code.

An estimate of the BER performance of three BCH codes, made using the method of Section 6.2.4, is given in Fig. 6.5. We observe that the coding gain is larger than for the Hamming codes of Fig. 6.4, and continues to increase with code length. This is confirmed by the estimates of coding gain given in Table 6.3. Note that, as suspected, the gain of the Hamming codes rapidly tends to a limit with increasing code length. There are, however, codes of

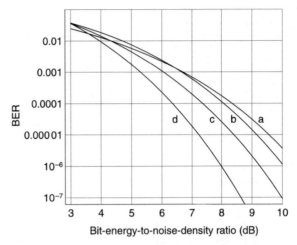

Figure 6.5 **Estimated BER performance of BCH codes: (b) (7, 4); (c) (15, 7); (d) (31, 16), compared with (a) uncoded transmission**

moderate length that yield useful coding gains, even with hard decision decoding. Note that the best codes in this respect have a rate around $\frac{1}{2}$.

6.3.6   Reed–Solomon codes

Reed–Solomon (RS) codes [6.3, pp. 170–7] are constructed using a superficially similar algorithm to that for BCH codes, which is also described in Appendix 1. However, it differs in that the resulting generator polynomial has coefficients that are themselves elements of the field. To make use of this polynomial, the data and the codeword must also be treated as being made up of symbols which are field elements. Thus in their fundamental structure RS codes are not binary, although, as we shall see, they are usually used in binary systems.

As mentioned above, in this section we simply treat the field elements as numbers on which two operations are defined, referred to as 'addition' and 'multiplication', although they behave differently from addition and multiplication over the natural numbers. Table 6.4 gives the addition and multiplication table for a simple example, the field GF(8). Note that addition of the element 0, or multiplication by 1, leave an element unchanged, as one would expect.

The length of an RS code defined over $GF(2^q)$ is always one less than the size of the field, i.e. $n = 2^q - 1$. We observe in Appendix 1 that the order of the generator polynomial of a t (symbol) error correcting code:

$$O[g(x)] = 2t = n - k$$
$$\therefore k = n - 2t = 2^q - 1 - 2t$$

$$(6.21)$$

	1	2	3	4	5	6	7
1	0						
2	3	0					
3	2	1	0				
4	5	6	7	0			
5	4	7	6	1	0		
6	7	4	5	2	3	0	
7	6	5	4	3	2	1	0

	2	3	4	5	6	7
2	4					
3	6	5				
4	3	7	6			
5	1	4	2	7		
6	7	1	5	3	1	
7	5	2	1	6	4	3

(a)   (b)

Table 6.4 (a) addition and (b) multiplication over the finite field GF(8)

Hence, we may relate the rate of the code to its error-correcting power more directly than we could for the BCH codes.

We consider next, with the aid of an example, how the non-binary RS codes can be used in binary systems.

Example 6.6

Find the generator polynomial of a length 7, 2-error-correcting RS code, and use it to encode some data. How might this be transmitted in binary form?

Solution The length implies that the code is defined over GF(8), for which addition and multiplication is tabulated above (Table 6.4). The order of the generator polynomial is 4, and the number of information symbols, k, is therefore 3. In Appendix 1 we determine the generator polynomial of this code as:

$$g(x) = (x - 2)(x - 2^2)(x - 2^3)(x - 2^4)$$
$$= 3 + 2 \cdot x + 1 \cdot x^2 + 3 \cdot x^3 + 1 \cdot x^4$$

The data to be encoded consists of three symbols from GF(8). As an example, let us encode data $\mathbf{d} = 105$:

$$d(x) = 1 + 5 \cdot x^2$$

$$c(x) = d(x)g(x) = (1 + 5 \cdot x^2)(3 + 2 \cdot x + 1 \cdot x^2 + 3 \cdot x^3 + 1 \cdot x^4)$$
$$= 3 + 2 \cdot x + 1 \cdot x^2 + 3 \cdot x^3 + 1 \cdot x^4 + 4 \cdot x^2 + 1 \cdot x^3 + 5 \cdot x^4 + 4 \cdot x^5 + 5 \cdot x^6$$
$$= 3 + 2 \cdot x + 5 \cdot x^2 + 2 \cdot x^3 + 4 \cdot x^4 + 4 \cdot x^5 + 5 \cdot x^6$$

$$\mathbf{c} = 3\,2\,5\,2\,4\,4\,5$$

Table 6.4 has been used for the addition and multiplication operations here.

However, in most cases we have binary data to be encoded and a binary channel to transmit across. Since the size of the field is 2^3, we can simply map groups of 3 bits onto the symbols of GF(8). It is not particularly important what mapping is used, but the simplest is an octal to binary conversion, so that in the example the data is 001 000 101, and the codeword is 011 010 101 010 100 100 101.

This approach can of course be generalized to any RS code, mapping the symbols onto groups of q bits. The parameters of the resulting binary code are then:

$$\left.\begin{array}{l} n = q(2^q - 1) \\ k = q(2^q - 1 - 2t) \end{array}\right\} \tag{6.22}$$

t here is the number of symbol errors corrected. Since each symbol contains q bits, and a single bit error will give rise to a symbol error, the number of bit errors corrected ranges from t to qt, depending on the distribution of bit errors.

The calculation of the exact hard decision BER following the approach of Section 6.2.4 above is rather involved, since we must calculate the probability of symbol error (which varies according to the number of bit errors), and then the probability of a word error. However, a good approximation is again given by considering the most probable type of word error: in which $t + 1$ symbols contain one bit error each. There are ${}^nC_{t+1}$ patterns of symbol error, with q^{t+1} patterns of bit error within each. We use the estimate of BER of Equation (6.18), except that each symbol error corresponds on average to $q/2$ bit errors out of q bits transmitted. Hence we approximate:

$$P_b \approx \frac{2t + 1}{2n} P_{ew} \approx \frac{2t + 1}{2n} {}^nC_{t+1} q^{t+1} p^{t+1} \tag{6.23}$$

Figure 6.6 shows the performance of three Reed–Solomon codes, in which the symbols are transmitted in binary form, compared with uncoded transmission. We note that the performance is not greatly improved compared with similar BCH codes: the advantage of Reed–Solomon codes is seen when concatenated with other codes (see Section 6.5.2). Figure 6.6 also compares the exact BER calculation with the approximation of Equation (6.23), showing that the latter is very accurate at most BERs of practical interest.

The binary mapping of their symbols results in a useful property of Reed–Solomon codes: a *burst-error correction* capability. This arises because any symbol error may be corrected as readily as any other symbol error, and hence a burst of errors that affects all bits in a symbol may still be corrected. In fact, it may be seen that a 2^q-ary, t-error-correcting RS code will correct burst errors of length up to $q(t - 2) + 2$. (An error burst of length b is a sequence containing a high proportion of errors of length b from first error to last.) This again is useful in concatenated code systems, since an error in the inner code is likely to give rise to a burst or errors that the outer code must correct.

In the context of radio systems using multilevel modulation, an intuitively appealing suggestion is to map the Reed–Solomon symbols to multilevel

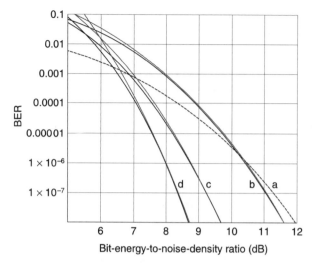

Figure 6.6 **BER performance of Reed–Solomon codes (symbols) (b) (7, 3), (c) (15, 9) (d) (31, 23) compared with (a) uncoded. The grey line in each case is an approximation of Equation (6.23); the black line is exact**

symbols. However, it has been shown [6.7] that there are limitations to this approach. Most significantly, because the code length is linked to the radix of the symbols (it is one less), this mapping limits the code lengths in most cases (e.g. 15 for 16-QAM), and thus limits the power of the code. Better results are obtained by mapping the RS symbols onto two or more multilevel symbols, which allows for much longer codes. However, this does not take into account that some symbol errors are more probable than others. As we shall see in Chapter 8, a better technique for coding multilevel symbols is available, which uses the concept of Euclidean distance introduced in Chapter 5.

6.3.7 Reed–Muller codes

Reed–Muller (RM) codes [6.8] are usually described in terms of their generator matrix, rather than the generator polynomial, although it has been shown [6.9] that they are in fact cyclic, and therefore have a generator polynomial. We follow the usual description here, since it is the most straightforward.

The length of all RM codes is a power of two, say $n = 2^l$. The generator matrix of the *zeroth-order* Reed–Muller code contains one row, consisting of all ones: thus the zeroth-order code is simply a repetition code. The generator matrix of the *first-order* code contains an additional l rows, whose columns consist of all n possible binary l-tuples. The *second-order* code generator contains, in addition to all these, $l(l-1)/2$ rows consisting of all possible logical AND combinations of two of the additional first-order rows. The third-order code adds to this all possible combinations of three of the first-order rows. In general the *m*th order code generator adds to the $(m-1)$th order generator all combinations of m of the first-order rows.

This will be clarified by a simple example.

Example 6.7

Construct all the possible length 8 RM codes. Find the rate and minimum Hamming distance of each.

Solution   The generator matrix for the zeroth-order code is a single row of '1's, length 8. The code is the 8-bit repetition code with two codewords: 00000000 and 11111111. $k=1$, and hence rate $R=\frac{1}{8}$. The minimum distance is 8.

The generator for the first-order code is:

$$\begin{bmatrix} 1 & 1 & 1 & 1 & 1 & 1 & 1 & 1 \\ \hline 0 & 0 & 0 & 0 & 1 & 1 & 1 & 1 \\ 0 & 0 & 1 & 1 & 0 & 0 & 1 & 1 \\ 0 & 1 & 0 & 1 & 0 & 1 & 0 & 1 \end{bmatrix}$$

The lower partition of this is the 'first-order part'. It consists of the columns $000, 001 \ldots 111$. $k=4$; $R=\frac{1}{2}$. A careful examination of the generator matrix shows that the minimum distance is 4 (in fact all codewords except the all zeros and the all '1's contain 4 '1's).

The generator matrix of the second-order code is:

$$\left[\begin{array}{cccccccc} 1 & 1 & 1 & 1 & 1 & 1 & 1 & 1 \\ \hline 0 & 0 & 0 & 0 & 1 & 1 & 1 & 1 \\ 0 & 0 & 1 & 1 & 0 & 0 & 1 & 1 \\ 0 & 1 & 0 & 1 & 0 & 1 & 0 & 1 \\ \hline 0 & 0 & 0 & 0 & 0 & 0 & 1 & 1 \\ 0 & 0 & 0 & 0 & 0 & 1 & 0 & 1 \\ 0 & 0 & 0 & 0 & 0 & 0 & 1 & 1 \end{array}\right]\begin{array}{l} 0 \\ \\ 1 \\ 2 \\ 3 \\ \\ 1\,\&\,2 \\ 1\,\&\,3 \\ 2\,\&\,3 \end{array}$$

This contains, in addition to the four rows of the first-order matrix, three rows formed of the bit-wise logical AND of all three combinations of two of the first-order rows 1–3, as shown. k is now 7, $R=\frac{7}{8}$. The minimum weight of the generator rows is 2, and this also (by inspection) is the minimum distance. Note that this is equivalent in rate and minimum distance to the SPC code.

One could also construct a third-order code, containing in addition the AND combination of all three first-order rows: $1\,\&\,2\,\&\,3 = 00000001$. This, however, would evidently have rate 1 and minimum distance 1, and as a FEC code would be trivial.

N	k	R	d_{min}
4	1	0.25	4
	3	0.75	2
8	1	0.125	8
	4	0.5	4
	7	0.675	2
16	1	0.0625	16
	5	0.3125	8
	11	0.6875	4
	15	0.9375	2

Table 6.5   Reed–Muller codes of length up to 16

We may generalize these calculations to other lengths, all powers of two. The first-order RM code of length $n = 2^l$ (sometimes written RM(l, 1)) has $k = l + 1 = {}^lC_0 + {}^lC_1$ and $d_{min} = n/2$. The mth order code RM(l, m) has $k = \sum_{i=0}^{m} {}^lC_i$ and $d_{min} = 2^{l-m}$. Table 6.5 summarizes the first few Reed–Muller codes. The fact that their minimum distance is always even makes them rather inefficient as FEC codes with hard decision decoding, but they nevertheless have a number of important applications, as we shall see.

6.3.8   Extending and shortening codes

It is frequently useful to create codes longer or shorter than an already existing code. There are means of creating codes of different length based on another code: *extending* and *shortening* [6.10, pp. 490–3].

A code can be extended simply by adding an extra parity check bit, for example to make the overall codeword weight even. If the minimum Hamming distance of the code is odd, this also increases the distance by 1, since the minimum weight codewords will have their weight increased by 1. In this way an (n, k, d) code may become an $(n + 1, k, d + 1)$. However, extension has only a trivial effect on a code whose codewords are already of even weight: thus a code can only be extended once.

Example 6.8

Find (n, k, d) for the extensions of the length 15 BCH codes.

Solution   BCH codes always have odd minimum distances; hence extension results in an increased minimum distance. The codes (reading from Table 6.3) become:

$$(16, 11, 4); \qquad (16, 7, 6); \qquad (16, 5, 8); \qquad (16, 1, 16)$$

Note that two of these have the same (n, k, d) as the Reed–Muller codes of the previous section; in fact they are equivalent to RM codes.

Conversely, shortening reduces the code length, but it is not the inverse operation to extension, since it also reduces k, while maintaining the same error-correcting power.

Consider the codewords of a systematic code in which a given set of l information bits (say the first l) are zero. There are 2^{k-l} such codewords, whose minimum distance is the same as the original code. Now we may use these codewords to form a new code, deleting the l zero bits, without affecting the minimum distance of the code. Thus we may shorten an (n, k, d) code to form an $(n-l, k-l, d)$ code. Note, however, that a shortened cyclic code is in general no longer cyclic, although it will still have a polynomial representation. Shortened codes do have the useful property that the original decoder can be used, simply by replacing the deleted zero bits.

We may be able to reduce code length without affecting k, by deleting one or more code bits (it is immaterial whether they are parity or information bits). The process is called *puncturing*. For most (in fact all non-trivial) codes this will, however, also reduce the minimum distance, to an extent that depends on which position(s) are punctured. This operation can be used to reverse the extension of a code. It is, however, more commonly used in convolutional codes than block codes.

We may also be able to *lengthen* a systematic code by adding information symbols (without additional parity symbols). However, this may eventually reduce its minimum distance. We can also change k without changing n by *augmenting* a code (adding codewords) or *expurgating* it (removing codewords). This will, in general, also change the minimum Hamming distance.

6.4   Soft decision decoding

In the above we have assumed hard decision decoding, as described in Section 5.6.1. As we have seen in Section 5.6.2, better performance can be obtained with soft decision decoding, in which the demodulator passes to the decoder additional information about the reliability of its decisions, in the ideal maximum likelihood (ML) case giving an exact likelihood ratio for each symbol. As we have seen, in the case of the AWGN channel this is equivalent to using Euclidean rather than Hamming distance as the decoding metric. On the AWGN channel, soft decision decoding gives an increase in coding gain of around 2 dB.

In Chapter 7, we will see that this is relatively straightforward to implement for convolutional codes, but for block codes it is much more difficult. The straightforward 'brute force' technique is to determine the Euclidean distance of the received word from all 2^k possible codewords, but clearly this is prohibitively complex for all but the very simplest codes. In fact, the optimum practical technique so far developed (at least for true ML decoding) is to express the block code in the form of a trellis, and then to use the Viterbi algorithm used for decoding convolutional codes. There are, however, some sub-optimum soft decision algorithms, of which the best established is the Chase algorithm.

6.4.1 Errors and erasures decoding

However, *errors and erasures decoding* provides a very simple sub-optimum approach [6.9, pp. 482–6]. Here we treat any symbol which the demodulator is unable to decide with sufficient certainty as an *erasure*. If the code originally had a minimum distance d_{min} and there are e erasures, there is still a minimum distance of $d_{min} - e$, counting only the un-erased places. Hence, the code is able to correct:

$$t < \frac{d_{min} - e}{2} \tag{6.24}$$

errors. Errors and erasures decoding can be implemented using a hard decision decoder by initially replacing all the erasures with '0's, then decoding. If fewer than half of the erasures should have been '1's, and Equation (6.24) is satisfied, then decoding will be correct. On the other hand, if more than half should have been '1's, then replacing all the erasures with '1's will result in correct decoding. We therefore repeat the decoding with the erasures replaced with '1's, and choose the decoded sequence closest to the received sequence (discounting erased symbol positions).

This could be regarded as a very simple form of soft decision decoding, using two thresholds instead of the one used in hard decision decoding. The gain given on the white Gaussian noise channel is quite limited – usually less than 1 dB – but may be useful in some circumstances for the relatively modest increase in complexity. For example, Fig. 6.7 compares errors and erasures decoding of the Hamming (15, 11) code with hard decision decoding and uncoded transmission. Note that if there are more than d erasures, the whole word will be erased: the probability of this occurring is also shown in Fig. 6.7.

6.4.2 The Chase algorithm

As mentioned above, the Chase algorithm [6.10, pp. 487–9] is a sub-optimum, but near ML, decoding algorithm. The principle is to generate a few candidate codewords using a hard decision decoder, and to find the closest of these to the received word using a soft decision criterion. The demodulator generates a hard decision estimate $\mathbf{r}$ of the received word, and then adds a set of test vectors $\mathbf{v}_1 \cdots \mathbf{v}_J$, each of which is decoded using the hard decision decoder. Chase suggested that the test vectors need have a Hamming weight no larger than $\lfloor (d - 1)/2 \rfloor$, and in fact a much smaller set is adequate in most cases.

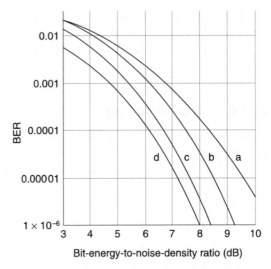

Figure 6.7 **Performance of errors and erasures decoding of the Hamming (15, 11) code and erasure threshold 0.3: (a) uncoded BER, (b) hard decision decoding BER, (c) BER with errors and erasures decoding, (d) word erasure ratio with errors and erasures decoding**

Clearly the '1's of the test vectors should preferably be in the least reliable symbol positions of the received word. Chase devised several algorithms based on these principles, of which his second algorithm is the most used:

(1) Generate hard decision estimate **r** of received word, locating the $\lfloor d/2 \rfloor$ least reliable symbols.
(2) Generate J test vectors with '1's in up to $\lfloor d/2 \rfloor$ of these positions.
(3) Perform hard decision decoding of all perturbed vectors $\mathbf{r} + \mathbf{v}_j, j = 1 \cdots J$.
(4) Find the soft decision metric (e.g. Euclidean distance) of each decoded vector, and choose the best.

The performance of this algorithm is normally negligibly poorer than true ML decoding.

6.4.3 Trellis decoding

Ever since the principle of soft decision decoding was first described, coding theorists have sought computationally efficient techniques for applying it to block codes. Indeed it was one of the main advantages of convolutional codes that they had a decoding algorithm, the Viterbi algorithm, in which soft decision decoding could readily be implemented, and led in large measure to the perception that convolutional codes are more practically useful. Wolf [6.11] first showed how the trellis, which is characteristic of convolutional codes, could also be applied to the decoding of block codes, and Forney [6.12] further stimulated research in the area. Since then the field has advanced rapidly. Lin *et al.* [6.12] describe the field in much more detail than can be accommodated here.

The basic principle, however, is simple. A trellis may be drawn to represent a block code in much the same way as for a convolutional code (Section 7.2.2). The Viterbi algorithm (Section 7.3.1) can then be applied to decode the received codeword using the appropriate soft-decision metric. Techniques have been developed to minimize the number of states in this trellis, and hence the decoding complexity.

The form of the trellis of a block code depends on the precise ordering of the parity bits, and on the basis codewords chosen (see Section 6.1.2 above). The number of states, and hence the decoding complexity, can therefore be minimized by appropriate operations on the generator matrix. We manipulate the matrix into *trellis-oriented form*, in which [6.12]:

- The leading '1' of each row appears in a column before the leading '1' of any row below it;
- No two rows have their trailing '1's in the same column

Example 6.9(a)
(see [6.12, p. 29])

Express the generator matrix of the (8, 4) Reed–Muller code in trellis-oriented form.

$$\begin{bmatrix} 1 & 1 & 1 & 1 & 1 & 1 & 1 & 1 \\ 0 & 0 & 0 & 0 & 1 & 1 & 1 & 1 \\ 0 & 0 & 1 & 1 & 0 & 0 & 1 & 1 \\ 0 & 1 & 0 & 1 & 0 & 1 & 0 & 1 \end{bmatrix}$$

This is not in trellis-oriented form, since the leading '1' of row (4) appears before that of row (3), and the trailing '1's of all four rows are in the same column. Interchange rows (2) and (4):

$$\begin{bmatrix} 1 & 1 & 1 & 1 & 1 & 1 & 1 & 1 \\ 0 & 1 & 0 & 1 & 0 & 1 & 0 & 1 \\ 0 & 0 & 1 & 1 & 0 & 0 & 1 & 1 \\ 0 & 0 & 0 & 0 & 1 & 1 & 1 & 1 \end{bmatrix}$$

and subtract row (4) from rows (1), (2) and (3):

$$\begin{bmatrix} 1 & 1 & 1 & 1 & 0 & 0 & 0 & 0 \\ 0 & 1 & 0 & 1 & 1 & 0 & 1 & 0 \\ 0 & 0 & 1 & 1 & 1 & 1 & 0 & 0 \\ 0 & 0 & 0 & 0 & 1 & 1 & 1 & 1 \end{bmatrix}$$

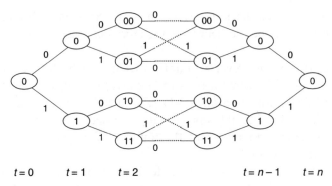

$t = 0$ $t = 1$ $t = 2$ $t = n-1$ $t = n$

Figure 6.8   **General form of trellis of block code**

This is now in trellis-oriented form. Note that each row has a non-zero span, called the *active span* between its leading and trailing '1's, with zeros before and/or after.

We shall return to this worked example in Example 6.9(b).

We now use the generator matrix in this form to draw up the trellis diagram. (See also Section 7.2.2 for a description of the trellis diagram for convolutional codes.) The trellis diagram treats the encoder as a finite state machine (FSM), and shows the state transitions and output bits from time $t = 0$ (before the codeword begins) to $t = n$ (at the end of the word). A trellis has the general form shown in Fig. 6.8. The ellipses (nodes) represent the states of the encoder at the given time: here they are labelled with the data input in order to reach that point. The branches represent the transitions corresponding to each output bit period: they are labelled with the appropriate output bit. Where two branches diverge from one node, they correspond to the two possible input bits. Where no other indication is given, the upper branch corresponds to input '0', the lower to'1'.

The encoder has memory only for data that will affect subsequent output bits. The other 'don't care' bits are omitted from the node label. This reduces the number of distinct states that need to be included in the trellis diagram. At the end of each bit period, only the data corresponding to active rows of the generator matrix at that point contribute to the state. Hence the number of states is 2^{n_a}, where n_a is the number of active rows: i.e. the number of rows that are active both to left and right.

Example 6.9(b)

Draw the trellis of the (8, 4) RM code.

We may now use the trellis-oriented form of the generator matrix obtained in Example 6.9(a) to obtain the trellis of the code. We first determine the *state*

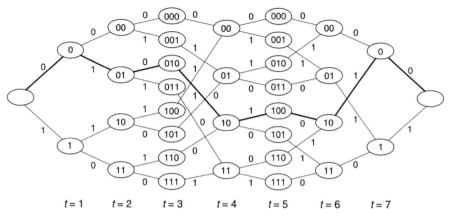

Figure 6.9 Trellis for (8, 4) RM code

profile: the number of states at each point in the trellis, namely:

$$\{1, 2, 4, 8, 4, 8, 4, 2, 1\}$$

Thus the trellis is as shown in Fig. 6.9. Here the node labels are related to the data bits as follows:

$t = 1$	d1	$t = 5$	d2 d3 d4
$t = 2$	d1 d2	$t = 6$	d2 d4
$t = 3$	d1 d2 d3	$t = 7$	d4
$t = 4$	d2 d3		

These correspond to the active rows of the generator matrix at each point. The matrix also shows how the branch labels (output bits) are calculated from the node labels and input data.

Then each path through the trellis corresponds to a codeword, which can be read from the branch labels. The path is determined by the input data: take the upward branch if the next data bit is '0'; the lower if it is '1'. Thus the data word 0100, corresponding to the path marked in heavier lines in Fig. 6.9, yields the codeword 01011010.

We shall return to the worked example in Example 6.9(c).

The trellis may now be used for decoding, using the Viterbi algorithm in much the same way as for a convolutional code. The Viterbi algorithm is described in more detail in Section 7.3.1: its principle is to find the trellis path (the *survivor* path) to each node at each time period that is closest to the received signal. The distance metric may then be Euclidean distance or other appropriate soft decision metric, and thus soft decision decoding may readily be implemented.

One significant difference between trellis decoding of block codes in comparison to convolutional codes is that the trellis is naturally *terminated*: that is, it converges to one node at the right-hand node, at which point there must remain only one survivor path, and decoding is complete with bounded delay. In contrast, for convolutional codes (unless they are artificially terminated), there will be a number of survivor paths throughout the trellis, leading to a potentially indefinite decoding delay (Section 7.3.1).

The computational complexity of trellis decoding clearly depends on the number of nodes in the trellis at each time period. Thus simplifying the trellis, particularly by minimizing the number of states, may also simplify the decoder. In many cases we may do this by *sectionalizing* the trellis: splitting it into sections corresponding to groups of code bits, rather than single bits as in the trellis described above. The best starting point is often the state profile, which indicates at which points in the trellis the fewest states are required.

Example 6.9(c)

Sectionalize the trellis of the (8, 4) RM code.

Consider the state profile of the (8, 4) Reed–Muller code obtained in Example 6.9(b), above:

$$\{1, 2, 4, 8, 4, 8, 4, 2, 1\}$$

If we group the code bits in pairs, then we need consider only every other entry: the new state profile becomes:

$$\{1, 4, 4, 4, 1\}$$

and the trellis becomes:

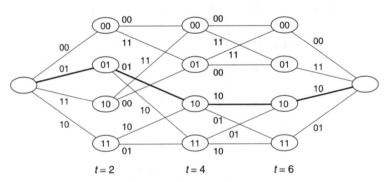

Figure 6.10 **Sectionalized trellis of (8, 4) Reed–Muller code**

This is significantly simplified, having at most four nodes. Note, however, that the first trellis period now corresponds to two data bits, and hence there are four branches from the left-hand node, each representing one of the four combinations of these bits. (The node label gives the combination).

6.5 System applications

6.5.1 Compact disks

Although it is not a radio system, the compact disk (CD) is perhaps the most significant current practical application of block codes [6.14, 6.15]. It was originally developed jointly by Sony and Philips for very high quality audio storage, although subsequently it has become widely used for multimedia storage in general, including computer data and video.

A CD is a plastic disk 120 mm in diameter onto which the data is encoded by forming pits in the surface, which can then be detected using a laser. When used for audio storage the stereo signal is sampled at 44.1 kHz, and each sample is quantized to one of 2^{16} levels (corresponding to 16 bits/sample). Hence, the disk encodes a useful data rate of $16 \times 44.1\,\mathrm{k} = 1.41\,\mathrm{Mbit\,s^{-1}}$. The process is prone to error due either to imperfections in the manufacturing process, or to subsequent damage to the disk, such as scratches or fingerprints. It is highly likely that the errors in reproduction caused by these will give rise to bursts of errors, since damage is likely to affect a group of bits in the same area of the disk.

To overcome these errors the digitized audio signal is encoded using powerful FEC codes, which also have error detecting capability. Specifically, concatenated Reed–Solomon codes are used. More detail on concatenated coding is given in Chapter 10, but the principle is illustrated in Fig. 6.11. Two (or more) encoders are used, the output of one, the *outer* encoder (here labelled C_1) being fed to the input of the next, the *inner* encoder (C_2). In the decoder the reverse process is performed. This leads to an effectively much more complex code, but one capable of being decoded by the simpler decoders of the two separate codes.

However, concatenated coding has the disadvantage that an error in decoding the inner code tends to give a burst of errors at the output of the

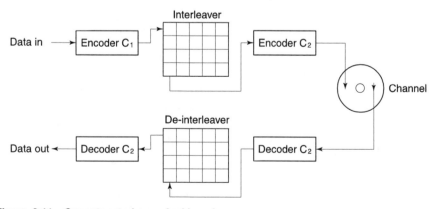

Figure 6.11   Concatenated encoder/decoder

decoder, which the outer decoder may not be able to cope with. For this reason an interleaver (see Chapters 9 and 11) is included between the two encoders/decoders. The effect of this is to spread these error bursts from the inner code over several codewords of the outer code, so that the outer code may now correct them. In a CD, interleavers are also added before encoder C_1 and after encoder C_2, so as to break up further bursts of errors from the disk. Remember that Reed–Solomon code symbols, which are elements of a Galois field $GF(2^q)$, are transmitted as groups of q bits, and that this gives a further degree of burst-error correction capability (Section 6.3.6).

In the CD system, both C_1 and C_2 are formed by shortening (rather drastically) the two symbol-error correcting (255, 251) Reed–Solomon codes (see Section 6.3.8), defined over $GF(2^8)$. For C_1 it becomes a (28, 24) code, while C_2 is (32, 28); both retaining two symbol-error correcting capability. The symbols are transmitted as groups of eight bits, so 192 bits are encoded as a total of 256 bits, an overall code rate of 0.75. Hence, the encoded data rate on the disk (when various overheads are included) is about $2\,\mathrm{Mbit\,s^{-1}}$.

If the error correction capability of the inner code is exceeded, the inner decoder may still be able to detect an error and signal an erasure. The outer decoder will take this into account, increasing the error correction power of the outer code. If the correction capability of the outer code is nevertheless exceeded, this code may signal an erasure of the corresponding sample. The decoder will then attempt to recreate the audio signal by interpolating between the samples on either side. *In extremis*, if too many samples are erased for interpolation to work, the system is muted for the duration of the burst. However, the system will cope with a burst of 4000 errors before correction fails, and 12 000 errors before interpolation fails, corresponding to a track length of 7.5 mm. At the normal uncorrected error rate of 10^{-3}, there should be less than one undetected error (producing an audible click) every 750 hours.

6.5.2 Deep space communications

One of the most extreme applications of radio communications is communication with deep space missions such as the *Voyager* mission to Saturn and Uranus [6.16]. Free space path loss over the distance (several hundred million kilometres), and limitations on transmit power, are such that power efficiency of the communication system is of the utmost importance. (The inverse square law implies that a coding gain of 6 dB due to the FEC coding scheme can double the range of the mission.) For the return link (spacecraft to Earth), very complex codes can be used, since powerful decoding hardware is available on Earth.

Until very recently these missions used concatenated codes in which once again Reed–Solomon codes formed the outer code. Here, however, the inner code was a half-rate convolutional code (see Chapter 7), with constraint length 7. Outer Reed–Solomon codes were used with block length 63–511 (symbol size 6–9

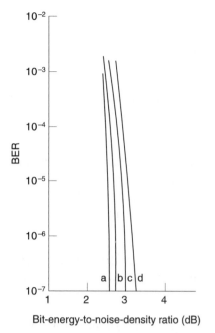

Figure 6.12 BER performance of concatenated codes used for deep space communications: (a) $n = 63$ **Reed–Solomon outer code, (b)** $n = 127$**, (c)** $n = 255$**, (d)** $n = 255$

bits). Convolutional codes also produce error bursts at the inner decoder output, and so once again an interleaver is used between the inner and the outer encoder/decoder. Figure 6.12 shows the BER curves for these codes.

The $n = 255$ code was used on the *Voyager* mission, achieving BER $= 10^{-6}$ at a bit-energy-to-noise-density ratio of 2.53 dB. Decoding was possible at a data rate of $2\,\text{Mbit}\,\text{s}^{-1}$. This was used for the transmission of the images obtained by the probe of these distant planets.

More recently turbo-codes (Chapter 11) have taken over from these codes, being used in the Mars mission. This allowed a significant cost reduction compared with the concatenated Reed–Solomon codes.

Problems

6.1 Write down a generator matrix for the code of Example 6.1. Does your generator matrix result in a systematic code? If not, change the matrix so that it does so.

6.2 Examine the (5, 3) code devised in Problem 5.2. Can it be described in terms of a generator polynomial? If so, is it cyclic? If possible, devise a (5, 3) cyclic code.

6.3 How many codewords has the length 8 cyclic code with generator polynomial $1 + x + x^2 + x^3$? Encode in systematic form the data words 100..., 010..., etc. and hence form the generator matrix. What is the minimum distance of this code?

6.4 Sketch a shift register encoder for the systematic code of Problem 6.3. Show how the data 10111 would be encoded. Check the result using long division of polynomials.

6.5 Repeat the calculation of syndromes from Example 6.5(a) using the polynomial formulation, remembering that the codewords are written in a different order in the two cases. Sketch a shift register syndrome former for this code, and show how the syndrome of the second example in 6.5(a) would be formed.

6.6 Draw up the parity check matrix $\mathbf{H}$ for a (15, 11) Hamming code, and thus find $\mathbf{P}$ and hence $\mathbf{G}$. Also find a generator polynomial for this code.

6.7 Write down the generator polynomial for the (15, 5) BCH code from Table 6.3. Multiply by the codeword corresponding to data 10000. Write down the resulting codeword, plus its first four right-ward cyclic shifts. Hence, find the generator matrix of this code in systematic form.

6.8 List the length 15 (symbols) Reed–Solomon codes, giving n and k in terms of both bits and symbols. Give the error correcting power in terms of symbols, and the burst-error correcting power in bits. For the three highest rate codes calculate the coding gain at $\mathrm{BER} = 10^{-6}$ assuming hard decision decoding, using the approximation of Equation (6.23).

How could a length 48 (bits) code with a burst correction capability of 10 bits be formed from a length 15 (symbols) Reed–Solomon code? What would be its rate?

6.9 Write down expressions for the code symbol error and erasure probability in errors and erasures decoding for received signal power S and erasure threshold $\theta\sqrt{S}$. Find the probability of decoded word error with e erasures (you need consider only the minimum number of errors which will cause decoding error for each number of erasures), and hence the BER. For the (15, 11, 3) BCH code, what is the optimum erasure threshold?

6.10 Find a trellis for the (7, 4) Hamming code of Example 6.2. Simplify the trellis by sectionalizing it.

References

6.1 Sweeney, P. (1991) *Error Control Coding: an Introduction*, Prentice-Hall.

6.2 MacWilliams, F.J. and Sloane, N.J.A. (1977) *The Theory of Error-Correcting Codes*, North-Holland.

6.3 Lin, S. and Costello, D.J. (1983) *Error Control Coding: Fundamentals and Applications*, Prentice-Hall.

6.4 Hamming, R.W. (1950) Error detecting and correcting codes. *Bell System Technical Journal*, **29**: 147–60.

6.5 Hocquenghem, A. (1959) Codes correcteurs d'erreurs. *Chiffres*, **2**: 147–56.

6.6 Bose, R.C. and Chaudhuri, D.K. (1960) On a class of error correcting binary group codes. *Inf. Control*, **3**: 68–79.

6.7 Sweeney, P. (1992) Coding of multi-level transmissions using cyclic codes. In C. Mitchell (Ed.) *Cryptography and Coding II*, Oxford University Press, pp. 273–84.

6.8 Muller, D.E. (1954) Applications of Boolean algebra to switching circuit design and to error detection. *IRE Transactions*, **EC-2**: 6–12.

6.9 Kasami, T., Lin, S. and Peterson, W.W. (1968) New generalisations of the Reed–Muller codes, Part I: Primitive codes. *IEEE Transactions on Information Theory*, **IT-14**: 189–99.

6.10 Wilson, S.G. (1996) *Digital Modulation and Coding*, Prentice-Hall.

6.11 Wolf, J.K. (1978) Efficient maximum-likelihood decoding of linear block codes using a trellis. *IEEE Transactions on Information Theory*, **24**: 76–80.

6.12 Forney, G.D. (1988) Coset codes II: Binary lattices and related codes. *IEEE Transactions on Information Theory*, **IT-34**: 1152–87.

6.13 Lin, S., Kasami, T., Fujiwara, T. and Fossorier, M. (1998) *Trellises and Trellis-based Decoding Algorithms for Linear Block Codes*, Kluwer.

6.14 Peek, J.B.H. (1985) Communications aspects of the compact disc digital audio system. *IEEE Communications Magazine*, **23**(2): 7–15.

6.15 Hoeve, H., Timmermans, J. and Vries, L.B. (1982) Error correction and concealment in the compact disc system. *Philips Technical Review*, **40**(6): 166–72.

6.16 McEliece, R.J. and Swanson, L. (1993) *Reed–Solomon Codes and the Exploration of the Solar System*, JPL Technical Report, August, at http://techreports.jpl.nasa.gov/1994/94-0881.pdf

Chapter 7

Convolutional codes

In this chapter we consider the second main type of error control code, the convolutional codes. As mentioned in Chapter 5, instead of treating each code block independently, these codes add dependence between successive blocks. Thus the current output block depends not only on information bits in the current input block, but also on those of one or more previous input blocks. This results in a more complex code structure, and means that we can no longer separate the code stream into separate codewords, but must consider instead complete, and potentially infinite, code sequences. The payoff for this extra conceptual complexity (which may not necessarily result in extra implementational complexity) is that the resulting codes may have desirable structure which improves performance. In practice, the block lengths used in convolutional codes are much shorter than those of block codes.

7.1 Code structure and encoding

The code structure is illustrated in Fig. 7.1. The braces in this diagram represent a sliding window, which moves along the input stream one block (k symbols) at a time. This shows how the current block of n code symbols depends on the current block of k data symbols, and also on $(\nu - 1)$ previous data blocks. The total number of input blocks, ν, is known as the *constraint length* of the code. The term $(\nu - 1)$ is sometimes called the *memory order* of the code; the *memory* of the code (in the sense of the number of previous data symbols the encoder must store) is clearly $k(\nu - 1)$.

The code may be *systematic*, in which case the data symbols from the current input block appear unchanged in the current code block, or *non-systematic*, in

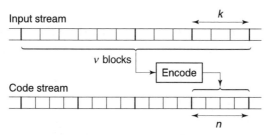

Figure 7.1   Structure of a general convolutional code

which case there is no such restriction on the code symbols. The data and code symbols are normally *binary*, but other radices are also possible. The encoder is normally *linear*, in the sense described in Section 5.3.4. The code is described as a (n, k, ν) code.

7.1.1   Encoder structure

The 'sliding window' is conveniently implemented using a shift register. Figure 7.2 shows the general case. The input data are presented a block at a time to k shift registers in parallel via a demultiplexer. (The shift registers are

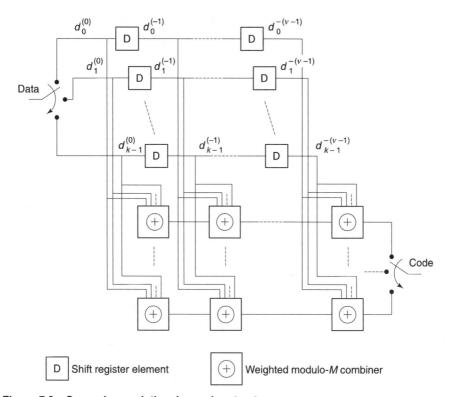

Figure 7.2   General convolutional encoder structure

clocked at the input block rate.) The outputs of the shift registers are combined by n sets of weighted modulo-M adders (where M is the code radix). For binary codes these are modulo-2 adders, i.e. exclusive-OR gates. The weighting is multiplication by an M-ary coefficient – in the binary case (where the coefficients are 0 or 1) this simply means the omission or inclusion of a connection to the relevant shift register element. This forms n code symbols, which are then multiplexed together to form the code stream. The output symbol rate is thus n/k times the input rate, so that the code rate is k/n.

The linearity of the code follows from this structure. Since it is composed only of shift registers (which implement a delay, a linear operation) and modulo-M adders, the modulo-M sum of two data sequences results in a code sequence which is the modulo-M sum of the corresponding code sequences. Hence, the sum of any two code sequences is also a code sequence. Further, the all-zeros sequence is a code sequence, resulting from the all-zeros data sequence. Hence the code is linear.

Example 7.1

Encode the data sequence 10000 using the rate 1/2 constraint length 3 binary (2, 1, 3) convolutional code, with the encoder shown in Fig. 7.3.

Solution   There is only one data bit per block, and hence no need for an input demultiplexer, and two code bits, generated by the two sets of modulo-2 adders shown. We will refer to this code from time-to-time in the sequel to illustrate the general case. To demonstrate its operation, consider the simplest possible data sequence: $10000\cdots$. We also assume that the encoder starts from the zero state: i.e. both shift register elements contain '0's. The state of various parts of the encoder during successive clock periods is shown in Table 7.1. It

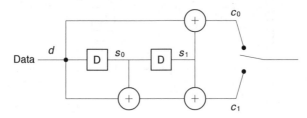

Figure 7.3   Encoder for code of Example 7.1

Data d_0	s_0	s_1	c_0	c_1
1	0	0	1	1
0	1	0	0	1
0	0	1	1	1
0	0	0	0	0

Table 7.1   Behaviour of encoder of Example 7.1 for data sequence $1000\cdots$

is evident that subsequent code outputs will all be '0'. The resulting code sequence is thus $11011100\cdots$.

___

7.1.2   Generator matrix and generator polynomials

The relationship of the pth code symbol to the data symbols can be described mathematically [7.1, p. 14] as:

$$c_i^{(p)} = \sum_{j=0}^{k-1} g_{ij}^{(0)} d_j^{(p)} + \sum_{j=0}^{k-1} g_{ij}^{(1)} d_j^{(p-1)} + \cdots + \sum_{j=0}^{k-1} g_{ij}^{(\nu-1)} d_j^{(p-(\nu-1))}$$

$$= \sum_{l=0}^{\nu-1} \sum_{j=0}^{k-1} g_{ij}^{(l)} d_j^{(p-l)}, \quad i = 0 \cdots n-1 \tag{7.1}$$

where all summations and additions are modulo-M. Note that this summation takes the form of a discrete convolution (although the operations are modulo-2): hence the name *convolutional*. We may reverse the order of summation, and express the inner sum as a polynomial in terms of the delay operator, D:

$$c_i^{(p)} = \sum_{l=0}^{\nu-1} \sum_{j=0}^{k-1} g_{ij}^{(l)} d_j^{(p-l)} = \sum_{j=0}^{k-1} \sum_{l=0}^{\nu-1} g_{ij}^{(l)} d_j^{(p-l)}$$

$$= \sum_{j=0}^{k-1} [g_{ij}^{(0)} + g_{ij}^{(1)} D + g_{ij}^{(2)} D^2 + \cdots + g_{ij}^{(\nu-1)} D^{\nu-1}] d_j^{(p)} \tag{7.2}$$

Multiplication by D corresponds to delay by one input block period, and therefore Dd_j refers to the corresponding data symbol in the previous input block. We may now express (7.2) in the form of a matrix multiplication:

$$\mathbf{c}^{(p)} = \mathbf{d}^{(p)} [\mathbf{G}(D)] \tag{7.3}$$

Here $\mathbf{c}$ is a length n row vector, $\mathbf{d}$ is a length k row vector, and $[\mathbf{G}(D)]$ is a $n \times k$ matrix. Note that for a systematic code, part of $[\mathbf{G}(D)]$ will be the identity matrix.

For the code of Example 7.1:

$$[\mathbf{G}(D)] = [1 + D^2 \quad 1 + D + D^2] \tag{7.4}$$

These polynomials in D are known as the *generator polynomials* of the code. For binary codes they are often expressed in octal form. The octal numbers may be converted back to binary, whereupon a '1' in bit i of the number (where bit 0 is the least significant bit) denotes a term in the polynomial in D^i. For example, for Example 7.1 the generator polynomials may be written as 5, 7.

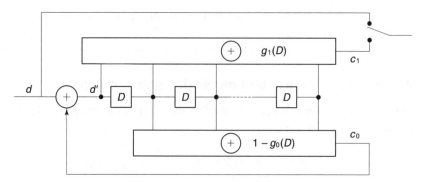

Figure 7.4   Recursive-systematic convolutional encoder

7.1.3   Recursive-systematic form of encoder

The encoder described above has no feedback, which means that if we input a data sequence that contains a finite number of '1's and then returns to all '0's, then the output code sequence will also contain a finite number of '1's. It is similar in this respect to a finite impulse response (FIR) digital filter (and is similar in structure). It is also possible to include feedback in an encoder [7.1, p. 36], in a similar way to that of an infinite impulse response (IIR) filter, as shown in Fig. 7.4 (for simplicity a $(2, 1, \nu)$ code is shown). This form is known as *recursive*, again using the terminology of digital filters.

The code shown is systematic, since one of the outputs is drawn directly from the input. Two weighted sums are also shown, one of which provides the second code output, while the other is fed back and summed with the input to the shift register. A systematic code is shown because it may be illustrated (7.2) that for any non-recursive, non-systematic code, there is a recursive-systematic code which is equivalent, in that it generates exactly the same set of code sequences, albeit from different data sequences.

To observe this, consider the $(2, 1, \nu)$ non-recursive, non-systematic code generated using the weighted sums given by the polynomials $g_1(D)$ and $1 - g_0(D)$. The input to this code would be the sequence d'. Now $d' = d + c_0$, and hence:

$$d = d' - c_0 = d' - d'[1 - g_0(D)] = g_0(D)d' \qquad (7.5)$$

Thus the recursive-systematic code generates the same code sequences as the non-recursive, non-systematic, but from the data sequence d' rather than d. Note that the code in this form is also linear, by the same argument as before.

Example 7.2

Consider the recursive-systematic code whose encoder is shown in Fig. 7.5. The behaviour of the encoder for the data sequence $10100\cdots$ is shown in Table 7.2.

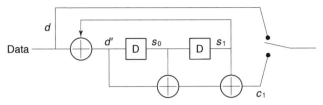

Figure 7.5   Encoder for Example 7.2

Data d	d'	s_0	s_1	c_1
1	1	0	0	1
0	0	1	0	1
1	0	0	1	1
0	0	0	0	0

Table 7.2   Behaviour of encoder of Example 7.2 for data sequence 1010 · · ·

Again, all subsequent code symbols will be zero. The resulting code sequence is 11101100 · · ·, as in Table 7.1, but the data sequence that generated it is different. Note, however, that the sequence d' is identical to the input data sequence in Table 7.1, as indicated above.

Note that not all data sequences leave the encoder in the zero state, as here. For example, the sequence 1001 would leave it in a non-zero state. If zeros continue to be input the encoder will, in general, then generate a repetitive pseudo-random sequence. Thus a finite-length input sequence can generate an infinite-length output sequence, unlike the non-recursive encoder. This difference in the way data sequences map to code sequences can result in some subtle differences between the performance of the two forms of the code.

7.2   Code representation

A number of useful tools for representing a convolutional encoder and the code it generates will be introduced in this section. Of these the most important is certainly the *trellis diagram*, but we will introduce this by way of the *tree diagram*, which, however, is also useful in its own right for certain decoding techniques. We will illustrate these techniques first in terms of Example 7.1, then more generally.

7.2.1   Tree diagram

The tree diagram [7.3, p. 472] represents the possible code sequences generated by an encoder as paths through a tree. The tree diagram for the code of

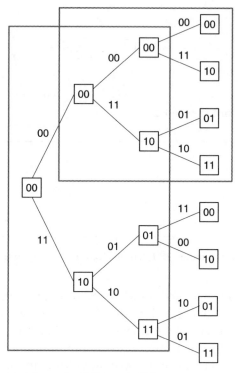

Figure 7.6   Tree diagram for code of Example 7.1

Example 7.1 is shown in Fig. 7.6. The labels in the boxes (which are the nodes of the tree) give the state of the encoder, in the form of the two bits in the shift register. The upper branch from each corresponds to input data '0'; the lower to '1'. The labels on the branches give the corresponding code output.

The diagram thus incorporates the effect of the encoder state as well as the incoming data. Thus any code sequence is represented as a path through the tree. This is a very useful conceptual tool in visualizing the action of the class of decoding techniques known as *sequential* algorithms.

It is clear that the number of nodes in the tree increases exponentially with the length of the data sequence, and very rapidly becomes unmanageable. However, we may also note that there is a lot of redundancy in the diagram. The two parts in grey boxes are topologically identical. In fact, any two parts starting at the same state are identical. This suggests that it may be possible to simplify the diagram greatly.

7.2.2   Trellis diagram

If, indeed, we merge all parts of the tree diagram in which the encoder takes the same state at the same time, we generate a diagram with no more than $2^{\nu - 1}$

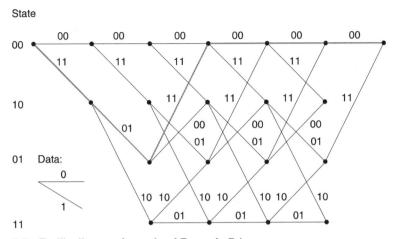

Figure 7.7   Trellis diagram for code of Example 7.1

nodes, without losing any of the information in the tree diagram. The result is the *trellis diagram*, first introduced by Forney [7.4]. Figure 7.7 shows the trellis diagram for Example 7.1.

We may summarize the correspondence between trellis diagram and code as:

Columns   ⇔   Information block periods (encoder clock periods)
Nodes   ⇔   State of encoder after each data bit
Branches   ⇔   State transitions (depending on input)
Branch labels   ⇔   Code output
Paths   ⇔   Code sequences

We retain the correspondence between paths through the diagram and code sequences, while the complexity of the diagram no longer grows exponentially. The path for the data sequence in Table 7.1 is shown in grey in the diagram.

A $(2, 1, \ldots)$ code like Example 7.1 gives rise to the simplest possible trellis diagram. In the general case it may be significantly more complex. Figure 7.8 shows schematically the trellis diagram for an (n, k, ν) code. It shows that, in general, there are 2^k branches leaving each node, and in the steady state, similarly, 2^k branches converging on a node. There are $2^{k(\nu-1)}$ nodes (corresponding to encoder states) and hence a total of $2^{k\nu}$ branches per trellis section, each labelled with n code symbols.

7.2.3   Free distance

The trellis diagram helps us to define a measure of code performance equivalent to the minimum Hamming distance of a block code. As we cannot divide the code stream into distinct codewords, we must consider the distance between complete code sequences. The *free Hamming distance* of a convolutional code

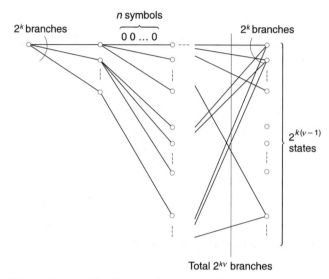

2^k branches

n symbols

0 0 ... 0

2^k branches

$2^{k(v-1)}$ states

Total 2^{kv} branches

Figure 7.8 **Schematic of trellis diagram for general (*n*, *k*, *ν*) convolutional code**

is defined as the smallest distance between any pair of code sequences beginning and ending on the same state [7.1, p. 50]. These are the closest sequences that could be confused by the decoder. As we shall see below, the free distance of the code has a significant effect on its BER performance, just as the minimum Hamming distance does on that of a block code.

Because the code is linear, we can without loss of generality consider only pairs of sequences that begin and end on the zero state. Other pairs can be expressed as the sum of such pairs and another code sequence. We can thus make comparison between the all-zero sequence and other sequences: in which case the Hamming distance becomes *Hamming weight*: the number of non-zero symbols. We can therefore equate the free Hamming distance of the code to the *free Hamming weight* of any sequence beginning and ending on the zero state.

For example, the free distance of the code of Example 7.1 may be determined by examining all paths in Fig. 7.7 starting from the left-hand node and returning to the zero state at some later point. We need, of course, consider only those that follow the lower branch from the start node: paths with zero in the first data block are simply right-shifted by one data block. We observe that the smallest Hamming weight is given by the path marked, which has weight 5. This is the free distance of the code. (As might be expected, the data sequence 1000···
usually leads to one of the lowest-weight code sequences, although it is not always the minimum weight sequence).

This example enables us to make an interesting general observation about non-systematic codes as compared with systematic non-recursive ones. The minimum weight sequence here begins and ends with branches of weight *n*: those which diverge from or merge to the zero state. It is possible, in

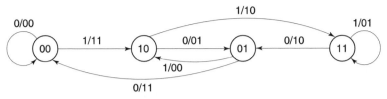

Figure 7.9 State diagram for encoder of Example 7.1

general, to ensure by appropriate choice of generator polynomials that this is always the case, and it will at least ensure that part of the closest sequence has maximum possible weight. However, the branch of a non-recursive code which re-merges with the zero state must correspond to data '0': which then does not occur in the code sequence. Hence, the optimum non-recursive code cannot be systematic.

This does not apply to recursive codes, since the relationship between data and code is different. We have in any case shown that in terms of free distance at least every non-recursive non-systematic code has a recursive-systematic equivalent, having the same distance properties.

7.2.4   State diagram

The convolutional encoder is a device that may take up a finite number of states, between which it moves at each block period according to the input applied. It may thus be described formally as a *finite state machine* (FSM). This is conveniently represented using a *state diagram*: a directed graph showing the states and the allowed transitions between them [7.1, p. 43; 7.5, pp. 295–302]. For example, the state diagram for Example 7.1 is shown in Fig. 7.9. The circles in the diagram represent the states; the arrowed lines the transitions between them. The branch labels give both the data input and the code output for each transition in the form *data/code*. Note the relationship between this graph and the trellis diagram in Fig. 7.7.

7.3   Decoding

As always, decoding is the most difficult and computationally complex aspect of the implementation of convolutional codes. It is further complicated in comparison with block codes because there are no distinct codewords, only potentially infinite code sequences. This means that, in principle, the decoder might have to wait an unlimited time before it is able to decide between two possible code sequences.

Decoding may be divided into two basic techniques: maximum likelihood sequence detection (MLSD), and sequential decoding. These have also been described as *breadth first* and *depth first* techniques, respectively. The first is also better known as Viterbi decoding.

7.3.1 Viterbi decoding

The Viterbi algorithm for MLSD in convolutional codes takes its name from Andrew Viterbi, who first applied it to decoding (although it was previously known in other disciplines) [7.6]. Its objective is to find the path through the code trellis that most closely resembles the received signal sequence, processing one code block at a time. The principle is to determine the path to each node (known as the *survivor path*) that is closest to the received sequence. It may be summarized in pseudo-code form as:

```
For each data block period (column on trellis diagram):
   For each final state (node on right of column):
      For each branch leading to this node:
         Calculate distance metric of received sequence from branch label
         Add to metric tally kept at initial node (on left of trellis column)
      Select branch with smallest distance metric. Store in a list of survivor paths
      Store total metric in tally kept at this node
      Delete the other paths from the list of survivors, and if this leaves some
      earlier paths 'floating', delete them too (leaving one survivor path to each final
      state node)
   If the deletion process leaves only one survivor path over some earlier data
   period, the corresponding data block can be output.
```

The algorithm searches every path through the trellis, but by noting that only one path to a given node may be the correct one, it restricts the number of paths to be considered to a manageable level. It is therefore guaranteed to find the closest path, as required, and is therefore a maximum-likelihood decoder (within the decoding metric being used).

Figure 7.10 shows the application of this algorithm to the trellis for Example 7.1 (see Fig. 7.7) in decoding the received code sequence 11010110111100, starting from the zero state. Those paths deleted at each stage of decoding are shown 'greyed out'. Here we assume hard decision decoding, and the distance metric is Hamming distance. In two cases (at the penultimate trellis period, or decoding epoch) there is a 'tie' between the metrics of two branches leading into one node: in this case an arbitrary decision can be made. Here we have applied the arbitrary rule that the higher of the two branches in the trellis is chosen: the choice could equally well be made randomly.

At the end of the received sequence the survivors have only the first trellis period in common: they diverge after that point. Hence, the algorithm has only succeeded in making a decision on the first data block (one bit in this case: it is '1'). Later bits may be resolved in subsequent decoding epochs, but it may be seen that a delay is introduced which is much more than one block

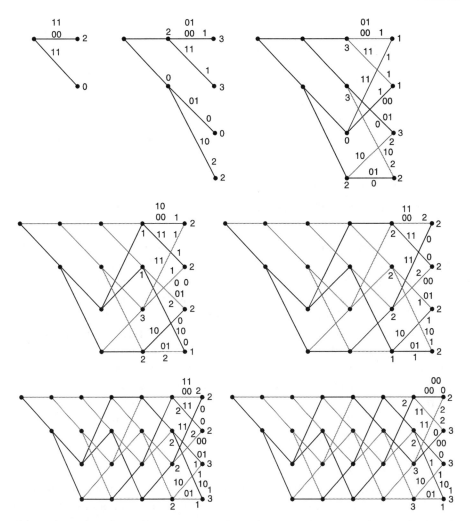

Figure 7.10 Action of Viterbi algorithm in trellis for Example 7.1, for received code sequence 11010110111100

period, and is in fact indeterminate. (There is no way of knowing how many subsequent epochs it will take before a given information bit may be decoded.) To ensure that a fixed, limited delay is introduced, most practical decoders apply a *truncation window*, storing only the portion of the survivor paths which fall within a window of a certain length (in block periods) [7.5, pp. 338–42]. At each decoding epoch a decision is then made on the data block that is about to leave the window. The most probable of the survivor paths is clearly that with the lowest distance metric. This path is traced back to the beginning of the window, and the data corresponding to that survivor is output.

187

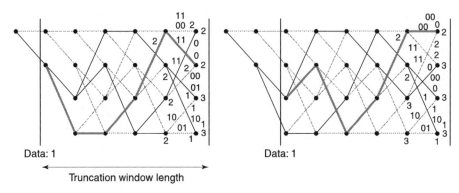

Data: 1   Data: 1

◄──────────────────►
Truncation window length

Figure 7.11   Truncation window applied to Viterbi decoding

Figure 7.11 shows this technique applied to the last two epochs of the decoding shown in Fig. 7.10. The truncation window has length 5 block periods (this is much shorter than would normally be applied). In the first of the decoding epochs shown, there is a tie between two of the survivors, at metric 2. The one shown is chosen at random. Tracing it back to the first period in the window, we note that it corresponds to data '1' (the downward of the branches out of the first node). Accordingly, we output this bit. At the next decoding epoch, however, there is no tie, and the survivor chosen is again marked. Tracing it back once again, we output data '1'. Note that it is not the same path as previously chosen: that path has now been shown to be sub-optimum. In the event, this has caused one data error, showing how a degradation in performance may be caused by the truncation. In practice, it is found that if the truncation window length is five or six times the constraint length, the degradation is negligible.

The implementation of the truncated decoder requires that the survivor paths within the truncation window be stored in some form, and then 'traced back' at each data period, as shown. This may be one of the more complex parts of the implementation of a decoder. There are two basic techniques: *register exchange*, in which each survivor is stored in its own register, which may have to be interchanged as decoding progresses; and *trace back* [7.7], in which the survivors are stored as linked lists, or similar, which must be traced at each stage.

If a convolutional code is used for encoding short packets of data, it is common practice to add $\nu - 1$ zero blocks, known as *tail bits*, to the end of the data before encoding in order to return the encoder to the zero state. If this is done, then the decoder need only look at the survivor that ends in the zero state. If this were the case in the example, the survivor marked (tinted line) in the latter part of Fig. 7.11 would be chosen. The data 1011000 is output (although the final two zeros would be tail bits). There is no performance degradation, but the cost has been to increase the redundancy of the code slightly.

The example above assumed hard decision decoding, using Hamming distance as the metric, but the algorithm is completely general, and may use any appropriate metric. Thus if soft information is available, Euclidean distance may be used, leading to soft decision decoding. On the white Gaussian noise channel this is optimum, as we have seen, and therefore the full Viterbi algorithm yields maximum-likelihood decoding, and is therefore the optimum decoder for a given code. Soft decision decoding typically increases the coding gain of a convolutional code by about 2 dB.

In practice, the decoder must be implemented with finite-precision soft decision information, which degrades performance slightly relative to true soft decision. However, quite coarse quantization may be used with very little degradation. Typically eight levels are used, corresponding to a 3-bit representation, and on the white Gaussian noise channel this gives rise to a degradation of only a small fraction of a dB.

It is usual to estimate the computational complexity of Viterbi decoding by counting the number of branches in the trellis per data bit. With each branch there will be associated a metric calculation and an addition, a comparison and a selection (ACS). Figure 7.8 shows that in the general case there are $2^{k\nu}$ branches per trellis section, and hence there are $2^{k\nu}/k$ operations per bit. This, of course, neglects the complexity and the storage required for the trace back. It has also been shown that the details of the implementation strongly influence what measure of complexity is appropriate: for example, a DSP processor implementation will have very different requirements from an ASIC or FPGA. Powerful ASIC decoders for a number of standard codes are now available, operating at data rates up to 30 Mbit s^{-1} [7.8].

7.3.2 Sequential decoding

The Viterbi algorithm performs maximum-likelihood decoding of a given code, but it has a computational complexity per data period that scales with the number of nodes (and to a lesser extent with the number of branches to and from each node). This increases exponentially with the constraint length of the code. Hence its application is limited, in practice, to relatively short constraint lengths. For example, decoders are readily available for a (2, 1, 7) code, which has 64 states. Constraint length 9, which has 256 states, can also be implemented, but significantly longer codes have prohibitive complexity.

Hence, for longer codes sub-optimum algorithms must be used. The class of sequential decoding algorithms are known as *depth first*, because they trace a given path in depth along the trellis before considering alternative paths. This is in contrast to the Viterbi algorithm, which is known as *breadth first*, because it explores all paths across the breadth of the trellis at one decoding epoch before it looks at subsequent epochs. The depth-first algorithms may in fact never explore the whole trellis, are therefore not guaranteed to find the closest path, and hence are not maximum-likelihood. However, by the same token, they are less computationally complex. In practice, coding gain may be increased for a given implementation complexity by using sub-optimal decoding of a long code rather than ML decoding of a shorter one.

The sequential algorithms [7.1, pp. 89–100; 7.5, pp. 350–84] are in fact somewhat older than the Viterbi algorithm, dating back to the 1950s [7.9]. They were the first algorithms to be shown to even approach the Shannon capacity bound (although they did not reach it, only a slacker bound known as the cut-off rate limit [7.10, p. 184]). Note that this is not inconsistent with the fact that they are sub-optimum for a given code, since the Shannon bound does not specify the code used.

The principle is probably best summed up in the *stack algorithm* [7.11, 7.12]. (The best-known alternative method is the *Fano algorithm* [7.13].) When it reaches a given node the algorithm searches the paths diverging from it, and lists them in metric order, placing them on a stack. It then further expands the best of these, and adds the resulting new paths to the stack, sorting again in metric order. It monitors the distance metric along the path it is currently following, and if it increases too rapidly (indicating that it is not the correct path), it selects the next path on the stack instead. This proceeds until the decoding reaches the end of the data. Figure 7.12 illustrates the process, showing the order in which nodes in a code tree might be visited.

This algorithm requires the comparison of paths of different lengths, which does not occur in the Viterbi algorithm, or in block codes. Clearly, it would be 'unfair' to use a simple Euclidean or Hamming distance metric, as longer paths

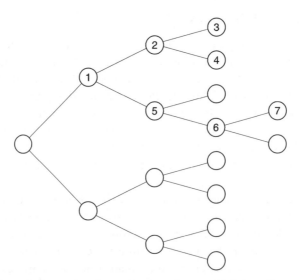

Figure 7.12   Tree diagram showing operation of sequential decoding

would be expected to show a larger distance. Instead the *Fano metric* [7.1, p. 89] is usually used, which subtracts an allowance dependent on the length of the path, and on the rate of the code. Another feature of the algorithm is that, unlike the Viterbi algorithm, the computation required per decoded bit may be highly variable. Some data may require a great deal of exploration of the code tree before the optimum path is found, especially if the signal-to-noise ratio is low; in other cases the decoder may follow the correct path without requiring any excursions.

7.3.3 Near MLSD

The full Viterbi algorithm performs maximum-likelihood sequence detection by examining paths from all nodes, but for a long constraint length this can be very computationally intensive. An alternative would be to examine only a sub-set of the paths, and clearly the best strategy is to select the nodes with smallest distance metric. Since those nodes with high distance metrics are unlikely to lie on the correct path, it may be expected that little performance would be lost by not exploring them.

There are two basic algorithms [7.14, 7.15]: the M-algorithm and the T-algorithm. The M-algorithm chooses a constant number M of the best nodes; those with the lowest metric. The T-algorithm explores all those nodes whose metric falls below a threshold T. The former thus has fixed complexity per bit; the latter variable. The choice between them is likely to depend on implementation details.

Unfortunately, the performance of these algorithms in decoding convolutional codes has been relatively disappointing. Both are subject to long bursts of errors due to *correct path loss*: if the correct path is not chosen as one of those for exploration, it is lost, and it is likely to take a long time for the decoder to return to it. While near-MLSD techniques are quite popular for equalization (see Chapter 9), they have not received much take-up for decoding.

7.4 Performance

We now describe techniques for evaluating the BER performance of convolutional codes. These are bounding techniques based on the union bound (see Section 5.7). Where appropriate, simulation results will be included to indicate their accuracy.

In block codes, we may distinguish between the bit error ratio (or probability) and the word error probability. As already discussed, we cannot consider distinct words in convolutional codes. The equivalent concept is perhaps the error-event probability, which we now discuss.

7.4.1 Error-event probability

An *error-event* is defined as the choice by the decoder of an erroneous path through the trellis which diverges from the correct path and re-merges with it at some later time [7.5, p. 325]. Since the code is linear, this may be regarded as the sum of the correct code sequence and an error sequence which begins and ends on the zero state. Then without loss of generality we may consider the probability only of error-events of this sort, illustrated schematically in Fig. 7.13.

At each data block period a number of erroneous paths branch from the correct one, a number of which are shown in Fig. 7.13. The decoder might choose any of them if the received sequence is closer to that path than to the correct one. The probability of choosing any given erroneous path is known as the *pairwise error-event probability*, and it is a function of the distance between the correct path and the erroneous one, as described in Section 5.7. For example, the pairwise error-event probability for a path of Hamming distance d_H from the correct one, using a binary code on the white Gaussian noise channel, is given (using Equation (5.43)) by:

$$P_{ev}(d_H) = Q\left(\frac{d}{2\sigma}\right) = Q\left(\frac{\sqrt{d_H}}{\sigma}\right) = Q\left(\sqrt{d_H \frac{2k}{n} \frac{E_b}{N_0}}\right) \tag{7.6}$$

where d denotes the Euclidean distance of the erroneous sequence. Of course d_H is also the Hamming weight of the error sequence: the number of non-zero symbols.

An upper union bound on the overall event-error probability may then be obtained by summing the pairwise probabilities of all erroneous paths:

$$P_{ev} \leq \sum_{d_H = d_{free}}^{\infty} A(d_H) Q\left(\frac{\sqrt{d_H}}{\sigma}\right) = \sum_{d_H = d_{free}}^{\infty} A(d_H) Q\left(\sqrt{d_H \frac{2k}{n} \frac{E_b}{N_0}}\right) \tag{7.7}$$

where $A(d_H)$ denotes the number of error sequences of Hamming weight d_H branching from the correct path at a given node (and returning to it at some later epoch). It is often known as the *weight spectrum* of the code. Note that for convolutional codes, the values of the weight spectrum increase without limit as d_H increases. However, since the Q function is a rapidly decreasing function of d_H, this does not in most cases of interest cause a continual increase in the error-event probability. That is, the sum to infinity in (7.7) converges for

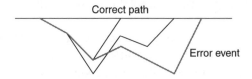

Figure 7.13   Schematic of an error event

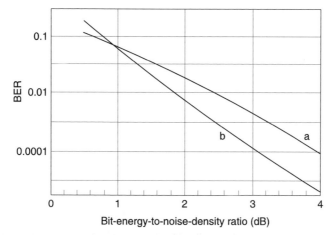

Figure 7.14   Upper bound on error-event probability for a (2, 1, 7) code: (a) with and (b) without truncation with window length 20

values of E_b/N_0 above a certain threshold. (This threshold turns out to correspond with the cut-off rate bound mentioned above in connection with sequential decoding.)

Recall, however, that in practice a Viterbi decoder operates within a truncation window, and thus error sequences are effectively truncated. We need not take into account infinitely long sequences. However, we do need to take into account the alternative survivors at the end of the truncation window. We may do this by counting not only sequences that re-merge with the correct sequence within the truncation window, but also those which reach a different node at the end of the truncation window. This tends to increase the values of the weight spectrum over a certain range of weights, giving rise to the performance degradation already mentioned, but also imposes an upper limit.

Figure 7.14 shows this effect. It gives the upper bound on error-event probabilities for the weight spectrum with and without truncation for a typical convolutional code. The truncation length is much shorter than would be used in practice, to show the difference.

At high E_b/N_0 the bound is in any case dominated by the minimum distance term, with $d_H = d_{\text{free}}$. A good approximation may be obtained by using this term alone. This underlines the importance of the free distance of the code as a determinant of its performance. A lower bound is in fact given by this term putting $A(d_{\text{free}})$ equal to unity, given in Equation (7.8). Figure 7.15 shows the upper bound, the partial bound using the first term only, and the lower bound. This shows that the lower bound is not very tight.

$$P_{\text{ev}} \geq Q\left(\sqrt{d_{\text{free}} \frac{2k}{n} \frac{E_b}{N_0}}\right) \tag{7.8}$$

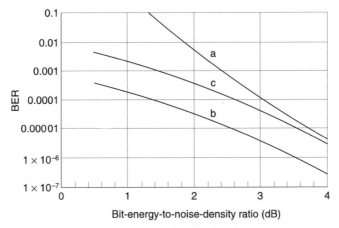

Figure 7.15   (a) Upper, (b) lower, and (c) partial bound on error-event probability

7.4.2   Bit error probability (BER)

The bit error probability, which of course is the same as the BER, is then obtained by multiplying the error-event probability by the number of data bit errors associated with each error event. This is encapsulated in a function which we will call $\theta(d_H)$, defined as the average data weight (number of data bit errors) associated with all error sequences of Hamming weight d_H. We must also divide by the number of data bits transmitted per code block. Then:

$$P_b \leq \sum_{d_H = d_{free}}^{\infty} \frac{\theta(d_H)A(d_H)}{k} Q\left(\frac{\sqrt{d_H}}{\sigma}\right) = \sum_{d_H = d_{free}}^{\infty} e(d_H)Q\left(\frac{\sqrt{d_H}}{\sigma}\right)$$

$$= \sum_{d_H = d_{free}}^{\infty} e(d_H)Q\left(\sqrt{d_H \frac{2k}{n} \frac{E_b}{N_0}}\right) \tag{7.9}$$

where $e(d_H) = \theta(d_H)A(d_H)/k$ is equivalent to the total error weight for erroneous codewords referred to in Equation (5.39). We will call it the *error-weighted distance spectrum*.

Even when we take into account the truncation window, this bound on BER remains a substantial over-estimate, and tends to 'blow up' towards infinity at low E_b/N_0. The effect may be seen for the error-event probability in Fig. 7.15, and it is very similar for BER. Figure 7.16 shows a series of *partial bounds* on the BER of a typical code, obtained by taking the first i terms in the summation of (7.9). These are not strictly bounds at all, but estimates, since one cannot prove that the true BER lies either above or below them, but they are commonly referred to as such. We will use the symbol $\lesssim$ to denote a partial bound.

Figure 7.16 also shows simulation results obtained for a $(2, 1, 5)$ code [7.16]. It shows that there is a partial bound (in this case $i = 3$) which is closer to the

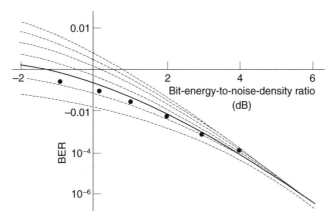

Figure 7.16 **Partial bounds on BER for (2, 1, 5) convolutional code, with simulation results**

true BER than the upper bound, and remains a good estimate of the BER up to quite low E_b/N_0 (or high BER). In general, it may be shown empirically that a partial bound based on the first three–ten terms is a good estimate for BER up to around 10^{-2} for nearly all codes. Table 7.3 gives the error-weighted distance spectrum for a range of popular rate 1/2 and rate 1/3 codes. The terms required in Equation (7.9) for the best approximation are shown in bold. Note that the generator polynomials g_0, g_1, (g_2) are given in octal form.

7.4.3 The transfer function

One way of obtaining $A(d)$ and $\theta(d)$ is by means of the *transfer function* [7.1, pp. 51–5; 7.5, p. 297 ff]. We make a slight change to the state diagram of the code, by separating the zero state node into a start node, representing the state of the encoder at the beginning of an error event, and a finish node,

Rate	ν	$g_0 \cdots g_{k-1}$	d_{free}	$e(d_{free} + i)$, $i = 0, 1, \ldots$
$\frac{1}{2}$	3	5, 7	5	**1, 4, 12, 32**, 80, 192, 448, 1024, 2304, ...
	4	15, 17	6	**2, 7, 18, 49, 130**, 333, 836, 2069, 5060, ...
	5	23, 35	7	**4, 12, 20, 72, 225**, 500, 1324, 3680, ...
	6	53, 75	8	**2, 36, 32, 62, 332, 701, 2342**, 5503, ...
	7	133, 171	10	**36, 0, 211, 0, 1404, 0, 11633, 0, 77433**, 0, 502690, ...
$\frac{1}{3}$	3	5, 7, 7	8	**3, 0, 15, 0, 58**, 0, 201, 0, 655, 0, 2052, 0, ...
	4	13, 15, 17	10	**6, 0, 6, 0, 58, 0, 118**, 0, 507, 0, 1284, 0, ...
	5	25, 33, 37	12	**12, 0, 12, 0, 56, 0, 320**, 0, 693, 0, ...
	6	47, 53, 75	13	**1, 8, 26, 20, 19, 62, 86, 204, 420**, 710, ...
	7	133, 165, 175	15	**11, 16, 19, 28, 55, 96, 169, 338, 636, 1276**, 2172, 3628, ...

Table 7.3 **Error-weighted distance spectra showing terms required for best approximation**

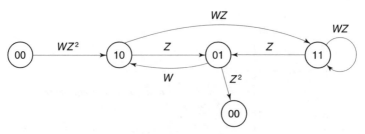

Figure 7.17 Modified state diagram for Example 7.1, for calculating transfer function

denoting its return to that state at the end of the event. We then associate with each branch a function denoting both the number of non-zero code symbols and the non-zero data symbols. Treating the modified state diagram as a signal flow graph, in which the branch functions give their gain, we may obtain a transfer function for the whole graph.

Taking the code of Example 7.1, whose state diagram is shown in Fig. 7.9, we obtain the modified re-labelled state diagram in Fig. 7.17. Here, the power of W on a branch label indicates the data weight; that of Z gives the code weight. It may be seen that the overall power of Z or W on any path through the graph gives the overall data or code weight of the sequence.

We solve the signal flow graph by setting up equations for each node:

$$\left.\begin{array}{l} X_{10} = WZ^2 X + WX_{01} \\ X_{01} = ZX_{10} + ZX_{11} \\ X_{11} = WZX_{10} + WZX_{11} \\ Y = Z^2 X_{01} \end{array}\right\} \tag{7.10}$$

where X and Y denote the input and the output of the graph, respectively. Solving this equation set, we obtain the transfer function:

$$T(W, Z) = \frac{Y}{X} = \frac{WZ^5}{1 - 2WZ} \tag{7.11}$$

This function encapsulates most of the spectrum values used above in calculating the error-event probability and the BER. For example, it may be expanded as an infinite series, with W set to unity:

$$T(1, Z) = \frac{Z^5}{1 - 2Z} = Z^5(1 + 2Z + 4Z^2 + 8Z^3 + \cdots)$$
$$= Z^5 + 2Z^6 + 4Z^7 + 8Z^8 + \cdots \tag{7.12}$$

in which the coefficients of Z are the values of the code weight spectrum, $A(d)$. In general:

$$T(1, Z) = \sum_{d = d_{\text{free}}}^{\infty} A(d)Z^d \tag{7.13}$$

For each power of Z the coefficient of W gives the number of data bits per error event. This can be used to obtain the error-weighted distance spectra of the code, since the power of W in $T(Z, W)$ (multiplied by the coefficient of the term) is given by $\partial T(Z, W)/\partial W|_{W=1}$. That is:

$$\frac{\partial T(W, Z)}{\partial W}\bigg|_{W=1} = \sum_{d=d_{\text{free}}}^{\infty} e(d)Z^d \tag{7.14}$$

In the example:

$$\frac{\partial T(W, Z)}{\partial W}\bigg|_{W=1} = \frac{Z^5(1 - 2WZ) - WZ^5(-2Z)}{(1 - 2WZ)^2}\bigg|_{W=1} = \frac{Z^5}{(1 - 2Z)^2}$$
$$= Z^5 + 4Z^6 + 12Z^7 + 32Z^8 + 80Z^9 + 192Z^{10} + \cdots \tag{7.15}$$

This is the $(2, 1, 3)$ code from the first row of Table 7.3, and it can be seen that its error-weighted distance spectrum agrees with the table.

It is possible to upper bound the pairwise error-event probability $P_{\text{ev}}(d)$ by a term of the form γ^d, both for soft and for hard decisions:

$$P_{\text{ev}}(d) \leq \exp\left(-d\frac{k}{n}\frac{E_b}{N_0}\right) = \left[\exp\left(-\frac{k}{n}\frac{E_b}{N_0}\right)\right]^d \tag{7.16}$$

$$P_{\text{ev}}(d) \leq [4p(1 - p)]^{d/2} = [\sqrt{4p(1 - p)}]^d \tag{7.17}$$

Then:

$$P_b \leq \sum_{d=d_{\text{free}}}^{\infty} e(d)\alpha\gamma^d = \frac{\partial T(W, Z)}{\partial W}\bigg|_{w=1, Z=\gamma} \tag{7.18}$$

This is known as the *transfer function bound* on the BER. However, Equations (7.16) and (7.17) do not provide very tight bounds, and hence tighter overall bounds may be obtained by using the exact expressions for soft and hard decisions. The transfer function method then becomes simply an alternative method for finding the various distance spectra.

7.5 Punctured codes

Convolutional codes are most easily implemented for the case $k = 1$, as in Example 7.1. However, this leads to a code rate of $1/n$, i.e. at most $1/2$. If we require higher rate codes, both encoder and trellis diagram become much more complex, as shown for the general case in Figs 7.2 and 7.8, respectively. Figure 7.8 shows that the trellis diagram contains $2^{k(\nu-1)}$ states, which will also increase the decoder complexity. For example, for a rate $7/8$ code, even for the lowest constraint length, say an $(8, 7, 2)$ code, the number of code states is 2^7. The complexity per bit as defined in Section 7.3.1 above is $2^{14}/7$, or about 2140 operations per bit.

Puncturing provides an alternative method to achieve high rate convolutional codes. The principle is simply to delete some of the code symbols, so that fewer code symbols are transmitted per data symbol. Symbols are deleted (punctured) according to a regular pattern. This is illustrated below, where the rate 1/2 code of Example 7.1 is punctured to provide a rate 2/3 code.

Example 7.3

The code of Example 7.1 is punctured every fourth code bit, choosing the first bit of every other trellis period. What is the resulting code rate? Draw the trellis, and find the minimum free distance.

Solution The resulting trellis is shown in Fig. 7.18. We now transmit 3 code bits for every two data bits, so the rate is 2/3. This of course affects the free distance of the code: the minimum weight sequence is shown in grey, and its weight is now 3. Note that if the second bit rather than the first had been punctured in each trellis section, the minimum weight would have been 2. This underlines the importance of the optimum choice of puncture pattern.

Note also that the minimum weight path does not in this case branch off from the zero state at the first trellis period. In this code a shift of one trellis period does not necessarily result in the same code sequence. Formally, we say that the code is *time-variant*, because the generator matrix varies cyclically from one trellis period to the next. This also implies that in finding the weight spectrum we must search paths branching from the zero state at the second period, as well as the first.

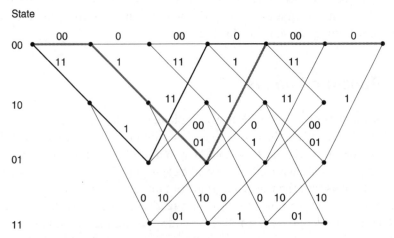

Figure 7.18 Punctured trellis diagram for Example 7.3

A major advantage of punctured codes is that the same decoder may be used as for the original unpunctured code. We simply re-insert the symbols that were deleted in puncturing the code. In soft decision decoding where $\{0, 1\}$ have been transmitted as $\{-1, +1\}$, we insert a zero value for the punctured symbols. Since this does not affect the metric value on that branch, we thereby implement a maximum-likelihood decoder for the punctured code.

The puncture pattern is commonly expressed in the form of an $l \times n$ matrix with elements from $\{0, 1\}$, each corresponding to the code bit generated by one of the n generator polynomials in each of the l code block periods spanned by the puncture pattern. A '0' indicates that the bit is deleted; a '1' that it is not. If the puncture pattern has m '1's, and the original code was $(n, 1, \nu)$, then the rate of the punctured code is:

$$R' = \frac{1}{n}\frac{nl}{m} = \frac{l}{m} \tag{7.19}$$

It may be shown, however, that a given punctured code is equivalent to an unpunctured rate k/n code. In the trellis of Fig. 7.18, merge each pair of trellis periods, considering only the final state. The result is shown in Fig. 7.19. Note that there are now four paths from each node, representing four routes through the original pair of trellis sections, and corresponding to two data bits. The branches from each node, reading from the upper to the lower, correspond to the data 00, 01, 10 and 11. We label the branches with the three code bits left after puncturing.

The resulting trellis is now time-invariant, and is the trellis of a $(3, 2, 2)$ code, which is equivalent to the punctured code. We can write down the generator matrix of this code, noting that the original data stream of the rate $1/2$ code (the code of Example 7.1), has now been de-multiplexed into two parallel

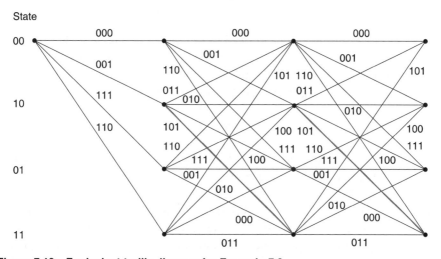

Figure 7.19 Equivalent trellis diagram for Example 7.3

streams. From Equation (7.2) we may write the original code as:

$$c_i^{(p)} = g_i^{(0)} d^{(p)} + g_i^{(1)} d^{(p-1)} + g_{ij}^{(2)} d^{(p-2)} + \cdots + g_{ij}^{(\nu-1)} d^{(p-\nu-1)}$$

We may then split this into two summations and write the data stream of the new code in terms of the original $d_j^{\prime(p')} = d^{(2p'+j)}$:

$$c_i^{(2p')} = g_i^{(0)} d^{(2p')} + g_i^{(2)} d^{(2(p'-1))} + \cdots$$

$$+ g_i^{(1)} d^{(2p'-1)} + g_i^{(3)} d^{(2(p'-1)-1)} + \cdots$$

$$= g_i^{(0)} d_0^{\prime(p')} + g_i^{(2)} d_0^{\prime(p'-1)} + \cdots$$

$$+ g_i^{(1)} d_1^{\prime(p'-1)} + g_i^{(3)} d_1^{\prime(p'-2)} + \cdots$$

$$c_i^{(2p'+1)} = g_i^{(0)} d_1^{\prime(p')} + g_i^{(2)} d_1^{\prime(p'-1)} + \cdots$$

$$+ g_i^{(1)} d_0^{\prime(p')} + g_i^{(3)} d_0^{\prime(p'-1)} + \cdots$$

Then the code stream of the new code $c_{i'}^{\prime p'} = c_{i' \bmod 2}^{(2p' + i' \operatorname{div} 2)}$, $i' = 0 \cdots 3$, and the new generator matrix becomes:

$$\begin{bmatrix} g_0^{(0)} + g_0^{(2)} D + \cdots & g_1^{(0)} + g_1^{(2)} D + \cdots & g_0^{(1)} + g_0^{(3)} D + \cdots & g_1^{(1)} + g_1^{(3)} D + \cdots \\ g_0^{(1)} D + g_0^{(3)} D^2 + \cdots & g_1^{(1)} D + g_1^{(3)} D^2 + \cdots & g_0^{(0)} + g_0^{(2)} D + \cdots & g_1^{(0)} + g_1^{(2)} D + \cdots \end{bmatrix}$$

Thus the generator matrix in the example becomes:

$$\begin{bmatrix} 1+D & 1+D & 0 & 1 \\ 0 & D & 1+D & 1+D \end{bmatrix}$$

of which the third code bit is punctured, leaving:

$$\begin{bmatrix} 1+D & 1+D & 1 \\ 0 & D & 1+D \end{bmatrix}$$

The same construction can be applied to any punctured code with a puncture pattern spanning l block periods, by merging these l trellis periods. However, the converse is not true: not all high rate codes can be expressed in the form of punctured codes. In general, the equivalent code is (n', k', ν'), where:

$$(n', k', \nu') = \left(m, l, \left\lceil \frac{\nu - 1}{l} \right\rceil + 1 \right) \tag{7.20}$$

Thus, for example, the rate 7/8 (8, 7, 2) code mentioned above is equivalent to a (2, 1, 7) code punctured using a pattern of length $l = 7$, with $m = 8$ '1's. The complexity per bit figure for this code is $2^7 = 128$, compared with 2140 for a direct implementation. (This comparison is not entirely fair, because the optimum (8, 7, 2) code may not be expressible as a punctured (2, 1, 7) code.)

Nevertheless, by careful choice of puncturing pattern, relatively high rate convolutional codes may be implemented with acceptable decoding complexity.

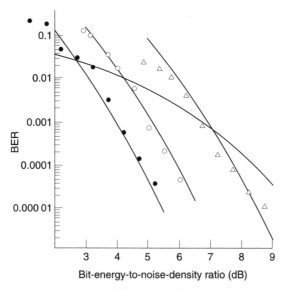

Figure 7.20 Estimated and simulated BER for some punctured convolutional codes: (●) rate 3/4; (○) rate 7/8; (△) rate 15/16, compared with uncoded (no symbol)

Figure 7.20 shows the performance of a number of codes of rate greater than 1/2 implemented by puncturing the rate 1/2 (2, 1, 7) code. As might be expected, the coding gain diminishes rapidly as code rate approaches unity, but a usable code remains even at rate 15/16. Table 7.4 gives the error-weighted distance spectrum

Rate	Puncture pattern	d_{free}	$e(d_{free})$, $e(d_{free}+1)$, ...
1/3		15	11, 16, 19, 28, 55, 96, 169
3/8	111 101 111	12	2, 25, 54, 88, 88, 298, 600
1/2		10	36, 0, 211, 0, 1404, 0, 11633
2/3	01 11	6	3, 70, 285, 1276, 6160, 27128, 116747
3/4	1011 0111	5	42, 201, 1492, 10391, 59996, 335016, 1756398
5/6	01011 01101	4	92, 528, 8572, 77158, 681054, 5530778, 40127485
7/8	0000001 1111111	3	14, 389, 7268, 155622, 3731671, 87265996, 1815436387
9/10	010100111 101011001	3	29, 1715, 33414, 588449, 9959144, 160441930, 2512601011
11/12	10000010001 01111101111	3	66, 4893, 105606, 2780898, 100425365, 3656102088, 2440980917
15/16	000001110011101 000011111011011	2	74, 5160, 158010, 8867369, 422664152, 938426262, 1843747548

Table 7.4 Error-weighted distance spectrum of punctured convolutional codes

of these codes, along with the puncturing pattern, from which BER estimates may be calculated. The original code is the (2, 1, 7) code with generator polynomials given in Table 7.3, except for the rate 3/8 code, which is based on the (3, 1, 7) code from the same table. Note that because these codes are really equivalent to codes having a somewhat larger block length, the truncation window length required may be somewhat greater if viewed in terms of the original code before puncturing. For example, high rate punctured codes may require a window of 200 trellis periods of the (2, 1, 7) codes, rather than the 35 that are normally required.

7.6 System applications

7.6.1 GSM mobile radio system

The second generation cellular mobile radio standard GSM (Global System for Mobile Communications – the main system in use in Europe and many other parts of the world at the time of writing) [7.17] makes use of convolutional codes for forward error correction, which greatly improve its robustness to poor propagation conditions. The main application of this system is speech, which is transmitted in a digitally encoded form [7.18], and therefore the coding scheme is adapted to the characteristics of speech encoded using the relevant algorithm.

The speech coding algorithm in GSM, chosen to give a good compromise between speech quality and bit rate, is *regular pulse excited linear predictive coding* (RPE-LPC), giving a net bit rate of $13\,\mathrm{kbit\,s}^{-1}$. It is a block-based scheme in which the speech is divided into 20 ms blocks, each yielding an output frame of 260 bits. Subjective testing has shown that of these 260 bits, 182 are more 'important', in the sense that errors in these bits cause a greater degradation in perceived speech quality. These are known as *class 1* bits. Errors in the remaining 78, the *class 2* bits, have much less effect. Within the class 1 bits there are 50 that are more significant still, and it has been determined that if any error occurs in these it is better to discard the entire speech frame. If this occurs, the speech signal can be reconstructed by extrapolation from previously received frames.

The coding is therefore designed primarily to protect those bits that are most significant for speech quality, i.e. the class 1 bits. First, the 50 most important class 1 bits are given added protection in the form of three parity check bits, generated by a cyclic redundancy check. This is effectively a cyclic block code with the generator polynomial $x^3 + x + 1$, but it is used for error detection only. If this parity check fails in the receiver, the whole frame is discarded. Four *tail bits*, set to '0', are added to the 182 class 1 bits, plus three parity bits, giving a total of 189 bits. These are then fed to a rate 1/2 convolutional encoder, which

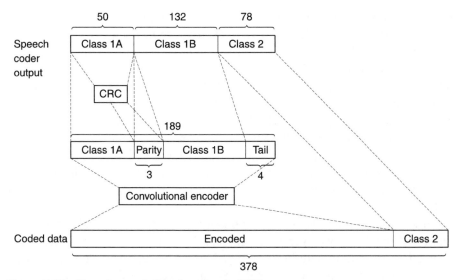

Figure 7.21   Use of convolutional coding in GSM

therefore outputs 378 bits. The generator polynomials are

$$[1 + D^3 + D^4 \quad 1 + D + D^3 + D^4]$$

so that the code has constraint length 5, and hence requires a comparatively simple 16-state decoder. The purpose of the tail bits is to ensure the encoder returns to the zero state at the end of the encoding, which assists the Viterbi decoder, as we have seen in Section 7.3.1 above. Finally, the class 2 bits are added uncoded, giving a total of 456 bits. Since these must still be transmitted in 20 ms, the data rate per channel is 22.8 kbit s^{-1}. The process is illustrated schematically in Fig. 7.21.

7.6.2   Deep space communications

The use of concatenated convolutional and Reed–Solomon codes in the *Voyager* mission to Jupiter and Saturn was described in Section 6.5.2. The inner convolutional code used in this mission has become something of an 'industry standard', used for a wide variety of applications, but still sometimes known as the 'NASA' code, having been developed by the Jet Propulsion Laboratory (JPL) on behalf of NASA for this mission.

There were, in fact, two codes developed for this purpose: (2, 1, 7) and (3, 1, 7) codes: rate 1/2 and rate 1/3, respectively. Both have constraint length 7, or a 64-state encoder. The generator polynomials for the (2, 1, 7) code are $1 + D + D^3 + D^4 + D^6$ and $1 + D^3 + D^4 + D^5 + D^6$ (in octal 133 and 171); these are also used in the (3, 1, 7) code together with $1 + D^2 + D^4 + D^5 + D^6$ (octal 165). In the *Voyager* mission these were concatenated with a (255, 233)

Reed–Solomon code over $GF(2^8)$, symbols being represented by 8-bit words. To ensure the outer code could correct error bursts due to errors in the convolutional code, a 5×255 symbol-wise interleaver was used.

Of the two inner codes it is the rate $1/2$ code which is particularly popular, since it represents a good compromise between performance and computational complexity without adding excessive redundancy. Coding gain of $5\,dB$ or more is available, yet a Viterbi decoder is readily implemented.

As mentioned above, ASIC Viterbi decoders are available for this code which can operate at up to $20\,Mbit\,s^{-1}$. As shown in Table 7.4, a range of other code rates can be obtained by puncturing this code. The resulting codes may still be decoded using the same decoder ASIC as the unpunctured code.

Earlier missions, such as the *Pioneer* missions, used convolutional codes alone. These had significantly longer constraint lengths, up to 32, but were designed for sequential rather than Viterbi decoding. The later *Galileo* mission again used concatenated convolutional and Reed–Solomon codes, this time with a more powerful inner code with constraint length 15, increasing coding gain by around $2\,dB$ at the cost of significantly more decoding complexity.

7.6.3 Digital Video Broadcast standard

The Digital Video Broadcast (Terrestrial) (DVB-T) standard [7.19] – see also Example 10.2 – the European standard for digital video transmission, which is used in the recently launched digital terrestrial television systems, also makes use of convolutional codes as inner codes of a concatenated coding scheme. Here a range of punctured codes is available, with rates from $1/2$ (unpunctured) up to $7/8$, all based on the 'NASA' rate $1/2$ constraint length 7 code mentioned above. The most appropriate code rate can then be picked from this range of options. In addition, there is an outer Reed–Solomon code, with interleaving both between the two encoders and before modulation. More detail is given in Example 10.2(b).

Problems

7.1 A convolutional code has the following generator matrix:

$$[1 + D + D^3 \quad 1 + D^2 + D^3 \quad 1 + D^3]$$

What is its block length n, the number of information bits per block k, the constraint length ν, and the rate R?

7.2 Draw the trellis diagram of the code of Problem 7.1 and label it with branch labels. Also label the states. Hence find its minimum free

Hamming distance, and the first three values of its error-weighted distance spectrum. This can most readily be done by inspection of the trellis. However, if you have access to a computer algebra package such as *Mathematica*, you could check your result using the transfer function method. (Carrying out the required procedure by hand is not recommended.)

Could a different choice of generator matrix yield a greater minimum distance?

7.3 Using the distance spectrum obtained in Problem 7.2 write down an approximate expression for the BER of the above code against bit-energy-to-noise-density ratio, assuming ideal soft decision decoding, and estimate the coding gain compared with uncoded transmission for $BER = 10^{-6}$.

7.4 Suggest a puncture pattern to provide a rate $2/5$ code from the basic code of Problem 7.1, and find the minimum free distance of the punctured code. Write down the generator matrix of the equivalent unpunctured rate $2/5$ code.

7.5 Draw the state diagram of the recursive systematic code of Example 7.2. Compare it with that of Example 7.1, as given in Fig. 7.9.

Use your state diagram to find the four lowest weight data sequences which, starting from the zero state, leave the encoder in the zero state (which may be called *terminating* sequences). Compare them with the poly-nomials obtained by multiplying $g_0(D)$ by $1, 1 + D, 1 + D^2, 1 + D + D^2$, etc. Use the relationship thus illustrated to find more terminating sequences.

7.6 Encode the data sequence 101011 using the code of Example 7.1, adding tail bits to return the encoder to the zero state. Add the error pattern $00000111000\cdots$ to the encoded sequence, and decode using the Viterbi algorithm. Compare your result with the result of Viterbi decoding the error sequence alone.

References

7.1 Lee, L.H.C. (1997) *Convolutional Coding: Fundamentals and Applications*, Artech House.

7.2 Costello, D.J. Jr (1969) Construction of convolutional codes for sequential decoding, PhD thesis, University of Notre Dame, Indiana.

7.3 Proakis, J.G. (1995) *Digital Communications*, 3rd Edition, McGraw-Hill.

7.4 Forney, G.D. Jr (1970) Convolutional codes. I: Algebraic structure. *IEEE Transactions on Information Theory*, **16**: 720–38.

7.5 Lin, S. and Costello, D.J. (1983) *Error Control Coding: Fundamentals and Applications*, Prentice-Hall.

7.6   Viterbi, A.J. (1967) Error bounds for convolutional codes and an asymptotically optimum decoding algorithm. *IEEE Transactions on Information Theory*, **13**(2): 260–9.

7.7   Truong, T.K., Shih, M.T., Reed, I.S. and Satorius, E.H. (1992) A VLSI design for a trace-back Viterbi decoder. *IEEE Transactions on Communications*, **40**(3): 616–34.

7.8   Qualcomm, Inc. (1998) *Forward Error Correction Data Book (Q1900 Viterbi decoder)*, 80-24128-1 A 8/98,
http://www.qualcomm.com/ProdTech/asic/vlsi/documents/FECDatabook.pdf

7.9   Wozencraft, J.M. (1957) Sequential decoding for reliable communications. *IRE National Convention Record* **5**(2): 11–25.

7.10 Blahut, R.E. (1987) *Principles and Practice of Information Theory*, Addison-Wesley.

7.11 Zigangirov, K.S. (1966) Some sequential decoding procedures. *Problemy Peredachi Informatsii*, **2**: 13–25.

7.12 Jelinek, F. (1969) A fast sequential decoding algorithm using a stack. *IBM Journal of Research and Development*, **13**: 675–85.

7.13 Fano, R.M. (1963) A heuristic discussion of probabilistic decoding. *IEEE Transactions on Information Theory*, **9**(4): 64–74.

7.14 Aulin, T.M. (1999) Breadth-first maximum likelihood sequence detection: Basics. *IEEE Transactions on Communications*, **47**(2): 208–16.

7.15 Osthoff, H., Anderson, J.B., Johannesson, R. and Lin, C.F. (1998) Systematic feed-forward convolutional encoders are better than other encoders with an M-algorithm decoder. *IEEE Transactions on Information Theory*, **44**(2): 831–8.

7.16 Burr, A.G. (1993) Bounds and approximations for the bit error probability of convolutional codes. *Electronics Letters*, **29**(14): 1287–8.

7.17 Hodges, M.R.L. (1990) The GSM radio interface. *British Telecom Technology Journal*, **8**(1): 31–43.

7.18 Cox, R.V. and Kroon, P. (1996) Low bit-rate speech coders for multimedia communication. *IEEE Communications Magazine*, **34**(12): 34–41.

7.19 European Standard EN 300 744 V1.1.2 (1997–8) *Digital Video Broadcasting (DVB); Framing Structure, Channel Coding and Modulation for Digital Terrestrial Television*, obtainable from http://www.etsi.org/eds/eds.htm

Chapter 8

Coded modulation

So far in this book we have developed techniques that can be used to improve the spectrum efficiency of a system at the expense of its power efficiency (namely, multilevel modulation), or power efficiency at the expense of its spectrum efficiency (namely, coding). The objective of this chapter is to introduce a combination of these techniques, called *coded modulation*, by which we may improve power and bandwidth efficiency simultaneously.

Some historical notes on the development of coded modulation might be of interest here. Previously it had been thought that since coding inherently required the introduction of redundant symbols, it must necessarily increase bandwidth required. It could therefore only be suitable for power-limited channels, for example satellite systems. Since at that time (the mid–late 1970s) the pressure on the available radio spectrum was mounting (a process that has only accelerated since), there seemed to be no advantage in using a technique that could only reduce spectrum efficiency.

The critical advance, however, came in a different field of communications technology, namely the voiceband modem: the device used for transmitting digital data, including FAX and computer data, over an analog telephone line. This is a channel severely restricted in bandwidth, to not much over 5 kHz; the bandwidth required for analog speech. To achieve the ever higher data rates needed by customers, a new advance was required. It was known from the Shannon bound that much higher capacities than the then current baud rates were possible. It was therefore proposed that coding should be combined with multilevel modulation. James Massey [8.1] and Gottfried Ungerböck [8.2], both working in Zurich, were chiefly instrumental in enunciating the principles by which this should be done; but, in fact, the same principles were being developed separately around the same time by researchers in Russia [8.3] and by Hideki Imai [8.4] in Tokyo. Ungerböck later published a review article [8.5], and the present author has also reviewed the forms of coded modulation [8.6].

8.1 Principles of coded modulation

The fundamental principle, then, of coded modulation is that redundancy should be added to the transmitted signal not by adding additional symbols to the code stream (which would increase its bandwidth), but by increasing the radix of the code symbols, which means increasing the size of the signalling constellation. For example (see Fig. 8.1), an uncoded QPSK system, which transmits 2 bits/symbol, could be replaced by an 8-PSK modulator (transmitting 3 bits/symbol) with a rate 2/3 code, so that the overall rate remains 2 bits/symbol.

The second principle concerns the design of the encoder/modulator, or rather of the linkage between the code and the modulation scheme used. Initial attempts in which an encoder was simply added at the input to a modulator designed on the principles of Chapter 2 gave rather disappointing results. Massey [8.1] then pointed out that it was necessary to integrate the design of the encoder and modulator, and to treat the code and modulation scheme as one entity, as shown in Fig. 8.1.

The principle on which the integrated scheme should be designed was that of Euclidean distance, as described in Section 5.5. Instead of maximizing the minimum Hamming distance of the code sequences, which has been the goal in both forms of coding we have considered (Chapters 6 and 7), we must now maximize the minimum Euclidean distance of the coded signals. Of course for binary modulation using BPSK, and also in fact for QPSK, the two goals are equivalent, since Euclidean distance is related to Hamming according to Equation (5.43), which is monotonic. For higher level modulation schemes, however, there is no such relationship, whatever mapping is used between code sequence and modulated signal.

This is a further application of the principle used in soft decision decoding, in which Euclidean distance becomes the decoding metric, and demodulation and decoding become a joint process. Now the application of the principle is

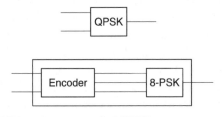

Figure 8.1   Coded 8-PSK replaces uncoded QPSK

complete in that Euclidean distance also becomes the metric for code design, and the processes of encoding and modulation also become joint.

8.1.1 Geometric principles of code design

As may be expected from the use of the term 'Euclidean distance' above, the geometric model introduced in Chapter 5 informs the principles of code design in a fundamental way. (Note that we will frequently use the term 'code' in a general way to refer to coded modulation schemes as well as to binary codes. It refers to the ensemble of coded signals that may be generated at the transmitter.)

Recall that the model represents coded signals as points in an n-dimensional space (*code points*), where n is the code length. The distance from the origin is proportional to the square root of the signal energy, which means that signals of a given maximum energy are restricted to a spherical volume of the space, which we call the *signal space*. Channel noise causes a displacement of the transmitted signal by a distance proportional to the noise energy. Hence, the distance in the space (the Euclidean distance) between code points determines the error probability.

In geometric terms an optimal code will have:

- as many signal points M as possible
  (This maximizes the number of information bits $k = \log_2(M)$ transmitted, and hence the code rate k/n.)
- in as small a volume as possible
  (This minimizes the radius of the signal space and, hence, the maximum transmit power. Clearly, the space should be spherical.)
- with as large minimum distance as possible between them.
  (This minimizes the error probability. It will tend to result in an equal distance between a given code point and all or most of its immediate neighbours. Of course, in practice, code design is a compromise between code rate (the first bullet principle) and required signal-to-noise ratio (the second two bullets).)

These principles are illustrated in Fig. 8.2, which represents the signal space in two dimensions. Its general principles, however, carry over to higher-dimensional spaces. In white are shown the optimum code point positions for a very low rate code, with only three codewords. They have been placed as far apart as possible in the space. In light grey we have additional points for a code with six codewords. The optimum positions of these are still on the perimeter of the signal space. Such codes, in which all coded signals have equal energy, are known as *spherical codes*, and include all binary codes and coded M-PSK schemes. (Some other coded modulation schemes may also be described as *quasi-spherical*.)

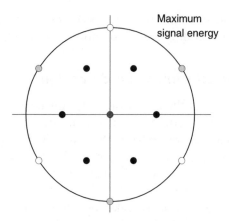

Figure 8.2   Optimum code design (in two dimensions)

However, if we add a seventh point (dark grey), its optimum position is now the origin – if it were added to the perimeter all the other points would have to be moved around, and the resulting minimum distance would be less than the signal space radius. Similarly, for yet higher rates the code points should be packed within the body of the signal space (points in black). Usually this results in a quite regular arrangement of points, as shown here. Thus the optimum low rate codes are spherical, while at higher rates (more than about 1 bit/dimension), optimum codes have unequal energy.

An alternative approach to the same problem begins with the 'spheres of uncertainty' mentioned in our discussion of the Shannon bound in Chapter 5. Recall that we may imagine a 'sphere of uncertainty' surrounding each signal point, its radius given by the noise power, within which the noisy received signal point must lie. Provided these spheres do not overlap, the code may be unambiguously decoded at the receiver. Thus the problem of optimum code design becomes how to pack as many spheres as possible into the signal space – the well-known *sphere-packing* problem [8.7]. This is, of course, the same as the problem illustrated in Fig. 8.2. We illustrate it for two dimensions in Fig. 8.3. The diagram shows how spheres of radius d result in a minimum Euclidean distance of $d_{\min} = 2d$.

Note the regular pattern that results, known as a *sphere packing*. Many (in fact nearly all) sphere packings have such regular structure. In three dimensions these packings in fact form the basis of crystal lattices, and the term is borrowed to refer to similar packings in n dimensions (as we will see later). Unfortunately, the sphere-packing problem in higher-dimensional space is much more difficult than in two or three, and only in some spaces are there known packings that can be shown to be optimal.

We should note here that in a coded modulation scheme the dimensionality of the signal space is determined by the number of degrees-of-freedom of the transmitted signals. Each symbol of a coded modulation scheme corresponds

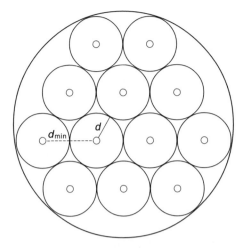

Figure 8.3 Sphere packing in two dimensions

to a modulated signal. This has two degrees-of-freedom: the in phase (I) and the quadrature (Q) components, which correspond to the two dimensions of the constellation diagram. Thus for a coded modulation scheme the number of dimensions n is twice the number of modulated symbols in the codeword.

8.1.2 Asymptotic coding gain

Asymptotic coding gain (ACG) provides a useful measure of the effectiveness of a coded modulation scheme that is usually much simpler to determine than the true coding gain (although there are pitfalls in its application, as we shall see).

> The *asymptotic coding gain* (ACG) of a coded modulation scheme is the limit of the coding gain, compared with a reference uncoded scheme, as signal-to-noise ratio (SNR) $\Rightarrow \infty$.

Normally, the reference scheme has the same rate in bits/symbol as the coded scheme: if not, a rate allowance should be applied by calculating the gain in terms of E_b/N_0, as in the definition of coding gain in Chapter 5. The concept of ACG stems from the observation that at very high signal-to-noise ratio (or equivalently very low BER) curves of BER versus SNR for coded and uncoded systems become almost parallel. The distance between them (in dB) is then the ACG. This is illustrated in Fig. 8.4.

Now, converting Equation (5.38) to logarithmic form:

$$\log(P_e) = \log(n_n) + \log\left[Q\left(\frac{d_{min}}{2\sigma}\right)\right] \approx \log\left[Q\left(\frac{d_{min}}{2\sigma}\right)\right] \quad (8.1)$$

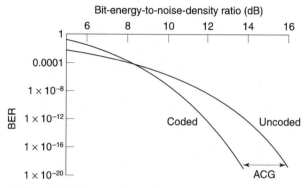

Figure 8.4   Definition of ACG

asymptotically, as $\log(P_e) \Rightarrow -\infty$ the term $\log(n_n)$ becomes negligible. Then the ACG is the difference between SNRs such that:

$$\left[P_{eu} = Q\left(\frac{d_u}{2\sigma_u}\right)\right] = \left[P_{ec} \approx Q\left(\frac{d_c}{2\sigma_c}\right)\right]$$

$$\therefore \text{ACG} = [\text{SNR}_u]_{dB} - [\text{SNR}_c]_{dB} = 10\log_{10}\left(\frac{\sigma_c^2}{\sigma_u^2}\right) = 20\log_{10}\left(\frac{d_c}{d_u}\right)$$

$$\left.\right\} \quad (8.2)$$

where d_c/d_u is the ratio of the minimum Euclidean distance of the coded scheme to the minimum distance of the reference scheme constellation, normalized to the same maximum signal power. Often it is much easier to find the minimum Euclidean distance of a scheme than its actual error probability, and the comparison with some suitable reference scheme is straightforward, as we shall see. However, for error rates of practical interest, the ACG should be treated with caution, because in some schemes the term n_n, the number of neighbours of a code point, may be very large, so that the difference between the ACG and the actual coding gain is large.

8.1.3   Set partitioning

We now begin to look at practical methods for applying codes to modulation constellations in such a way as to fulfil the above principles. The first principle behind most of these schemes, originally described by Gottfried Ungerböck [8.2, 8.5], is *set partitioning*. This provides a formal means of taking into account the Euclidean distance of pairs of points in the constellation, and of relating Euclidean distance to the binary label of each constellation point.

The principle is to partition the constellation in a series of *sub-sets* of diminishing size, in such a way that minimum Euclidean distance within the sub-sets increases down the partition chain. In general terms this means taking every other point from the constellation to form one sub-set, the remaining points forming the other. The partition is usually binary at each level. This can of course best be explained by means of an example.

Example 8.1

Establish a partition chain for the 8-PSK constellation, and determine the minimum distances within each sub-set.

Solution   The partition chain for the 8-PSK constellation is shown in Fig. 8.5.

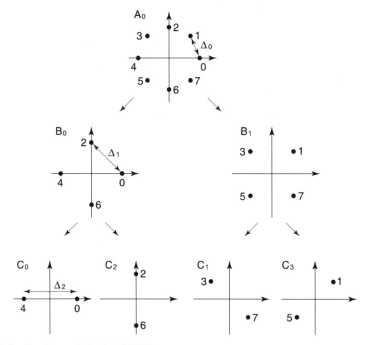

Figure 8.5   Partition chain for 8-PSK

The minimum distances within the sub-sets are as follows. We make the normalizing assumption that the constellation radius is unity. In the case of constellations that are not of equal energy, the usual normalizing assumption is of unity energy, i.e. the mean square radius is unity.

$$\left.\begin{array}{lll} \text{A sub-set} & \Delta_0 = 2\sin(\pi/8) = 0.765 \text{ or } \sqrt{2 - \sqrt{2}} \\ \text{B sub-sets} & \Delta_1 = \sqrt{2} \\ \text{C sub-sets} & \Delta_2 = 2 \end{array}\right\} \qquad (8.3)$$

The code is then chosen so as to protect more strongly those coded signals within the same upper-level sub-set (whose Euclidean distance may be small), rather than those within the same lower-level set, for which we know that the Euclidean distance is relatively large. For example, if the point 0 is used in a given position of a given codeword, then we can freely use the point 4 in the same position of another codeword, because these points are in the same sub-set C_0. However, if we use point 1, which shares only the A_0 sub-set, then we must ensure that that codeword differs in a number of positions, i.e. that the Hamming distance is large.

Set partitioning allows us to assign binary labels to constellation points according to which sub-set they are in, and therefore according to their Euclidean distance. The least significant bit (LSB) is assigned according to which of the two sub-sets a point is in on the first level of partition, the next bit on the next level, and so on until the most significant bit (MSB) identifies the point within the bottom-level sub-set. In Example 8.1 (PSK), the labelling is given in Fig. 8.6.

In the example this process has led to a natural numbering of the points around the circle of the constellation. This is not always the outcome of labelling by set partitioning, and indeed other equally valid label schemes could be devised for 8-PSK. We note, however, that those points that differ only in the MSB lie in the same C sub-set, and are furthest apart in Euclidean

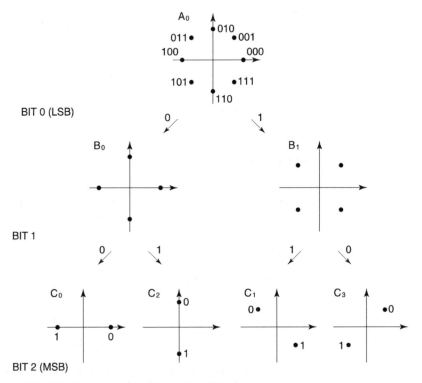

Figure 8.6 Labelling (mapping) by set partitioning

distance, while those that differ in the LSB may be close together. Now we can say that the LSB requires most protection from the code; the MSB is already unlikely to be in error, since that would require a large displacement in Euclidean distance within the constellation.

The different forms of coded modulation represent different means of providing these different degrees of protection to the different bits of the constellation label, or alternatively of packing the code points optimally into the signal space. The best-known form is *trellis coded modulation* (TCM) [8.2], which we will describe first (Section 8.2).

8.1.4 Optimum constellation expansion

As shown in Fig. 8.1, coded modulation involves an M-ary modulator preceded by a rate $l/\log_2(M)$ encoder, where k is the number of data bits per channel symbol. This is equivalent to an uncoded 2^l-ary modulation scheme. In his classic paper on the subject [8.2], Ungerböck addressed the question of what degree of constellation expansion is appropriate; i.e. what value of M is required for a given l. This was done by calculating the capacity for a channel under the restriction that an M-ary constellation is used, and comparing it with the unrestricted Shannon capacity of the channel (according to Equation (5.22)). The result is shown in Fig. 8.7 for the QAM constellations along with a related set, the AMPM constellations.

This diagram shows the signal-to-noise advantage possible with coding of unlimited complexity through expanding the constellation. For example, an

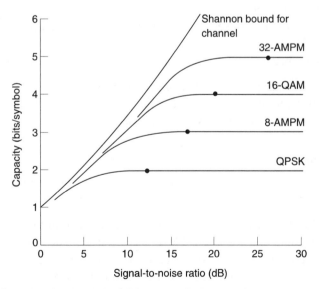

Figure 8.7 Capacity of various signalling constellations, to determine optimum constellation expansion: (●) required SNR for BER = 10^{-5}

uncoded QPSK system would require 12.9-dB signal-to-noise ratio (for a BER of 10^{-5}). For the same capacity in bits per symbol, a coded 8-AMPM scheme would theoretically require SNR of only 5.9 dB (in terms of its Shannon capacity). Unrestricted coding (which yields the Shannon capacity, and which is equivalent to a constellation of unlimited size) could yield only a further 1.2 dB. A further factor of 2 expansion, to 16-QAM, would yield a negligible improvement. Hence, Ungerböck argued, an expansion by a factor of two is adequate, and the returns diminish very rapidly for larger constellations. Examining the diagram, we see that this applies to each constellation, and hence we take it as a general rule. We therefore use a rate $l/(l + 1)$ encoder.

8.2 Trellis coded modulation (TCM)

Trellis coded modulation, as the name suggests, is based on the trellis as used in convolutional coding. It was the form of coded modulation first proposed by Ungerböck, although arguably block coded modulation had been proposed previously in various forms. Rather than trellis branches being labelled with binary code sequences, they represent constellation points from the signalling constellation.

Ungerböck gave four rules for the mapping of constellation points onto the code trellis:

(1) All constellation points to be used equally often.
(2) All trellis branches starting from the same node to be assigned points from the same B sub-set.
(3) All trellis branches converging to the same node to be assigned points from the same B sub-set.
(4) All parallel branches to be assigned points from the same C sub-set.

(We will see an example of parallel branches shortly).

We will illustrate these rules, in using the set partitioning for 8-PSK given in Example 8.1 to develop an 8-PSK TCM scheme.

Example 8.2(a)

Develop a trellis coded 8-PSK scheme with rate equivalent to uncoded QPSK (i.e. 2 bits/symbol, cf. Fig. 8.1) and a four state trellis.

Solution Two bits/symbol, or per trellis branch, imply that four branches must emanate from each node. One possible trellis for such a code is shown in Fig. 8.8. It may be described as a *fully connected* trellis, since each state is connected to every other state. The application of rule 2 (above) would suggest that the branches diverging from node zero should be labelled with points from sub-set B_0, as shown. Applying rule 3, this would then mean that all other nodes

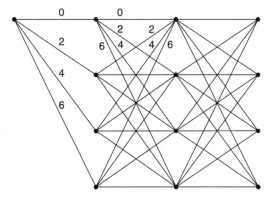

Figure 8.8 Possible trellis for Example 8.2

would also have to use sub-set B_0. This would violate rule 1, and also result in an effectively QPSK scheme, which could not provide coding gain.

We are therefore obliged to use a different trellis structure, that shown in Fig. 8.9. To avoid creating a fully connected trellis, this trellis includes *parallel branches*. These are pairs of branches that both begin and end on the same node, and therefore are given no error-protection from the code. For this reason their constellation points must be as far apart as possible, from the same C sub-set, as per rule 4.

An appropriate labelling scheme is shown in Fig. 8.9. It fulfils all the requirements of Ungerböck's rules, making full use of the 8-PSK signalling constellation.

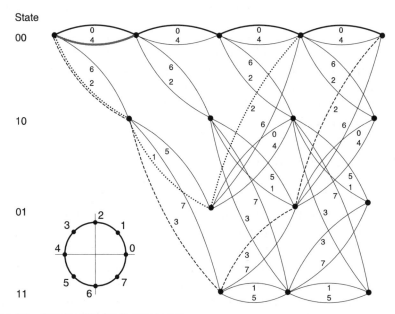

Figure 8.9 Final trellis for Example 8.2

We now evaluate the performance of this scheme, in terms of its minimum Euclidean distance, which will then give the asymptotic coding gain. Because this is a trellis scheme, we use the concept of free distance, as for convolutional codes, but in this case we are concerned with free Euclidean distance rather than Hamming distance. Once again this is a group code, and we can, without loss of generality, take one reference path and compare all others with it. The reference will be the all-zero path, shown in bold black on Fig. 8.9. Three other paths are shown; these are candidates for the minimum-distance path in Euclidean distance terms. Table 8.1 shows the calculation of Euclidean distance for these paths. We determine from the trellis and the constellation diagram the squared distance in each symbol period (it is given by the appropriate sub-set distance). The overall squared distance is then the sum of these squared distances up to the point at which the path remerges with the reference path.

Path	Symbol sub-set	Distance²	Symbol sub-set	Distance²	Symbol sub-set	Distance²	Symbol sub-set	Distance²	Total squared distance
——	4	Δ_2^2		0		0		0	
	C_0	4.0		0.0		0.0		0.0	4.0
.....	2	Δ_1^2	1	Δ_0^2	2	Δ_1^2		0	
	B_0	2.0	A_0	0.568	B_0	2.0		0.0	4.568
- - - -	2	Δ_1^2	3	Δ_0^2	3	Δ_0^2	2	Δ_1^2	
	B_0	2.0	A_0	0.568	A_0	0.568	B_0	2.0	5.136

Table 8.1   Calculation of minimum Euclidean distance of scheme of Example 8.2

From this calculation, the closest path is that which takes one of the parallel branches for one symbol, and then reverts to the reference. The two remaining paths enumerated are clearly more distant, and it is also clear that any other paths will also be at least as far from the reference. Hence, the minimum squared Euclidean distance is 4.0, and the ACG is $10 \log_{10}(4.0/2.0) = 3$ dB.

We will return to this worked example in Example 8.2(b).

Table 8.2 gives the asymptotic coding gain for a number of coded 8-PSK schemes, using different constraint length codes, but all sending 2 bits/symbol. Note that for constraint lengths greater than three, parallel transitions are not used, as it is possible to avoid a fully connected trellis without them. The table also gives the number of states of the encoder, which yields a measure of decoder complexity. For codes of higher constraint length, the direct design method illustrated above becomes too complex, and the optimum codes have been found by a computer search for the largest minimum distance, using the rules as a filter for candidate code generators. Similarly, Table 8.3 gives the gains for coded 16-QAM schemes, this time at 3 bits/symbol.

Constraint length	States	d^2_{min}	Asymptotic coding gain (dB)
2	2	2.59	1.1
3	4	4.0	3.0
4	8	4.58	3.6
5	16	5.17	4.1
7	64	6.0	4.8
9	256	7.52	5.7

Table 8.2.   Asymptotic coding gains for coded 8-PSK schemes at 2 bits/symbol

Constraint length	States	d^2_{min}	Asymptotic coding gain (dB)
3	4	4.0	3.0
4	8	5.0	4.0
5	16	6.0	4.8
7	64	7.0	5.4
8	128	8.0	6.0

Table 8.3   Asymptotic gains for coded 16-QAM schemes at 3 bits/symbol

8.2.1   Encoder structure

We have shown above that the encoder should have a rate of $l/(l + 1)$. For TCM it is a parallel convolutional encoder, with l inputs and $l + 1 = \log_2(M)$

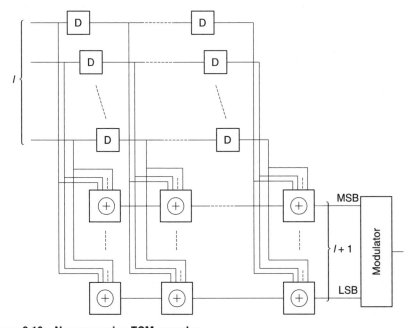

Figure 8.10   Non-recursive TCM encoder

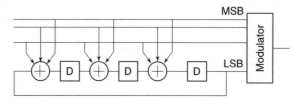

Figure 8.11   Recursive-systematic TCM encoder

outputs, connected directly to the modulator. The modulator then uses the mapping-by-set-partitioning rule.

There are two possible encoder structures for trellis codes, based on the non-recursive and the recursive-systematic forms of the convolutional encoder, respectively. These are illustrated in Figs 8.10 and 8.11.

Example 8.2(b)

As an example, we will obtain the non-recursive form of the encoder for the code of Example 8.2.

Solution   Figure 8.12(a) gives the trellis labelling, using mapping by set partitioning. Note how the MSB, and only the MSB, differs between parallel branches. Hence, the data bit that chooses between these two branches can be used as the MSB of the label, and is not fed into the encoder. It is effectively uncoded. If we then disregard the MSB and the parallel branches, we obtain the reduced trellis of Fig. 8.12(b), which determines the encoding of the two least significant bits from one of the data bits. The encoder which results in

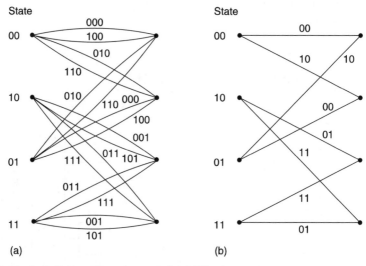

Figure 8.12   Labelled trellises for coded 8-PSK scheme

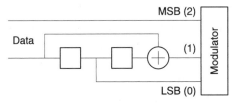

Figure 8.13   Encoder for coded 8-PSK scheme

this trellis is shown in Fig. 8.13. This may be obtained by drawing up a truth table for the branch labels in terms of the state of the encoder and the data input. A convenient way of drawing this is as a Karnaugh map:

	0	1
00	0	1
01	1	0
11	1	0
10	0	1

Label bit 1

	0	1
00	0	0
01	0	0
11	1	1
10	1	1

Label LSB (bit 0)

The map shows that the label LSB depends only on the state LSB. It also shows that the label bit 1 depends only on the data and the state of the MSB, and that the dependence is exclusive-OR (XOR).

By re-arranging it in much the same way as for the recursive-systematic convolutional codes of Chapter 7, this encoder can be obtained in the recursive-systematic form mentioned above. This is shown in Fig. 8.14.

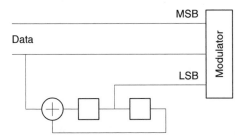

Figure 8.14   Recursive-systematic form of encoder for coded 8-PSK scheme of Example 8.2

8.2.2   Decoding

Decoding of trellis codes is almost invariably by means of the Viterbi algorithm over the trellis. Soft decision decoding is essential, particularly since the codes have been developed using this as a design metric. Given this, the only difference in decoding is that Euclidean distances are calculated using the distances of the received signal from the possible constellation points. Note, however, that since coded modulation schemes (other than coded M-PSK schemes) may not be spherical, the simplified metric calculation implied in Equation (5.32) may not always apply.

The performance of TCM schemes can also be estimated in exactly the same way as for convolutional codes, assuming soft decision decoding, except that the Euclidean distances do not necessarily take integer values as the Hamming distances do. We therefore adapt Equation (7.9) slightly:

$$P_b \leq \sum_{d \geq d_{\text{free}}} e(d) Q \left(d \sqrt{\frac{k}{2} \frac{E_b}{N_0}} \right) \tag{8.4}$$

where d denotes the Euclidean distance, which may now take any value greater than or equal to d_{free}, the free Euclidean distance of the scheme; k is the number of bits per symbol, assuming one symbol per trellis period. We assume that the Euclidean distances are normalized such that the mean constellation power is unity (i.e. unit radius for an M-PSK constellation).

In the scheme shown in Example 8.2, using the set of distances found in Table 8.1, we have:

$$P_b \approx Q \left(\sqrt{4.0 \frac{E_b}{N_0}} \right) + 8Q \left(\sqrt{4.568 \frac{E_b}{N_0}} \right) + 12Q \left(\sqrt{5.136 \frac{E_b}{N_0}} \right) + \cdots \tag{8.5}$$

Note that the distances quoted are the squared Euclidean distances, and that there are four possible paths at a squared distance of 4.568, corresponding to the alternative parallel branches, and similarly for the next distance. The results are shown in Fig. 8.15, which compares this estimate with the equivalent uncoded QPSK, and with a lower bound (which we may call the *asymptotic*

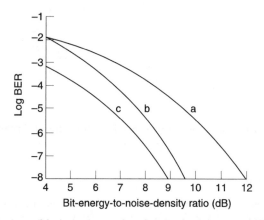

Figure 8.15 BER versus bit-energy-to-noise-density for (a) uncoded QPSK, (b) estimate of Equation (8.5), and (c) asymptotic lower bound based on single term

lower bound) obtained from just the first term of Equation (8.5), with its co-efficient set to unity. This corresponds to the uncoded curve left-shifted by the asymptotic coding gain. Simulation shows that the true BER is very close (within 0.2 dB) of the estimate in this case. This indicates that the asymptotic coding gain is not very close to the true coding gain, except at very low BER. For example, at $BER = 10^{-3}$ only 1.1 dB of the 3 dB of asymptotic coding gain is realized.

8.2.3 CPM and TCM

We have described continuous phase modulation (CPM), in Section 3.3.6, as an FSK scheme with pre-filter to reduce sidelobes. Figure 3.29 showed the *phase trellis diagram*, which has some obvious similarities to the trellis diagram used in TCM. This suggests an equivalence between the two schemes, which we may show more formally, in that both may be generated by a *finite state machine* (FSM) followed by a memory-less modulator (Fig. 8.16(b)) [8.8]. For TCM, the FSM is the shift register of the trellis encoder. For CPM, it is the memory of the pre-filter, plus the memory of the continuous phase modulator, that stores the phase of the previous symbol so as to begin the next symbol transmission without phase discontinuity. The CPM modulator is shown in Fig. 8.16(a), in which the continuous phase modulator memory element is marked by a heavier outline. For a binary CPM scheme the number of states of the filter part is clearly $2^{\nu-1}$, where ν is the length of the filter impulse response in symbol periods. The number of states of the continuous phase modulator part is the number of different phase states of the basic unfiltered modulation, which is $2q$ where q is the denominator of the modulation index h. Thus for schemes based on MSK ($h = 1/2$) this is 4, which agrees with the 4-phase states of the MSK constellation

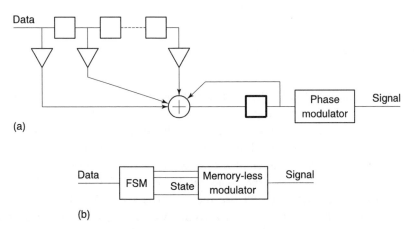

(a)

(b)

Figure 8.16 Finite state machine representation of CPM

(Fig. 3.18). Thus the total number of states is $2q2^{\nu-1} = 2^{\nu}q$. This alternative representation is particularly useful when additional convolutional coding is to be added to a CPM scheme, since it allows the coding to be integrated into the modulation and optimized for a given total number of encoder/modulator states. It also allows joint decoding and demodulation operating on a single trellis.

8.3 Block coded modulation

Block coded modulation (BCM) is the counterpart of TCM, using block codes in place of convolutional. It is also an example of *multilevel coded modulation* (MLCM) which will be described in general in Section 8.4. It was, in fact, discovered in the 1970s, [8.2, 8.3], before TCM was announced, although it did not attract much attention at that time, and was subsequently 're-discovered' in the earlier 1980s by Cusack [8.9] and by Sayegh [8.10].

We have seen that when constellation labels are applied according to the rule of mapping by set partitioning, different bits of the label require different degrees of protection from the code. In BCM, we provide this by encoding the different bits with different codes, having different minimum Hamming distances and redundancy.

Specifically, we encode the LSB with a powerful code, with large Hamming distance, and encode the MSB with the least powerful code, which also has least redundancy. It is useful to arrange the point labels in an array, forming columns with the LSB at the top, as illustrated in Table 8.4. Here $\{a_0\ b_0\ c_0\}$ forms the label for the first symbol, and so on. The illustration is for a coded 8-PSK scheme, and hence has three rows; in general it will have $\log_2(M)$ rows.

$$\begin{bmatrix} a_0 & a_1 & \cdots & a_{n-1} \\ b_0 & b_1 & \cdots & b_{n-1} \\ c_0 & c_1 & \cdots & c_{n-1} \end{bmatrix}$$

Table 8.4 Array for BCM scheme

Vectors **a**, **b** and **c** should then form codewords of three different length n binary codes, in which the top row code has the greatest Hamming distance, and the bottom row has smallest Hamming distance, or may be uncoded.

To determine the optimum choice of codes, we will consider the relationship between the Hamming distance of the codes on each row, known as *row codes* or (more generally) *component codes*, and the overall minimum Euclidean distance of the scheme. We will use the all-zeros array $(\mathbf{a} = \mathbf{b} = \mathbf{c} = \mathbf{0})$ as a reference, and compare it with non-zero arrays. Let the minimum Hamming distances of the three codes (top to bottom row) be d_{H0}, d_{H1}, d_{H2}, respectively.

The minimum Euclidean distances within the corresponding sub-sets are Δ_0, Δ_1, Δ_2. The number of data bits are k_0, k_1, k_2. The code length n is of course the same for all the codes.

Consider first the array with $\mathbf{b} = \mathbf{c} = \mathbf{0}$ and $\mathbf{a} \neq \mathbf{0}$. $\mathbf{a}$ has '1' in at least d_{H0} places: i.e. it differs from the reference value by at least Δ_0 in at least d_{H0} symbols. Therefore, the total squared Euclidean distance from the reference array is:

$$d_0^2 = d_{H0}\Delta_0^2 \tag{8.6}$$

Similarly for an array with $\mathbf{a} = \mathbf{c} = \mathbf{0}$ and $\mathbf{b} \neq \mathbf{0}$, etc. In general:

$$d_i^2 = d_{Hi}\Delta_i^2 \tag{8.7}$$

where d_i is the ith *level* (or *row*) *Euclidean distance*. Hence, the overall minimum squared Euclidean distance:

$$d_{min}^2 = \min_i\{d_{Hi}\Delta_i^2\} \tag{8.8}$$

d_{min} is clearly maximized if the row Euclidean distance is equal for all rows (otherwise it could be improved by increasing just one minimum Hamming distance). The design goal is therefore to equalize these distances.

Example 8.3

Design a block coded 8-PSK scheme, of equivalent rate to uncoded QPSK (and therefore also equivalent to Example 8.2).

Solution We begin by choosing a bottom level code, which we will assume to be uncoded: Then $d_{H2} = 1$, and $d_2 = 1\Delta_2 = 2$. Hence on the next level up $d_1^2 = d_{H1}\Delta_1^2 \geq d_2^2$, and $d_{H1} \geq d_{H2}\Delta_2^2/\Delta_1^2 = 2$. This corresponds to a single parity check code (SPC).

On the top level $d_{H0} \geq d_{H2}(\Delta_2^2/\Delta_0^2) = 6.83$. We choose 7, which corresponds to a length 7 repetition code. The structure of the code array is thus as illustrated in Table 8.5.

$$\begin{bmatrix} D & P & P & P & P & P & P \\ D & D & D & D & D & D & P \\ D & D & D & D & D & D & D \end{bmatrix} \begin{bmatrix} \text{repetition } (7,1,7) \\ \text{SPC } (7,6,2) \\ \text{uncoded } (7,7,1) \end{bmatrix}$$

Table 8.5   Code array for Example 8.3

The present author has more recently shown [8.11] that better results may be obtained at practical BERs if the row Euclidean distances are not equalized. While this reduces the overall minimum Euclidean distance, and hence reduces the ACG, it also reduces the codeword multiplicity at minimum distance (the number of nearest neighbours), and at practical BER this gives rise to an improvement. The principle becomes instead the equalization of the stage BERs in the multistage decoder (see Section 8.4.2). This also allows the scheme to be optimized for a particular operating BER, and thus to be adapted to the requirements of the service being provided. For example, coded speech requires a BER of around 10^{-3}, which results in a different code from the one optimized for high-integrity data, at a BER of perhaps 10^{-8}.

8.3.1 Decoding

Maximum likelihood decoding of BCM requires, in general, an exhaustive search among all possible combinations of codewords on all levels, of which there are a total of $2^{k_0} \times 2^{k_1} \times 2^{k_2} = 2^{(k_0+k_1+k_2)}$ combinations. For Example 8.3 this would be 2^{14}, or over 16 000. This problem may be solved, in general, by the *multistage* decoding technique, which is not maximum likelihood, but has the same performance asymptotically (as the signal-to-noise ratio increases). This allows the problem to be broken down into the separate decoding of each component code, then the results are fed forward one level to inform the decoding on the next. We will deal with this technique in more detail in Section 8.4, as it is applicable to multilevel codes in general.

However, for a range of BCM codes, including many of practical interest, maximum likelihood decoding is possible using trellis decoding, as in trellis decoding of block codes. In fact, a trellis can be created for any BCM scheme, but for some (including that of Example 8.3) it is particularly simple [8.12]. The trellis for Example 8.3 is shown in Fig. 8.17. This may be perceived as a combination of the simple trellises shown in Fig. 8.18: a repetition code (a), a single parity check (SPC) code (b), and the trellis of uncoded data (c). The Viterbi decoding algorithm may be applied to this trellis in the same way as for trellis decoding of block codes.

We can estimate the BER performance of this scheme using an expression similar to Equation (8.4). Estimating $e(d)$ by a rather detailed inspection of

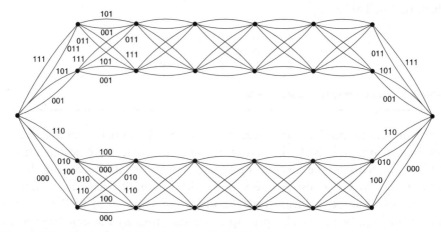

Figure 8.17   Trellis for BCM scheme of Example 8.3

Fig. 8.17, we obtain:

$$P_b \le \frac{1}{14}\left[7Q\left(\sqrt{\Delta_2^2\frac{E_b}{N_0}}\right) + 36Q\left(\sqrt{2\Delta_1^2\frac{E_b}{N_0}}\right) + 64Q\left(\sqrt{\Delta_0^2\frac{E_b}{N_0}}\right) + \cdots\right]$$

$$= \frac{43}{14}Q\left(\sqrt{4\frac{E_b}{N_0}}\right) + \frac{32}{7}Q\left(\sqrt{4.10\frac{E_b}{N_0}}\right) + \cdots \tag{8.9}$$

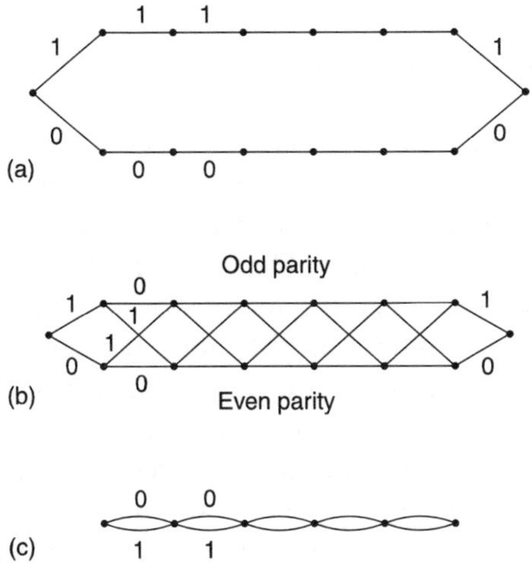

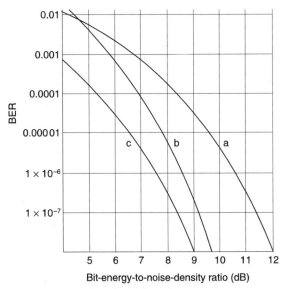

Figure 8.18   Constituent trellises of Fig. 8.17: (a) repetition code, (b) single parity check code, (c) uncoded

Figure 8.19   BER of code of Example 8.3, using trellis decoding (a) uncoded QPSK, (b) estimate from Equation (8.9), (c) asymptotic lower bound

This yields curve b in Fig. 8.19, where it is compared with the equivalent uncoded modulation scheme, uncoded QPSK (curve a), and with the asymptotic lower bound, curve c. It is again clear that the asymptotic bound is not attained in practice except at very low BER. Indeed performance compared with asymptotic is poorer than for TCM, which is commonly the case in block coded schemes, since the error multiplicity, or number of nearest neighbours, tends to be larger.

8.4 Multilevel coded modulation

Multilevel coded modulation is, in fact, a generalization of BCM, from the observation that the binary component codes do not have to be block codes of equal length, but could be convolutional codes, or even a mix of both block and convolutional. The general structure of the encoder is shown in Fig. 8.20. Note that the modulator uses mapping by set partitioning, and that the demultiplexer distributes data to the component encoders according to their relative rate. Equation (8.8) applies as for BCM, and hence the design rules are the same, replacing minimum Hamming distance by free Hamming distance as necessary. The first example of MLCM was probably the BCM scheme of Imai and Hirakawa [8.4], but the generalization to other types of code was given a firm basis by Calderbank [8.13].

As we have seen, some multilevel codes lend themselves to maximum likelihood decoding, using trellis decoding, for example. However, a general algorithm also exists, which can be used for all multilevel codes, namely the multistage decoder, due originally to Imai and Hirakawa [8.4]. It is not true ML, but it may be described as *asymptotically ML*, in the sense that its performance tends to ML as the signal-to-noise ratio tends to infinity. It was more recently shown [8.14] that despite this sub-optimality multistage decoding can nevertheless approach the Shannon bound. We describe this technique and its performance next.

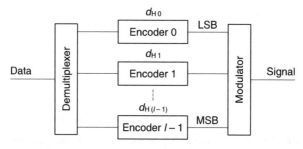

Figure 8.20   General structure of multilevel encoder

8.4.1 Multistage decoding

The principle of multistage demodulation is to decompose the joint decoding problem for the whole scheme into a series of decoders for the individual component codes taken separately, in stages. The structure of the decoder/demodulator is shown in Fig. 8.21. (This shows the decoder for a three-level code, such as coded 8-PSK, but it readily generalizes for other constellations.)

At each stage the demodulator examines the received signal and compares it with the two sub-sets of the constellation at that stage, outputting a soft value to indicate its relative closeness. (This will be discussed shortly.) The decoder then uses the demodulator output to decode that component code, thereby selecting one of the two sub-sets. This choice is then fed forward to the next stage decoder, using a re-encoder. A delay is inserted to compensate for the delay in the decoding/re-encoding process. The next stage then chooses between the two sub sub-sets of the chosen sub-set on the next level, and so on.

The optimum soft value to feed from the demodulator to the decoder is the log likelihood ratio (see Section 5.6.3). As we have seen, Euclidean distance is, in effect, a proxy for this metric. For example, consider the demodulation of the received symbol Y as shown in Fig. 8.22. The LLR for the LSB of this is given by Equation (5.34) in terms of the distance of Y from the nearest point of each of the sub-sets (shown in white and in grey). Using the cosine rule in the diagram in Equation (5.34):

$$\Lambda('1','0'|Y) \approx \frac{d_0^2 - d_1^2}{2\sigma^2} = \frac{(1 + y^2 - 2y\cos\theta_0) - (1 + y^2 - 2y\cos\theta_1)}{2\sigma^2}$$

$$= \frac{y}{\sigma^2}(\cos\theta_1 - \cos\theta_0) \qquad (8.10)$$

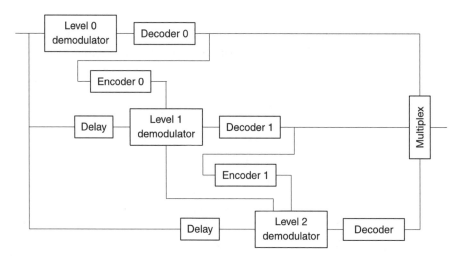

Figure 8.21   Multistage decoder for MLCM

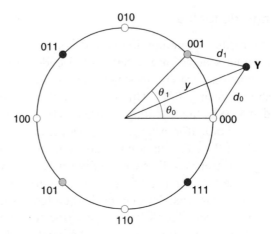

Figure 8.22   Stage demodulation

Note that $y = |\mathbf{Y}|$, the signal amplitude. Plotting the LLR against $\theta = \arg(\mathbf{Y})$ (for the first stage demodulator) we obtain Fig. 8.23. (The result for the second stage is only slightly less linear.) This (taken with Equation (8.10)) shows that the demodulator output for M-PSK should be given by a simple linear function of the phase of the received signal, multiplied by the signal amplitude.

Similarly, Fig. 8.24 shows part of a QAM constellation. Again, using the geometry of the diagram and substituting in (5.34) we have:

$$\Lambda('1','0'|\mathbf{Y}) \approx \frac{d_0^2 - d_1^2}{2\sigma^2}$$

$$= \frac{[(1-x)^2 + (1-y)^2] - [(1-x)^2 + (1+y)^2]}{2\sigma^2} = \frac{-2y}{\sigma^2} \quad (8.11)$$

for the region where the received symbol is closest to the two points marked. Again we have a simple linear relationship to the received signal.

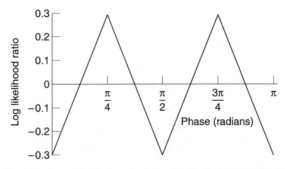

Figure 8.23   LLR against received signal phase for first stage demodulation

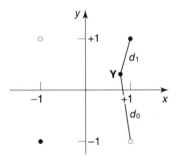

Figure 8.24   Demodulation of QAM constellation

The decoder may then be any suitable decoder for the component code. Ideally, of course, it should be maximum likelihood, and usually performance is very poor if it is not soft decision.

8.4.2   Performance of multistage decoder

We can then estimate the performance of the multistage decoder from that of the binary component code decoders. There are, however, two factors that degrade the multistage decoder.

First, each point has more than one neighbour in its constellation: for example, there are two in 8-PSK and in all its partitions except the smallest. Both of these are labelled with the same bit in the corresponding partition. For example, if we take 000 as a reference in Fig. 8.22, it has two neighbours, 001 and 111, both of which have '1' as LSB. For every pair of codewords of the first component code (at Hamming distance d), there are therefore two neighbours for each symbol in which the words differ. Hence overall there are 2^d neighbours resulting from that pair of codewords. In general there are a_i^d for each neighbour codeword of the ith component code, where:

$$\{a_i, i = 0 \cdots 2\} = \{2, 2, 1\} \tag{8.12}$$

for 8-PSK, and:

$$\{a_i, i = 0 \cdots 3\} = \{3, \tfrac{9}{4}, 2, 1\} \tag{8.13}$$

for 16-QAM.

Second, an error in an earlier stage is clearly going to affect the decoding of later stages. For example in Fig. 8.22 suppose 000 were transmitted, but that the first stage was wrongly decoded. The next stage would then try to decide between the light and the dark grey sub-sets, and of course the error probability would be 0.5. This is called *error propagation*. We therefore estimate an *error propagation factor* ε_i, defined as the ratio of bit errors occurring in the ith decoder and all subsequent ones, to the total number of bits transmitted. An error event (whether in a convolutional or block code) at the ith stage of

Hamming distance d symbols, causing dR_i bit errors in its own decoder, is likely on average to result in $dR_{i+1}/2$ errors at the next stage, $dR_{i+1}/4$ at the next, and so on. (Note that because the later component codes are likely to have smaller minimum Hamming distance, they are unlikely to correct these errors.) Then:

$$\varepsilon_i \approx \frac{R_i + R_{i+1}/2 + R_{i+2}/4 + \cdots}{R} \tag{8.14}$$

where R_i is the rate of the ith component code and $R = \sum_i R_i$ is the overall rate of the scheme in bits/symbol. Then we may upper bound the *stage BER*, defined as the ratio of the bit errors caused by errors in the ith stage decoder to the total bit transmitted, as:

$$P_{ei} \lesssim \varepsilon_i \sum_{d=d_{Hi}}^{d_{\max}(i)} e_i(d) a_i^d Q\left(\frac{\Delta_i}{2}\sqrt{\gamma d}\right) \tag{8.15}$$

where:

$$\gamma = \frac{E_c}{N_0} = \frac{RE_b}{N_0} \tag{8.16}$$

The overall BER is then:

$$P_b = \sum_{i=1}^{m} P_{ei} \tag{8.17}$$

Figure 8.25 compares the performance of this decoder for Example 8.3 with the ML decoder of Section 8.3.1. We note that there is a further degradation, but only of a fraction of a dB.

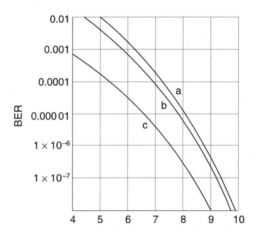

Figure 8.25 Performance of multistage decoder for Example 8.3 (a), compared with ML decoder (b), and asymptotic bound (c)

8.5 Lattice codes

Lattice codes [8.7] are block coded modulation schemes that arise directly from geometrical considerations, as described in Section 8.1.1. As mentioned there, good codes may be based on dense sphere-packings in n dimensions, and these tend to have a regular repetitive structure, like that of crystal lattices. (n here is the number of dimensions of the coded signal, which for coded modulation is twice the number of symbols per code block.) Formally:

A *lattice* is a regular structure created by the repetition of a unit cell throughout space.

We use a three-dimensional example, in order to be able to illustrate it:

Example 8.4
Construct the *body-centred cubic* (BCC) lattice illustrated in Fig. 8.26 from the Z^3 (cubic) lattice.

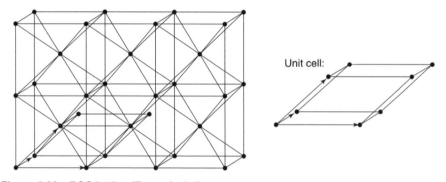

Figure 8.26   BCC lattice (Example 8.4)

Solution   Being a regular structure, a lattice can be constructed by selecting points from a rectangular lattice (known as Z^n), which is in fact equivalent to $n/2$ uncoded QAM constellations. For example, Fig. 8.27 shows how a BCC lattice can be constructed as a sub-set of the points of a Z^3 lattice. If we label alternate points in each dimension '0' and '1', as shown, then we select points whose label contains either zero or three '1's, we obtain the BCC lattice. This selection may be carried out by applying a binary code to the point labels.

   This shows that lattice codes have a close relationship to block coded modulation, since in both cases a binary code of fixed length is applied to

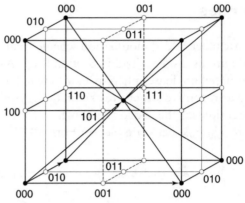

Figure 8.27   BCC lattice as a sub-set of Z^3

constellation point labels. This may be illustrated further with a more complex example.

Example 8.5

Construct a lattice code from the 64-point constellation as shown in Fig. 8.28, which has been 'shaped' so as to reduce its peak amplitude. Explore the effect of phase rotation on this scheme.

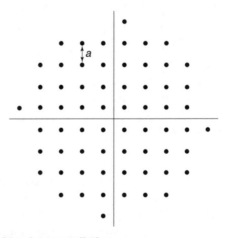

Figure 8.28   Shaped 64-point constellation

Solution   Figure 8.29 shows how this constellation may be partitioned into four (rather than two) sub-sets, each being a 90° ($\pi/2$) rotation of the previous one. Each point within the sub-set is given a 4-bit label, which rotates with the sub-set. In encoding data, four bits per codeword are used directly to select a

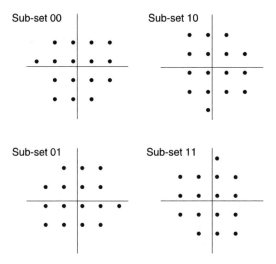

Figure 8.29 Partition of constellation of Fig. 8.28 into four sub-sets

point from the sub-set. These are uncoded, like the bottom-level component code of Example 8.3. The sub-set is chosen using a binary code: an $(8, 4, 4)$ Reed–Muller code, which is in fact the same as a $(7, 4, 3)$ Hamming code with an additional parity check bit added (an *extended Hamming code* – see Section 6.3.8). The generator matrix is given in Equation (8.18):

$$\begin{bmatrix} 1 & 1 & 1 & 1 & 1 & 1 & 1 & 1 \\ 1 & 0 & 1 & 0 & 1 & 0 & 1 & 0 \\ 1 & 1 & 0 & 0 & 1 & 1 & 0 & 0 \\ 1 & 1 & 1 & 1 & 0 & 0 & 0 & 0 \end{bmatrix} \tag{8.18}$$

Four data bits per codeword are input to this encoder, and its output gives the four sub-set labels (two bits each). Thus the code transmits $4 + 4 \times 4 = 20$ bits/codeword, or 5 bits/(two-dimensional) symbol. This construction forms a lattice known as E_8, or rather that portion of it that lies within a region around the origin.

The minimum distance of the coded signal is clearly $2a$ for the uncoded data in each of the sub-sets. For the encoded data used to select the sub-set, there will be a distance of at least a in each of at least four dimensions (the minimum distance of the code), giving a total squared distance of $4a^2$, so the minimum distance is $2a$ here also. Comparing this with an uncoded 32-point constellation, which would also transmit 5 bits/symbol, and in which the minimum distance would be $a\sqrt{2}$, the ACG is 3 dB. Simulations [8.15] show that, in practice, this scheme can achieve about 1.8 dB at BER $= 10^{-6}$.

This scheme also has an important property called *rotational invariance* [8.16]. In practice, if a constellation is symmetrical like the one described here, it may be difficult for the receiver to synchronize with it in the correct phase. (This constellation, like the QAM constellations, is said to have 90° rotational symmetry.) This can be overcome by suitable differential encoding of the data before transmission. However, this requires that any codeword still remains a codeword if all the constellations within it are rotated by a multiple of 90° ($\pi/2$). This is the property of rotational invariance.

Since the sub-sets are 90° rotations of one another, and the labels also rotate with the codewords, the uncoded data directly transmitted in these labels is unaffected by a rotation. The effect of a 90° rotation on the sub-set label will be to transform it around the cycle $\{00 \Rightarrow 10 \Rightarrow 11 \Rightarrow 01 \Rightarrow 00\}$. Thus we must ensure that any such transformation, applied pairwise to the bits of a codeword, results in another valid codeword. A careful examination of the generator matrix of the $(8, 4, 4)$ Reed–Muller code given in Equation (8.18) shows that this is always the case. Indeed, it can be shown that it will always be the case for any Reed–Muller code of first order or greater.

8.6   System applications

8.6.1   Voiceband modems

As mentioned above, the application that gave the initial impetus for the development of trellis coded modulation was the voiceband modem: the device that allows digital services like FAX and Internet access over a conventional telephone line. This is designed to handle speech signals of rather restricted quality, and has a bandwidth extending from 300 Hz to 3.4 kHz. As such it is clear that to achieve data rates greater than about 2.4 kbit s^{-1} (the maximum rate available in the early 1980s) requires multilevel modulation techniques. This was an ideal application for trellis coded modulation. The first standard using TCM in voiceband modems appeared in 1984: the CCITT (later ITU-T) standard V.32 [8.17, p. 239; 8.18].

The modulation constellation (with labelling scheme) and encoder are shown in Fig. 8.30. The constellation is in fact a 32-CROSS constellation (i.e. a 6×6 square constellation with the four corner points omitted), but it is conventionally illustrated rotated through 45°, as shown. The labelling scheme is best understood in terms of a partition into eight sub-sets defined by the three least significant bits. For example the labels of the sub-set XX111 are shown in italics in Fig. 8.30(a). Observe that the sub-sets XX100, XX011 and XX000 are 90° rotations of this sub-set. Similarly, the remaining sub-sets, XX001, XX110, XX101 and XX010 are 90° rotations of one another. This is required so that the code is 90° rotationally invariant, as in Example 8.5.

Note that the convolutional encoder here is non-linear, containing two AND gates as well as the modulo-2 adders (XOR gates). It is given in recursive form,

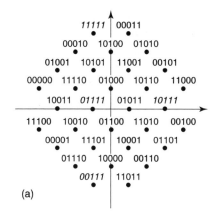

(a)

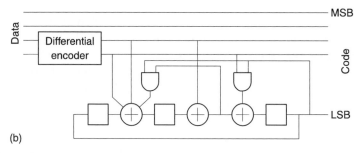

(b)

Figure 8.30   Constellation (a) and encoder (b) for the ITU-T V.32 voiceband modem standard

as in Fig. 8.11. The two encoded data bits are differentially encoded, again ensuring rotational invariance. Considerable care has been taken in the design of this and subsequent standards not only to maximize the asymptotic coding gain, but also to minimize the code multiplicity, so as to minimize the nearest neighbour effect (Section 8.1.2).

Since the V.32 standard sends 4 bits/symbol, it can transmit at $9.6\,\mathrm{kbit\,s^{-1}}$ over conventional telephone lines: a very substantial improvement on the previous state-of-the-art. It has a coding gain of around 4 dB in practice. Further increases became available in 1991 with the V.32(bis) standard, capable of $14.4\,\mathrm{kbit\,s^{-1}}$, and in 1994 with V.34 (which was code-named 'VFast' during development), now commonly used for dial-up Internet links, at up to $28.8\,\mathrm{kbit\,s^{-1}}$. V.32(bis) and V.34 use, respectively, a coded 128- and 960-point constellation, with 16- and 64-state trellis codes [8.17, pp. 236–42; 8.19; 8.20].

Further developments in these systems are now limited more by the quantization noise introduced by digital transmission over the core telecommunications network than by the noise on the local access loop of the telephone system. Such circuits are inherently limited to the $64\,\mathrm{kbit\,s^{-1}}$ used for a telephone circuit over the core network. The recently introduced 56-kbit s^{-1} modems (for which a unified standard is still under development) provide this rate on the down-stream connection (exchange to customer) by transmitting digitally direct to the exchange, so that no analog-to-digital conversion is required in this direction. Higher rates (up to several Mbit s^{-1}) will be achieved only when an asymmetric digital subscriber line (ADSL) [8.21] is introduced by the network operators.

Problems

8.1 Construct the partition chain for 16-QAM, determine the sub-set distances, and devise a mapping by set partitioning.

8.2 Devise a TCM scheme for 16-QAM at 3 bits/symbol, using an 8-state trellis. Determine whether parallel branches should be included in the trellis. Draw the trellis structure if they are not. A suitable basic trellis structure, if they are included, is given in the figure below. Devise a trellis labelling for your chosen trellis, using Ungerböck's principles and maximizing the minimum Euclidean distance of the code.

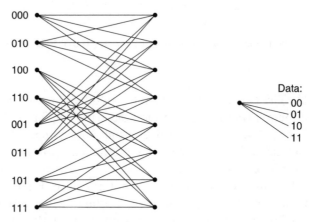

8.3 Find the asymptotic coding gain (ACG) of the scheme devised in Problem 8.2 compared with 8-AMPM.

8.4 Devise an encoder for the scheme of Problem 8.2.

8.5 Find the possible length 63 block-coded 8-PSK modulation schemes, using BCH codes (plus the single parity check code where appropriate) as the component codes. k and d of the length 63 BCH codes are:

$$(57, 3), (51, 5), (45, 7), (39, 9), (36, 11), (30, 13),$$

$$(24, 15), (18, 21), (16, 23), (10, 27), (7, 31), (1, 63)$$

Start with the bottom row code, beginning with the smallest Hamming distance code (i.e. uncoded), and then considering codes with increasing Hamming distance. For each bottom row code:

- Find the bottom row Euclidean distance.
- Find middle and top row codes to maintain Euclidean distance on these rows just greater than the bottom row Euclidean distance.
- Find the rate R of the overall scheme in bits/symbol.
- Find the asymptotic coding gain of the scheme compared with uncoded QPSK. If the rate R is different from uncoded QPSK, add a rate allowance of $10\log_{10}(R/2)\,\mathrm{dB}$.

8.6 Assuming that the minimum distance is limited by the uncoded bits, find the asymptotic coding gain of the V.32 standard, compared with uncoded 16-QAM.

References

8.1 Massey, J.L. (1974) Coding and modulation in digital communications. In *Proceedings of the International Zurich Seminar on Digital Communications*, March, pp. E2(1)–(4).

8.2 Ungerböck, G. (1982) Channel coding with multilevel/phase signals. *IEEE Transactions on Information Theory*, **IT-28**: 55–67.

8.3 Blokh, E.L. and Zyablov, V.V. (1994) Coding of generalised concatenated codes. *Problems of Information Transmission* (*Problemy Peredachy Informatsii*), **10**: 218–22.

8.4 Imai, H. and Hirakawa, S. (1977) A new multilevel coding technique using error-correcting codes. *IEEE Transactions on Information Theory*, **IT-23**(3): 371–7.

8.5 Ungerböck, G. (1987) Trellis coded modulation with redundant signal sets, Part I: Introduction, Part II: State-of-the art. *IEEE Communications Magazine*, **25**(2): 5–11, 12–21.

8.6 Burr, A.G. (1993) Block versus trellis: an introduction to coded modulation. *Electronics and Communication Engineering Journal*, **5**(4); 240–8.

8.7 Conway, J.H. and Sloane, N.J.A. (1988) *Sphere Packings, Lattices and Groups*, Springer-Verlag, New York.

8.8 Rimoldi, B. (1988) A decomposition approach to CPM. *IEEE Transactions on Information Theory*, **34**: 260–70.

8.9 Cusack, E.L. (1984) Error control codes for QAM signalling. *Electronics Letters*, **20**: 62–3.

8.10 Sayegh, S.I. (1986) A class of optimum block codes in signal space. *IEEE Transactions on Communications*, **34**: 1043–5.

8.11 Burr, A.G. and Lunn, T.J. (1997) Block coded modulation optimised for finite error rate. *IEEE Transactions on Information Theory*, **43**(1): 373–85.

8.12 Peng, X.-H. and Burr, A.G. Efficient optimum soft-decision decoding for multilevel block modulation codes. *IEE Proceedings – Communications*, in press.

8.13 Calderbank, A.R. (1989) Multilevel codes and multistage decoding. *IEEE Transactions on Communications*, **37**: 222–9.

8.14 Huber, J. and Wachsmann, U. (1995) Power and bandwidth efficient digital communication using turbo codes in multilevel codes. *European Transactions on Telecommunications*, **6**(5): 557–67.

8.15 Sheppard, J.A. and Burr, A.G. (1997) Performance of lattice codes on the AWGN channel. In *IEEE International Symposium on Information Theory*, Ulm, July.

8.16 Wei, L.-F. (1984) Rotationally invariant convolutional channel coding with expanded signal space. *IEEE Journal of Selected Areas in Communications*, **2**(5): 672–86.

8.17 Lee, L.H.C. (1997) *Convolutional Coding: Fundamentals and Applications*, Artech House.

8.18 CCITT Study Group XVII (1984) *Recommendation V.32 for a Family of 2-wire, Duplex Modems Operating on the General Switched Telephone Network and on the Leased Telephone-type Circuits*, Document AP VIII-43-E.
http://www.itu.int./itudoc/itu-t/iec/v/index.html

8.19 CCITT Recommendation V.32*bis* (1991) *A Duplex Modem Operating at Data Signalling Rates of up to 14400 bits/s for use on the General Switched Telephone Network and on Leased Point-to-point 2-wire Telephone-type Circuit*,
http://www.itu.int./itudoc/itu-t/iec/v/index.html

8.20 ITU-T Recommendation V.34 (1994) *A Modem Operating at Data Signalling Rates of up to 28800 bits/s for use on the General Switched Telephone Network and on Leased Point-to-point 2-wire Telephone-type Circuit*,
http://www.itu.int./itudoc/itu-t/iec/v/index.html

8.21 Czajkowski, I.K. (1999) High-speed copper access: a tutorial overview. *Electronics and Communication Engineering Journal*, **11**(3): 125–48.

Chapter 9

Modulation and coding on multipath channels

An inherent characteristic of a radio system is that it is difficult to restrict the radio signal to a single route. Often, significant signals are received by reflection and scattering from buildings, etc.: there are *multiple paths* from transmitter to receiver. Indeed in many systems, and especially in personal and mobile radio systems, it is rare for there to exist one strong line-of-sight path between transmitter and receiver. Usually the signals on these paths are subject to different delays, phase shifts and Doppler shifts, and arrive at the receiver in random phase relation to one another. The interference between these signals gives rise to a number of deleterious effects which are the most serious problems of the mobile and many other radio channels, and which are collectively known as *multipath*. The most important of these problems are *fading* and *dispersion*.

This chapter describes the effects of the multipath channel on digital radio systems, including coded modulation systems, and introduces a number of countermeasures against these effects. First we describe the effects and obtain mathematical models for the channel.

9.1 Multipath and its effects

Figure 9.1 illustrates the origin of multipath in a variety of radio systems, showing the propagation mechanism which results in multiple paths. Table 9.1 summarizes an even wider range of systems, underlining the ubiquity of the effect, even in non-free-space systems, such as cable. In all these systems fading and dispersion may potentially occur [9.1].

Fading is due to the interference of multiple signals with random relative phase. Constructive and destructive interference between them cause random

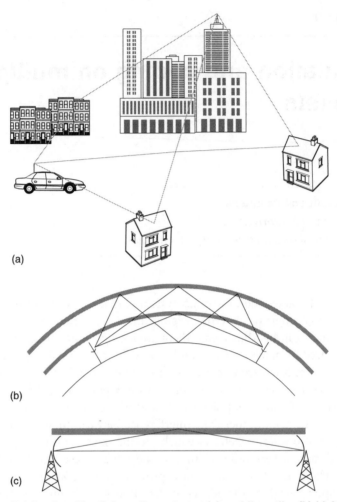

(a)

(b)

(c)

Figure 9.1   Origin of multipath in radio systems: (a) mobile radio, (b) high frequency ionospheric propagation, (c) microwave line-of-sight links

	System	Multipath mechanism
1	HF radio	Reflection from multiple ionospheric layers
2	Mobile and personal radio	Reflection and scattering from buildings, terrain, etc.
3	Microwave point-to-point links	Atmospheric refraction and reflection
4	Satellite–mobile systems	Ground and building reflection
5	Radio LAN/indoor radio	Reflection from walls and building structure
6	Diffuse infra-red	Reflection from walls
7	Multimode optical fibre	Multimode propagation
8	Telephone/cable network	Reflections from terminations

Table 9.1   Multipath mechanisms

variations in the amplitude of the received signal. This will increase the error rate in digital systems, since errors will occur when the signal-to-noise ratio drops below a certain threshold. Dispersion is due to differences in the delay of the various paths, which disperses transmitted pulses in time. If the delay differences are comparable with the symbol period, delayed signals from one symbol may interfere with the next signal, giving rise to *inter-symbol interference* (i.s.i.).

If the transmitter or receiver is in motion, as for example in a mobile radio system, then the relative phase shifts of the different paths will change with time, potentially quite rapidly. Similar effects, though generally less rapid, may occur in fixed systems due to the movement of the scatterers. In effect the different components of the signal are subject to different Doppler frequency shifts, because of the differences in their angle of arrival [9.2]. Thus overall the signal is subject to a Doppler spread, so that a single trans-mitted signal is received as a band of frequencies. This makes carrier recovery difficult in coherent systems, and may also give rise to errors in non-coherent demodulators.

9.1.1 Multipath channel models

It is helpful to create mathematical models of the multipath channel, for three main purposes. The first is to aid in the understanding of the channel, and its effects on communication signals. The second allows us to analyze these effects, and derive some results mathematically. For the third, the models may form the basis for computer simulation of the channel, which can be used in situa-tions that are too complex to analyze mathematically.

There is a hierarchy of available models, starting from the most detailed and general, and descending to the most specific and simplest [9.3]. The relationship between them is shown in Table 9.2.

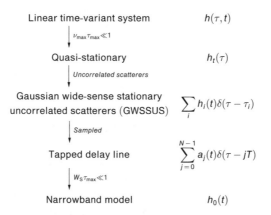

Table 9.2 Mathematical models of the multipath channel

The most general, models the channel as a *linear time-variant system*. This is described by its *time-variant impulse response*, $h(\tau, t)$ [9.4]. This gives the response of the channel at time t to an impulse at time $t - \tau$. It therefore gives the channel impulse response and shows how it varies with time. $h(\tau, t)$ is also related to three other functions, which give the same information in a different form. These are illustrated in Table 9.3, in which **F** denotes Fourier transformation with respect to the subscripted variable. The most interesting of these functions are $H(f, t)$, the *time-variant frequency response*, and $S(\tau, \nu)$, the *scattering function*. Since ν can be interpreted as a Doppler shift, the latter function gives the Doppler spectrum of the received signal as a function of the delay.

$$
\begin{array}{ccc}
h(\tau, t) & \xrightarrow{\textbf{F}_\tau} & H(f, t) \\
\textbf{F}_t \downarrow & & \textbf{F}_t \downarrow \\
S(\tau, \nu) & \xrightarrow{\textbf{F}_\tau} & B(f, \nu)
\end{array}
$$

Table 9.3   Relationship of functions describing channel

If the time-variation of the channel is slow, we may treat it as *quasi-stationary*, or *piecewise stationary*: in other words, as a linear system whose parameters vary with time, but which are constant for periods of a few transmitted symbols. We can strengthen this condition because if the maximum Doppler shift $\nu_{\max}$ is much less than one upon the maximum delay in the channel, $\tau_{\max}$, then the channel is said to be *separable*, so that the delay parameter τ and the time t can be treated separately. If we further assume that the signals on the different paths are uncorrelated and have Gaussian distributions, we have the well-known Gaussian wide-sense stationary uncorrelated scatterers (GWSSUS) model [9.5]. Here the impulse response may be treated as the sum of a series of impulses with delays τ_i, representing the different paths, with complex amplitudes (incorporating also the phase) h_i which vary with time, giving the form shown in Equation (9.1). This is illustrated in Fig. 9.2.

$$h(\tau) = \sum_{i=0}^{n-1} h_i(t)\delta(\tau - \tau_i) \tag{9.1}$$

where n is the number of multipath components. The squared amplitude of this impulse response is known as the *power-delay profile* of the channel. It may be given as a series of discrete delays and amplitudes, as in Fig. 9.2, or as a continuous function. The latter representation allows for the fact that, in practice, there are usually a very large number of paths, and it is difficult to separate them. Various models have been used for the power-delay profile in particular environments. The best-known for mobile radio channels are the COST 207

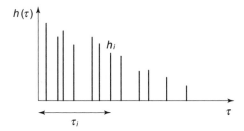

Figure 9.2   Impulse response for GWSSUS model

profiles used in the definition of GSM [9.6] (Section 9.1.2). More arbitrary shapes, such as exponential, Gaussian or two-ray have also been used. For indoor channels, statistical models have been developed in which the arrival of rays is treated as a Poisson process. These are reviewed in more detail in the next section.

The most important parameter of the power-delay profile response is the *delay spread* Δ, which is the standard deviation of the delay:

$$\Delta = \sqrt{\frac{\int_0^\infty (\tau - D)^2 |h(\tau, t)|^2 \, d\tau}{\int_0^\infty |h(\tau, t)|^2 \, d\tau}} = \sqrt{\frac{\sum_i (\tau_i - D)^2 |h_i|^2}{\sum_i |h_i|^2}} \qquad (9.2)$$

where D is the mean delay. The inverse of this is called the *coherence bandwidth*, because it gives the frequency range over which the propagation varies by about 3 dB: i.e. over which the frequency response of the channel remains nearly flat.

Another important parameter is the total range of multipath delays, $D_{max} = \tau_{n-1} - \tau_0$. In practice, however, it is difficult to define the maximum multipath delay, and therefore we use the length D_{90} of a delay window which includes (say) 90% of the multipath power, defined as:

$$D_{90} = \tau_{n_{90}} \quad \text{s.t.} \quad \sum_{i=0}^{n_{90}} |h_i|^2 = 0.9 \sum_{i=0}^{n} |h_i|^2 \qquad (9.3)$$

For practical purposes we are not interested in the response of the channel outside the bandwidth of the signal we intend to transmit over it. We can thus sample the channel at the symbol rate, leading to the *tapped delay-line model* [9.5]. Here the delayed signals on the different paths are lumped into delays of multiples of the symbol period. This can be represented by a tapped delay line (Fig. 9.3) with delays of one symbol period. Each tap is weighted by a (complex) coefficient a_j, $j = 1 \cdots n - 1$, and multiplied by a *fading envelope*, which implements the time-variable element of the channel.

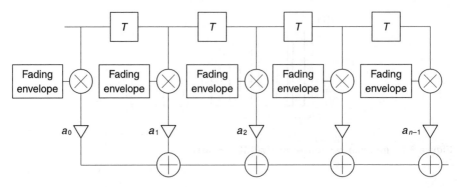

Figure 9.3 Tapped delay-line model

For the GWSSUS channel, this is a complex Gaussian process. For a mobile system its spectrum is represented by the Doppler spectrum at the given delay: i.e. by the scattering function $S(\tau, \nu)$. Various models have been used for this, but the bandwidth is of the order of the maximum expected Doppler shift. For stationary terminals, as is usually the case in wireless local access networks (WLAN) and fixed wireless access systems, the only Doppler effects are due to the motion of other objects in the environment, including people. These are generally very slow compared with the data rate, and for many practical purposes the channel can be regarded as stationary.

The Doppler spectrum is related to another important parameter of the channel. The *coherence time* $\nu_{\max}$ can be regarded as the dual of the coherence bandwidth, and measures the time over which the channel fading remains approximately constant. It can be obtained from the inverse Fourier transform of the Doppler spectrum, and is approximately the inverse of the Doppler bandwidth. As we will see in Example 9.3, it is important when determining the performance of coded systems on a fading channel.

The coefficients a_j are derived from the GWSSUS coefficients according [9.7] to:

$$a_j = \sqrt{\sum_{i=0}^{\infty} g^2(jT - \tau_i)\overline{|h_i|^2}} \qquad (9.4)$$

where $g(t)$ is the shape of the signalling pulse at the receiver, after the receiver matched filter. Note that if $g(t)$ lasts for more than one symbol period (which is usually the case), there may be non-zero taps for $j < 0$. If the component amplitudes are subject to Rayleigh fading (Section 9.1.3), then so is the tap amplitude, and (9.4) gives the r.m.s. amplitude. The power-delay profile can also be given in continuous form, in which case the summation becomes an integral. This model, as well as forming the basis for analysis, is readily implemented as a computer simulation of the channel.

The final simplification of this model can be made when the symbol period T is much greater than the channel delay spread, or equivalently when the signal bandwidth is much less than the coherence bandwidth. Under these conditions dispersion is negligible, and only one tap is required in the model, and hence the tapped delay-line reduces to the first branch only. This may be called the *narrowband model*. Note that for quite a wide range of channels (those with delay spreads comparable with the symbol period) a two-tap model is appropriate.

These models highlight the differences between narrowband and wideband signals in terms of how they are affected by a multipath channel. 'Narrowband' here means that the bandwidth is much less than the coherence bandwidth of the channel; 'wideband' means that it is comparable with or greater than the coherence bandwidth. Narrowband signals are not subject to *dispersion*, but only to *fading*; wideband channels are subject to both dispersion and fading. Equivalently, narrowband channels have a frequency response that is flat across the signal bandwidth; wideband channels do not: they are described as *frequency-selective*. This may be an advantage for very wideband channels, where the delay-line model has a large number of taps, since it implies that not all the spectrum is likely to fade simultaneously. Some types of equalizer for wideband systems, such as the RAKE receiver in code division multiple access (CDMA) systems, can utilize this feature to mitigate the effects of fading. These issues are dealt with below for the two types of channel.

9.1.2 Power-delay profiles

As mentioned above, the behaviour of a wideband multipath channel is characterized by its power-delay profile. To provide a basis for evaluation and comparison of systems, various mathematical models have been proposed for the power-delay profiles of multipath channels for different environments.

For the outdoor mobile radio channel at 900 MHz (as used for GSM) the best-known models are the COST 207 models. These were developed under the European collaborative research programme COST 207 ('Digital land–mobile radio communications') [9.6] for use in evaluating the GSM proposals. The profiles are in fact given as continuous functions, rather than discrete paths. They consist of one or two 'clusters' of paths, within which the amplitudes decay exponentially with excess delay. The general form is illustrated in Fig. 9.4. Mathematically it may be expressed as follows, the values of the parameters being given in Table 9.4:

$$|h(\tau)|^2 = \begin{cases} \exp(-a\tau), & 0 \leq \tau < t_0 \\ \alpha \exp[-b(\tau - t_1)], & t_1 \leq \tau < t_2 \\ 0, & \text{elsewhere} \end{cases} \qquad (9.5)$$

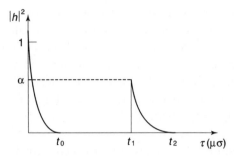

Figure 9.4   COST 207 power-delay profiles

For indoor propagation a number of statistical models have been proposed. The best-known, at least for UHF frequencies, are those by Rappaport *et al.* [9.8] and by Saleh and Valenzuela [9.9]. These describe statistical models derived from measurements made, respectively, in open-plan factories and in office buildings. The former is assumed also to apply to open-plan offices.

Rappaport's model is somewhat *ad hoc*, and thus more difficult to construct a general model from. However, its main features (for the present purpose) are that the probability of receiving a multipath component with given delay decreases exponentially with the delay, and that the amplitudes of components are log-normally distributed. A distinction is made between obstructed and line-of-sight paths: in the former, the maximum probability occurs for a delay of 75 ns.

Saleh and Valenzuela [9.9], similarly, model arrival of multipaths as a random process, with Poisson statistics, but in their model the amplitudes have a Rayleigh distribution (although it is noted that the log-normal distribution would also fit the data quite well). They note from their measurements that multipath components tend to arrive in 'clusters', which they surmise are due to the large-scale structure of the building, while the components within the clusters are due to reflections from features in the immediate vicinity of the transmitter and receiver. Both the clusters themselves and the components within the clusters form a Poisson random process, which means that each arrives at random with the inter-arrival time having an exponential distribution. The mean inter-arrival time for the clusters is much larger than that of the

Environment	a $(\mu s)^{-1}$	t_0 (μs)	α	t_1 (μs)	b $(\mu s)^{-1}$	t_2 (μs)
Rural (non-hilly) area (RA)	0.7	9.2	0			
Typical (non-hilly) urban area (TU)	1.0	7.0	0			
Bad case for (hilly) urban area (BU)	1.0	5.0	0.5	5.0	1.0	10.0
Typical hilly terrain (HT)	3.5	2.0	0.1	15.0	1.0	20.0

Table 9.4   Parameters for COST 207 power-delay profiles

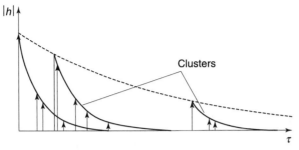

Figure 9.5   Power-delay profile in Saleh and Valenzuela model

components within the clusters. Likewise, the mean amplitude of both clusters and components decays exponentially with delay. The model is illustrated in Fig. 9.5.

Mathematically:

$$|h(\tau)|^2 = \sum_{l=0}^{\infty} \sum_{k=0}^{\infty} |\beta_{kl}|^2 \delta(\tau - T_l - t_{kl}) \tag{9.6}$$

where T_l is the delay of the lth cluster and t_{kl} that of the kth component within the cluster, relative to the start of the cluster. The mean square amplitude of the components:

$$\overline{|\beta_{kl}|^2} = \exp\left(-\frac{T_l}{\Gamma}\right) \exp\left(-\frac{t_{kl}}{\gamma}\right) \tag{9.7}$$

and the distributions of the inter-arrival time of clusters and components are:

$$\left.\begin{array}{l} p(T_l - T_{l-1}) = \Lambda \exp[-\Lambda(T_l - T_{l-1})] \\ p(t_{kl} - t_{k-1,l}) = \lambda \exp[-\lambda(t_{kl} - t_{k-1,l})] \end{array}\right\} \tag{9.8}$$

As mentioned, the distribution of the component amplitudes, $|\beta_{kl}|$, is assumed to be Rayleigh (see below). Figure 9.6 shows a typical power-delay profile

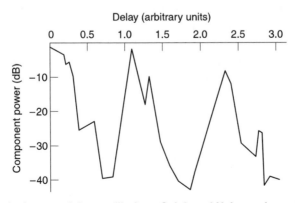

Figure 9.6   Typical power-delay profile from Saleh and Valenzuela model

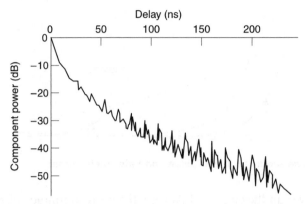

Figure 9.7 Power-delay profile for rectangular room obtained by two-dimensional ray tracing

taking all these random effects into account: three clusters can clearly be seen.

Another approach, for both indoor and outdoor propagation (particularly in urban areas) is to use a deterministic *ray-tracing* model. Here the paths of multipath components reflected or scattered from known obstacles are determined by tracing each individual ray, taking into account diffraction and other effects. This approach is clearly extremely computationally intensive, and relies on very accurate knowledge of the environment. Figure 9.7 shows an example for an indoor scenario, modelling reflection from walls only in two dimensions.

Finally, there are a number of more arbitrary models that are frequently used. The first is the two-ray model:

$$|h(\tau)|^2 = \delta(\tau) + \alpha\delta(\tau - T) \tag{9.9}$$

In this model there are two degrees-of-freedom: either the two rays are made equal in amplitude, and the delay T of the second is varied, or the delay is kept constant and the power α of the second ray is varied. If T is set to the symbol period, the second of these has the advantage of being a good model of the sampled channel for relatively small delay spreads, as noted above. The equal-ray version does not correspond accurately to any practical channel, but is used for simplicity of analysis. The delay spread in either case is given by:

$$\Delta = \frac{T\sqrt{\alpha}}{1 + \alpha} \tag{9.10}$$

The second is the continuous exponential model:

$$|h(\tau)|^2 = \exp\left(-\frac{\tau}{\Gamma}\right), \quad 0 \leq \tau < \infty \tag{9.11}$$

It will be noted that many of the more detailed models described above have an exponential trend to them, and indeed this agrees with many measurements. The continuous function provides quite a good approximation to a profile with many components, and hence the exponential model is likely to be quite a good approximation for the profile of an unknown radio channel. The delay spread is equal to the time constant Γ.

A third model has been proposed: the Gaussian model, where the power-delay profile is given a Gaussian shape, but this is not a good model of radio systems in general. It has been used to show the insensitivity of many systems to the actual shape of the profile.

9.1.3 Narrowband channels: fading

We consider now the effects of multipath on narrowband signalling, namely fading. Fading arises because the signals on the multiple paths interfere constructively and destructively at random. Since there are normally a very large number of paths, which are normally assumed to be independent, according to the central limit theorem these signals add to give a random process with a complex Gaussian distribution. The amplitude r of the received signal therefore has the Rayleigh distribution (which is the distribution of the amplitude of a complex Gaussian process) [9.10, p. 45]:

$$p(r) = \frac{r}{\sigma^2} \exp\left(-\frac{r^2}{2\sigma^2}\right) \qquad (9.12)$$

where σ^2 is the total power in the multipath signal. If, however, there is a significant line-of-sight signal, not subject to multipath, the signal amplitude will have the Rician distribution [9.10, p. 47]:

$$p(r) = \frac{r}{\sigma^2} \exp\left(-\frac{r^2 + s^2}{2\sigma^2}\right) I_0\left(\frac{rs}{\sigma^2}\right) \qquad (9.13)$$

where s^2 is the power of the line-of-sight component, and I_0 denotes the zeroth-order modified Bessel function of the first kind. The Rician fading situation is often characterized by the ratio s^2/σ^2, known as the *carrier-to-multipath ratio*, or C–M.

The spectrum of this process depends on the variation of the channel with time. Equivalently, we can regard it as the Doppler spectrum of the received signal. Since, in general, it comes from a different direction relative to the motion of the mobile, each path will be subject to a different Doppler shift (Fig. 9.8). Hence the received signal suffers a Doppler 'spread', rather than a single Doppler shift [9.2]. The Doppler spectrum can be determined by evaluating the energy from each direction, on the assumption that the received power comes from all directions equally, and calculating the Doppler shift for each direction.

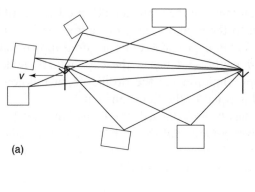

(a)

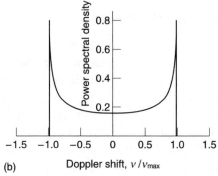

(b)   Doppler shift, v / v_{max}

Figure 9.8   Doppler shift of components: (a) model; (b) spectrum

The resulting spectrum (Fig. 9.8(b)) is given by:

$$S(\nu) = \frac{1}{2\pi\nu_{\text{max}}\sqrt{1 - (\nu/\nu_{\text{max}})^2}}, \quad -\nu_{\text{max}} < \nu < \nu_{\text{max}}, \quad 0 \text{ elsewhere} \quad (9.14)$$

where $\nu_{\text{max}} = v/\lambda$ is the maximum Doppler shift due to the mobile velocity. Note that this applies also to the individual taps of the tapped delay-line model, except that the fading spectrum may vary with delay, according to the scattering function $S(\tau, \nu)$. Other models are also used: for example the COST 207 [9.6] model assumes a Gaussian fading spectrum for some delay, and a first-order Butterworth response has also been used.

The effect of fading is first to increase the bit error ratio (BER), because during fades the signal drops below the threshold signal-to-noise ratio required to maintain a low BER. It can be shown that for coherent PSK on a Rayleigh channel the BER P_e is given [9.10, pp. 772–5] by:

$$P_e = \frac{1}{2}\left(1 - \sqrt{\frac{E_b/N_0}{1 + E_b/N_0}}\right) \quad (9.15)$$

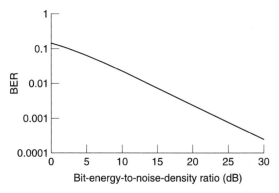

Figure 9.9 Average BER *versus* bit-energy-to-noise-density ratio for Rayleigh fading channel

This is plotted against bit-energy-to-noise-density ratio in Fig. 9.9. Note, however, that errors on a fading channel tend to occur in bursts, lasting for the duration of a link fade.

9.1.4 Wideband channels: dispersion

Wideband channels were defined above as channels in which the signal bandwidth is comparable with or greater than the coherence bandwidth of the channel. Thus the channel is frequency-selective. Equivalently, it means that the symbol period is comparable with or less than the delay spread, Δ. Hence the signal is subject to dispersion, as well as to fading. The appropriate model is the tapped delay line of Fig. 9.3. The dispersion gives rise to *intersymbol interference* (i.s.i.) (Fig. 9.10). The transmitted rectangular pulses are distorted by the channel, and received with a long 'tail' due to multipath dispersion. This interferes with the reception of subsequent symbols, and may give rise to errors (termed *irreducible errors* because they cannot be eliminated by increasing the signal power).

If successive data symbols are uncorrelated, and the fading of the taps of the model is also independent, then it is possible to model the i.s.i. as an additional source of noise, uncorrelated with the received data. Further, if all taps other than the first are undergoing Rayleigh fading (i.e. the fading is a complex Gaussian process), then this noise is Gaussian. The power is given [9.7] by:

$$\overline{N_{\text{i.s.i.}}} = \sum_{k=1}^{\infty} \overline{|d_k|^2} \sum_{i=0}^{\infty} g^2(kT - \tau_i) \overline{|h_i|^2}$$

$$= \overline{|d|^2} \sum_{i=0}^{\infty} \overline{|h_i|^2} \sum_{k=1}^{\infty} g^2(kT - \tau_i) \qquad (9.16)$$

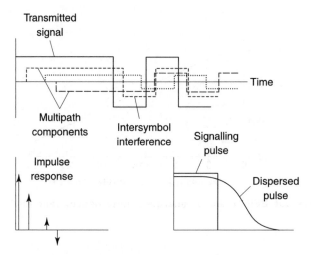

Figure 9.10   Intersymbol interference due to dispersion

Similarly, the signal power:

$$\overline{S} = \overline{|d|^2} \sum_{i=0}^{\infty} g^2(-\tau_i) \overline{|h_i|^2} \tag{9.17}$$

where $\overline{|d|^2}$ is the mean symbol power; $g(t)$ is the cascaded impulse response of the receive and transmit filters; T is the symbol period; and τ_i and $\overline{|h_i|^2}$ are the delay and mean power, respectively, of the ith multipath component. Note, comparing this with Equation (9.2), that the signal power is proportional to the squared amplitude of the first tap of the tapped delay-line model, while the i.s.i. power is proportional to the sum of the squares of the remaining taps.

Usually, the function $\sum_{k=1}^{\infty} g^2(kT - \tau)$ follows a square law with τ, at least for small values. (This applies for most practical receive and transmit filters.) This means that in most systems the i.s.i. power is proportional to the square of the ratio of the delay spread to the symbol period, and is independent of the shape of the power-delay profile. Hence in most mobile radio systems, where the signal is subject to Rayleigh fading (and hence the BER follows Equation (9.15)), the irreducible BER is also proportional to this ratio (e.g. Fig. 9.11). Simulation shows that this is indeed valid over a wide range of symbol rates regardless of the actual shape of the power-delay profile.

Note, however, that this is a mean BER: in the short-term the BER may vary widely around this mean, depending on the fading both of the channel taps and of the signal. Hence if the channel is fading only slowly, as in most WLAN or fixed access systems, then it may be a very long-term mean, in which case other means, such as adaptive modulation or frequency-hopping, might be required to overcome it.

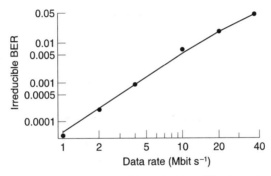

Figure 9.11   Irreducible BER for QPSK with no Nyquist filtering, channel delay spread 20 ns

9.2   Multipath countermeasures

We now discuss the most commonly used countermeasures to these two main effects of multipath: fading and dispersion. Their effect in a system using FEC coding, which also acts as another form of countermeasure, will be discussed in the Section 9.3.

9.2.1   Fade countermeasures: diversity

Fading on a radio channel is usually countered by means of *diversity* [9.11]. The principle of diversity is to provide two or more channels, or *branches*, for the same information signal, subject to statistically independent fading. Then if one path fades we may expect that the other(s) do not, and hence a satisfactory error ratio is maintained. Diversity techniques may be classified according to the means by which the additional channels are provided, and according to how the multiple signals are combined.

The three main diversity techniques are called *space*, *frequency* and *time* diversity (Fig. 9.12). The most commonly used is space diversity. Here independently fading signals are provided by receiving the same signal at two or more different antennas, separated in space. Because Rayleigh fading is due to small phase differences in the multipath signals, it can be expected to vary rapidly in space, and be completely uncorrelated within the space of a few wavelengths at the transmission frequency. Implementation feasibility is very system-dependent: for example at the usual frequencies for mobile radio transmission, these separations are feasible at base stations, and sometimes for vehicle-mounted mobiles, but not usually for hand-portables.

If space diversity is not feasible, frequency or time diversity may be used. Here the same signal is transmitted on multiple channels, either at a different frequency, or it is repeated at a different time. The frequency or time separation

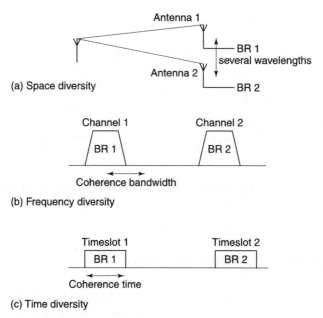

(a) Space diversity

(b) Frequency diversity

(c) Time diversity

Figure 9.12   Diversity techniques (BR, branch)

must again be sufficient that the fading is uncorrelated: several times the coherence bandwidth $1/\Delta$, or the coherence time (Section 9.1.1). Frequency and time diversity have the obvious disadvantage that additional spectrum-space is used, which may reduce the overall capacity.

There are also three main combining methods (Fig. 9.13) [9.11], each of which may be used with any of the diversity techniques. The optimum technique (in that it provides a maximum-likelihood detection method) is *maximum ratio combining* (MRC). Here the diversity branches are weighted proportionately to the signal amplitudes and then added. The weights minimize the noise that is added from faded branches. It may be shown that the symbol error probability for L-branch MRC diversity is given [9.10, p. 781] by:

$$P_e = \left(\frac{1-\mu}{2}\right)^L \sum_{k=0}^{L-1} {}^{L-1+k}C_k \left(\frac{1+\mu}{2}\right)^k \approx {}^{2L-1}C_L \left(\frac{1}{4E_c/N_0}\right)^L \qquad (9.18)$$

where

$$\mu = \sqrt{(E_c/N_0)/(1+E_c/N_0)}$$

where E_c denotes the received signal energy per bit per diversity branch, and hence total bit energy $E_b = LE_c$. Figure 9.14 compares the performance of diversity reception, in terms of total bit energy, with no diversity (curve a). Curves b and c show the BER performance of MRC with 2 and 4 branches, respectively. This confirms the implication of the approximation in (9.18)

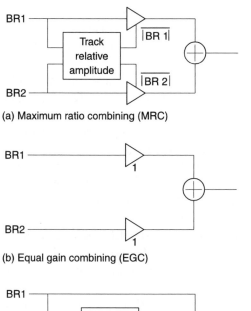

(a) Maximum ratio combining (MRC)

BR1

BR2

(b) Equal gain combining (EGC)

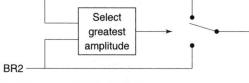

(c) Selection combining (SC)

Figure 9.13   Combining techniques

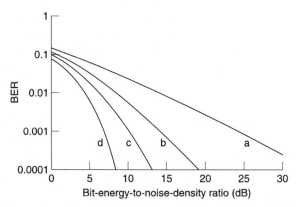

Figure 9.14   BER *versus* **bit-energy-to-noise-density ratio for (a) Rayleigh fading channel, (b) Rayleigh channel with two-branch diversity, (c) with four-branch diversity, compared with (d) AWGN channel**

that diversity results in plots that (on the log–log scale) are steeper by a factor equal to the number of diversity branches. This results in very significant gains in bit-energy-to-noise-density requirements, making diversity highly advantageous if it can be achieved.

Clearly, MRC requires that the received signal amplitudes are tracked and the weights changed in step. If this is not feasible, *equal gain combining* (EGC) may be used. Here the branches are equally weighted. Both MRC and EGC require that the signals may be added in phase, or coherently. The third combining technique, *selection* (or *switched*) *combining* (SC), switches between branches according to which has the strongest signal. This does not require coherence between the branches. Both EGC and SC incur a penalty of a dB or so compared with MRC, but this still gives a very large advantage over systems without diversity.

As we shall see, the performance of FEC coding in fading channels can also be understood in terms of diversity. If a code has a Hamming distance d_{min} (i.e. any two codewords differ in at least d_{min} symbols), then any decision in the decoder is taken on the basis of at least this number of symbols. If the symbols fade independently, then this is equivalent to time diversity with d_{min} branches, but with a much smaller penalty in terms of spectrum usage.

9.2.2 Fade countermeasures: power control, 'frequency jumping' and adaptive modulation

An alternative to diversity reception (of one kind or another) when fading is relatively slow is to adapt the transmission to the channel conditions. Here we consider three such techniques. All three assume that a reverse communication channel is available to signal the channel conditions back to the transmitter. This occurs naturally in a duplex communication system; it is clearly not feasible in broadcast systems. It also assumes that the channel changes slowly enough that the delay inherent in such a feedback path may be tolerated.

The most obvious method for this is *power control*: we increase the transmit power when the channel fades. Some of the impetus behind such a development comes from spread spectrum CDMA systems, in which very accurate power control is essential to overcome the 'near–far' problem, by ensuring that all signals are received at the base station at the same power level. It was discovered that this would have the additional advantage of overcoming slow Rayleigh fading [9.12, 9.13]. It has been shown that schemes of this sort will cope with fade rates (maximum Doppler shifts) of the order of a few Hz, which is adequate for most fixed systems, or even for movement of pedestrians, but not for vehicle-borne mobiles.

Figure 9.15 shows a simulation of a scheme of this sort. A fading channel with a maximum Doppler of around 1.25 Hz is simulated, and power control which changes the transmit amplitude up or down by 0.5 dB on the basis of

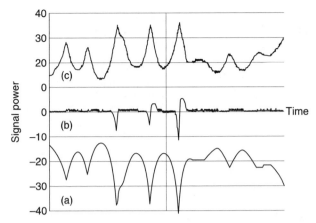

Figure 9.15 **Simulation of power control as a fade countermeasure: (a) channel propagation, (b) received power, (c) transmitted power. Fade rate, 1.25 Hz; refresh rate, 250 Hz; power control step, ±0.5 dB**

a feedback bit every 4 ms is applied. (These figures are typical for cellular radio with stationary or very slow-moving terminals.) The results show that perfect power control (constant receive power) is achieved except during a few very deep fades, when the transmit power cannot increase rapidly enough. Clearly, however, the fade rate could not be much greater than this. Further, very large transmit powers may occur, up to 20-dB more than the mean level, and this may degrade the overall capacity of the cellular system by causing excess interference to neighbouring cells [9.13].

Other parameters of the radio link could also be adapted to the fading conditions. For example, instead of increasing transmit power, the code rate could be reduced during deep fades, to allow the system to operate at lower signal-to-noise ratio. This would avoid increasing interference. If fading is frequency selective, then not all the frequency channels available to the transmitter in an FDMA system may be equally affected, and it may be possible to 'jump' from a faded to a less-faded channel [9.13]. The effect of these schemes on the average power required to maintain a link is shown in Fig. 9.16. (*Frequency hopping* is also shown here: this will be considered in Section 9.3.3.) The results show that an improvement in the required power margin of up to 15 dB is possible by using a combination of frequency jumping and adaptive coding. It is also possible to trade power for bandwidth efficiency: the number of users can be increased at the cost of an increased power margin.

9.2.3 Dispersion countermeasures: linear equalization

Dispersion can be countered by correcting the frequency response of the channel. As noted above, a dispersive channel has a non-flat frequency

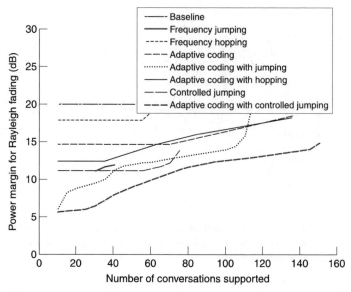

Figure 9.16   Frequency jumping and adaptive modulation as fade countermeasures

response over the signal bandwidth. This may be corrected by adding a filter of frequency response $G(\omega)$ in the receiver, which exactly cancels the variations in frequency response $H(\omega)$ in the channel, resulting in a flat response overall. This is known as *linear equalization* (Fig. 9.17) [9.10, pp. 601–21; 9.14]. Normally the equalizer is implemented as an adaptive FIR filter, with some suitable adaptation algorithm used to select the filter weights.

The required frequency response for the equalizer is then:

$$G(\omega) = \frac{1}{H(\omega)} \tag{9.19}$$

In z-transform terms:

$$H(z) = \sum_i h_i z^{-i} = \prod_j (z - q_j)$$

$$G(z) = \frac{1}{H(z)} = \frac{1}{\prod_j (z - q_j)} \tag{9.20}$$

where h_i is the tap(s) of the tapped delay-line channel model (Fig. 9.3), and q_j is the zero(s) of the z-transform. The equation shows that the ideal equalizer positions poles at each of the zeros of the channel response in the z-domain.

Unfortunately, the performance of the linear equalizer is very poor on many radio channels, those which exhibit so-called *amplitude distortion*. The frequency response of such channels tends to exhibit deep nulls, which gives rise to compensatory peaks in the equalizer response. These amplify the

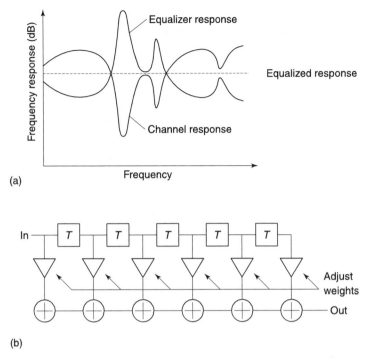

(a)

(b)

Figure 9.17   Linear equalizer: (a) principle, (b) structure

noise at these frequencies, giving rise to a *noise multiplication* effect. This makes linear equalizers unsuitable for channels such as mobile radio, except where a strong line-of-sight component exists and can be guaranteed.

Example 9.1(a)

Figure 9.18 shows the magnitude of the impulse response of a channel containing *precursors* (multipath components arriving in advance of the

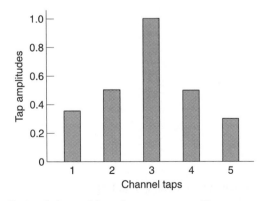

Figure 9.18   Magnitude of channel impulse response with precursors

strongest component). Plot the frequency response and pole-zero diagram for this channel, and comment on the performance of a linear equalizer.

Solution Figure 9.19 shows the frequency response of the channel (frequency with respect to carrier, normalized to symbol rate). This shows a minimum at $f = 0.31$, which will clearly give rise to substantial noise amplification if perfectly equalized. Note, however, that this does not take account of the phase response of the channel. Figure 9.20 shows the positions of the zeros for this channel, relative to the unit circle in the z-plane. The ideal equalizer would position poles on top of these zeros – some of which are outside the unit circle. This implies that the equalizer must be unstable, which may lead to infinite noise amplification and implementation difficulties. This problem arises in a high proportion of channels having precursors.

We return to this worked example in Example 9.1(b).

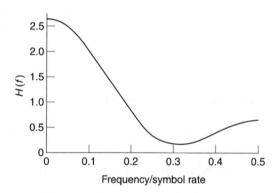

Figure 9.19   Frequency response of channel of Fig. 9.18

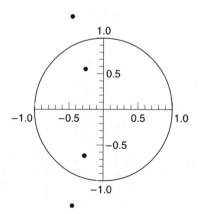

Figure 9.20   Zero positions for channel of Fig. 9.18

The criterion for 'ideal' equalizer design in Equations (9.19) and (9.20) is known as the *zero-forcing* (ZF) criterion [9.10, p. 603], and it guarantees to eliminate i.s.i., albeit at the cost of noise amplification, as we have seen. A more robust criterion is the *minimum mean-square error* (MMSE) criterion [9.10, p. 607], which aims to minimize the total error at the output of the equalizer, including the (amplified) noise and the i.s.i. In z-domain terms the optimum MMSE linear equalizer has:

$$G(z) = \frac{1}{H(z) + N_0} \tag{9.21}$$

where N_0 is the noise density on the channel. This overcomes many of the problems of noise amplification, but the overall performance remains poor on many channels, such as those with precursors. Note that as the noise tends to zero, the MMSE equalizer tends to the zero-forcing. In fact the signal-to-noise ratio must often be quite poor for the MMSE criterion to make much difference to the tap weights.

Example 9.1(b)

Comment on the performance of an MMSE equalizer for the channel of Example 9.1(a), with $N_0 = 1.5$.

Substituting in Equation (9.21), the MMSE equalizer for this channel has the transfer function:

$$G(z) = \frac{1}{1.85 + 0.5z^{-1} + z^{-2} + 0.5z^{-3} + 0.3z^{-4}}$$

Note that this corresponds to a rather poor signal-to-noise ratio. Figure 9.21(a) shows the frequency response of this equalizer, compared with that of the zero-forcing equalizer, while Fig. 9.21(b) shows its pole positions. We note that the

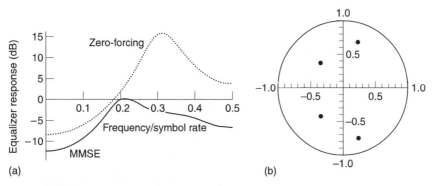

Figure 9.21 (a) Frequency response of MMSE equalizer of Example 9.1(b) compared with zero-forcing; (b) poles of MMSE equalizer

poles are now all within the unit circle, and hence the equalizer is stable. The frequency response also shows significantly less noise enhancement.

The equalizers described by Equations (9.20) and (9.21) are clearly IIR (recursive) digital filters. The attempt to approximate this by a finite-length FIR filter leads to further difficulties. This approximation can be obtained by a series expansion of the IIR z-transform. In this example the MMSE equalizer z-transform becomes:

$$G(z) = 0.5404 - 0.1461z^{-1} - 0.2527z^{-2} + 0.0012z^{-3} + 0.0881z^{-4} + 0.0675z^{-5}$$
$$- 0.0252z^{-6} - 0.0537z^{-7} - 0.0044z^{-8} + 0.0261z^{-9} + 0.0139z^{-10}$$
$$- 0.0080z^{-11} - 0.0117z^{-12} - 0.0005z^{-13} + 0.0064z^{-14} + \cdots$$

The FIR form would require an infinite number of taps for a perfect reconstruction. Simply to truncate the filter means that the truncated terms contribute to the intersymbol interference. An optimized truncated form can be found, but there will always be some remanent i.s.i. and, in practice, the FIR equalizer will need to be two to three times the length of the channel impulse response. Note that because it has poles outside the unit circle, the zero-forcing equalizer cannot be approximated in this way, since the series expansion does not converge.

9.2.4   Dispersion countermeasures: non-linear equalization

The structure of the linear equalizer can be viewed slightly differently, as shown in Fig. 9.22. Here we regard the FIR filter as containing an estimator of the i.s.i. This then allows the i.s.i. to be subtracted from the signal, regenerating an undistorted version of the original signal. We may also include a pre-filter, as shown, because in some cases it may ease the task of equalization. In this case the i.s.i. estimate includes the effect of the pre-filter. In the linear equalizer the i.s.i. subtraction is effectively incorporated into the filter structure, but other non-linear estimators are also possible.

For example, in the *decision-feedback equalizer* (DFE) (Fig. 9.23) [9.10, pp. 621–7; 9.15] we make use of symbol decisions already made to estimate

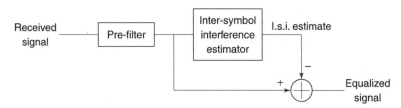

Figure 9.22   General equalizer structure

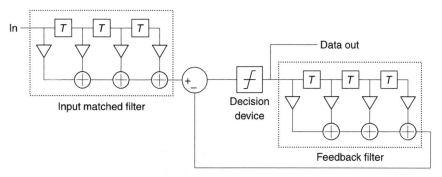

Figure 9.23   Decision feedback equalizer (DFE)

the i.s.i. An input matched FIR filter is used to condition the received signal, i.s.i. due to previous symbols is subtracted, and the current symbol decision is made. The i.s.i. due to this decision is then estimated using another FIR filter, and fed back. The optimum feed-forward coefficients c_j, $j = -K \cdots 0$, with c_0 the last coefficient, have been determined in order to minimize the mean squared error at the input to the decision device [9.10, pp. 622]. The coefficients may be obtained from the solution of:

$$\sum_{j=-K}^{0} \psi_{ij} c_j = h_{-i}, \quad \text{where } \psi_{ij} = \sum_{m=0}^{-i} h_m^* h_{m+i-j} + N_0 \delta_{ij}, \quad i, j = -K \cdots 0$$

$$(9.22)$$

where $h_0 \cdots h_{L-1}$ are again the taps of the channel model, N_0 is the noise density and δ_{ij} is the Kronecker delta: $\delta_{ij} = 1$ for $i = j$, $\delta_{ij} = 0$ otherwise. The effect of the feed-forward filter is to maximize signal energy in the main peak of its output while minimizing power in any precursors. The feedback filter can then perfectly cancel the i.s.i. due to post-cursors.

Example 9.2

Figure 9.24 shows the coefficients and filter response for the channel of Example 9.1, optimized using the MMSE criterion for three different noise levels, chosen to represent zero noise (a), for which the equalizer is the same as a zero-forcing equalizer, moderate noise (b), and extremely high noise (c). In each case we show the feed-forward and feedback taps, and the impulse response of the combination of feed-forward filter and channel.

At zero noise the feed-forward filter contains only one tap (i.e. its frequency response is flat). The decision device then operates on the signal from the first channel tap, treating all the rest as post-cursors, even though they are larger. The feedback filter response exactly mirrors these post-cursors, and so perfectly cancels all the i.s.i. For larger noise, taking the decision on the

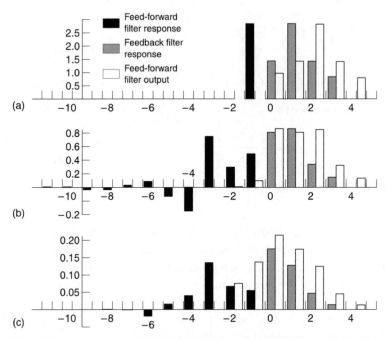

Figure 9.24   Filter responses for DFE for the channel of Fig. 9.18, optimized for

first channel tap is clearly sub-optimum, since the signal-to-noise ratio is small. Here, therefore, the feed-forward filter operates to boost the precursor so that now the decision is taken on the largest component of the combined response. Some small precursors to this largest response remain, which will cause i.s.i. since the feedback filter cannot cancel them, but this is small. Again, the feedback filter mirrors the post-cursors of the combined channel and feed-forward filter response, and therefore cancels them. For large noise (larger than would normally be encountered in practice), we note that the feed-forward filter response becomes close to the channel response: in fact it tends to a matched filter, matched to the channel. This maximizes the signal-to-noise ratio at its output, at the cost of leaving quite large precursors in the combined response and so leaving some i.s.i. that cannot be cancelled.

The DFE remains sub-optimum, since it suffers from a number of degrading effects. First, as we have seen, there will be some i.s.i. that cannot be cancelled due to precursors in the combined channel–feed-forward filter response. Second, the feed-forward filter may introduce some noise enhancement, although much less than the linear equalizer. Third, the equalizer may suffer from *error propagation*, since errors in the decision device will cause incorrect i.s.i. estimates to be fed back, which may give rise to further errors.

The optimum technique is Viterbi equalization, which is *maximum likelihood sequence estimation* (MLSE) performed by means of the Viterbi algorithm (see Section 7.3.1) [9.16]. The channel may be treated as a finite state machine, in which the different states represent the different combinations of input data. The Viterbi algorithm is a means of tracing all the possible data sequences, and selecting the one which is most likely to have been transmitted (hence the term MLSE).

The complexity of a Viterbi decoder is proportional to the number of channel states, which is exponentially related to the length of the multipath spread in symbol periods. It can be evaluated as M^{L-1}, where M is the modulation order and L is the number of taps in the channel model. This is related to the total range of multipath delays on the channel (which is usually significantly greater than the delay spread) and hence as the data rate increases, the complexity quickly becomes excessive. *Reduced-state sequence estimation* (RSSE) techniques have been developed to reduce the complexity of these techniques at the cost of a small degradation in performance (of a few dB) [9.17]. These consider only the most probable states, or group states together. The simplest version of this ignores the last few taps of the channel, resulting in increased i.s.i., which is treated as noise. Of course an RSSE with one state only reduces to a DFE.

Example 9.3

In developing the GSM standard, the committee of the European Telecommunication Standards Institute (ETSI) wished to ensure that the most effective equalizers could be used, since it was predicted that multipath dispersion would be one of the most serious problems for a digital standard using time division multiple access (TDMA). They had therefore to ensure that it would be feasible to implement a Viterbi equalizer on the worst-case channel. Comment on the limit this imposes on the maximum bit rate.

Solution The complexity of a Viterbi equalizer depends on the length of the channel impulse response, and therefore the worst case channel is the hilly terrain (HT) model (Table 9.4). We first find the 95% power-delay window D_{95} for this channel. Using the values from Table 9.4 we find that:

$$\int_0^\infty |h(\tau)|^2 = 0.385 \quad \text{and that} \quad \int_0^{16.6} |h(\tau)|^2/0.385 = 0.949$$

and hence $D_{95} = 16.6\,\mu\text{s}$. (We may adapt Equation (9.3) to give D_{95}.) Examining Equation (9.4) and remembering that the duration of the pulse $g(t)$ is at least twice the symbol period T (since it is the pulse shape after the receive matched filter, which will broaden the pulse), we find that the number of significant taps in the channel model, $L = D_{95}/T + 1$. Then the number of states in the Viterbi equalizer, $2^{L-1} = 2^{D_{95}/T} = 2^{16.6 \times r_b}$, where r_b

here is the channel bit rate in Mbit s^{-1}. Thus to limit the number of states to 16 required a maximum r_b of around 250 kbit s^{-1}. In the event, the raw bit rate of 270 kbit s^{-1} was chosen. This of course limited the number of channels that could be combined using TDMA on one carrier, and led to the choice of eight channels.

9.3 Coded systems on the multipath channel

In this section we consider the performance of coded systems, including coded modulation, on the multipath channel, in the presence of both fading and dispersion. We also describe multipath countermeasures that are applicable to coded systems in particular. We will deal separately with the effects of fading and dispersion, although in practice, of course, both may occur together.

9.3.1 Fading in coded systems

As mentioned above, the use of FEC coding on a fading channel is equivalent to an implicit time diversity. The receiver will choose between two possible codewords differing in d_H symbols (the Hamming distance of the two). The metric will be formed by combining the received signals for these d_H symbols. Hence, *provided the symbols fade independently*, this is equivalent to d_H-fold diversity combining [9.10, p. 809]. Usually, the overall error probability will be dominated by the pairwise error probability having the smallest diversity order, which will of course be the minimum Hamming distance of the code.

We may evaluate the pairwise error probability for a coded system in Rayleigh fading using Equation (9.18). This expression may then be substituted into Equations (5.37)–(5.39) in place of $Q(d/2\sigma)$. The expression becomes:

$$P_b \le \sum_j e_j \left(\frac{1-\mu}{2}\right)^{d_j} \sum_{k=0}^{d_j-1} {}^{d_j-1+k}C_k \left(\frac{1+\mu}{2}\right)^k \tag{9.23}$$

This assumes maximum ratio combining, which in the context of a coded system implies that symbols are combined according to the fading they experience. This requires that each received symbol is weighted by the fading amplitude before the metric is calculated, which can be implemented by simply multiplying it by the appropriate value before entering the decoder. This does, however, require an estimate of the channel fading (so-called *channel-state information* or CSI) to be available at the receiver. If it is not, the symbols may all be weighted equally, equivalent to equal gain combining, giving a poorer performance by a few dB.

This implicit diversity gives a considerable advantage over direct time diversity in that it greatly reduces the redundancy of the transmitted signal. L-fold time diversity requires repetition of the data L times, reducing the spectral efficiency by this factor. The same diversity order may be obtained in a coded system with a code of much higher rate. Thus two-fold diversity could be achieved using a single parity check code of rate very close to unity, instead of an effective rate of one-half. Four-fold diversity could be provided by (say) a $(32, 26, 4)$ extended Hamming code of rate over 0.8, instead of one-quarter rate.

Example 9.4

Estimate the performance of a rate $2/3$ constraint length 7 punctured convolutional code on a Rayleigh fading channel.

Solution The estimate may be obtained using Equation (9.23) with the error-weighted distance spectrum from Table 7.4. The first five terms of the distance spectrum are used, as for the AWGN channel. In Fig. 9.25 the resulting estimate is compared with simulation results, showing quite close agreement for BER up to 0.1. Note that it is important to use the exact expression for BER, as in Equation (9.23), rather than the asymptotic approximation given alongside the exact expression in (9.18). The code has a minimum Hamming distance of 6. Notice that the use of this code returns performance to very close to that of the unfaded channel (also shown in Fig. 9.23), and provides very large coding gains compared with uncoded transmission on the fading channel (for example, 16.8 dB even for BER $= 10^{-3}$).

This result applies for coded BPSK in which all symbols in the codeword (or in a relatively short length of code sequence) fade independently. We have noted previously (Section 2.1.1) that QPSK with Gray code labelling can be

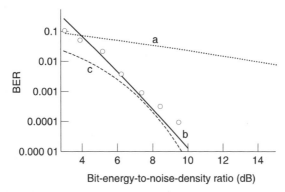

Figure 9.25 Performance of rate 2/3 coded BPSK estimate (b) and simulation (○) on a Rayleigh fading channel, compared with uncoded transmission on the same channel (a), and with uncoded transmission on an AWGN channel (c)

treated as two independent binary channels, and therefore binary codes can be applied to it. However, in the fading case, the two code symbols transmitted on the same QPSK symbol will not fade independently, and thus to achieve the performance described above they must be separated by interleaving prior to modulation (see Section 9.3.3).

9.3.2   Fading in coded modulation

We have noted that the implicit diversity order of coded systems is determined by the minimum *Hamming* distance of the code. However, in designing optimum coded modulation schemes we showed that performance was determined by minimum *Euclidean* distance. In coded BPSK and QPSK (subject to the proviso of the previous paragraph), there is no conflict between these requirements, since maximizing Hamming distance also maximizes Euclidean distance. However, this is not the case in higher-order coded modulation schemes, as we saw in Section 8.1. This means that new criteria must be applied in the design of coded modulation schemes for the Rayleigh fading channel.

It has been shown [9.17, 9.18] that, in fact, it is the Hamming distance that is most significant, and the Euclidean distance of relatively small importance. In order of importance, the code parameters are:

- The minimum Hamming distance: the minimum number of coded channel symbols in which two possible coded sequences differ.
- The *product distance*: the product of the Euclidean distances between symbols which differ on the two coded sequences.
- The error multiplicity, or the number of nearest neighbours.
- The minimum Euclidean distance.

These principles have been used to design coded modulation schemes specifically for the fading channel. For example, a constraint length 8 TCM 8-PSK scheme can be found [9.17] that has a minimum Hamming distance of 5, compared with 3 for the equivalent conventional Ungerböck scheme. The Ungerböck code suffers a degradation of some 8 dB on the Rayleigh fading channel (at BER $= 10^{-4}$); the optimized scheme performs about 2-dB better.

Other approaches have been proposed. For example, multilevel coded modulation, by applying a binary component code at each level, means that the minimum Hamming distance of the code is the smallest of the Hamming distances of the component codes [9.19]. To optimize the asymptotic performance on a fading channel, therefore, we may choose component codes with the same minimum Hamming distance. For example, for a 2-bit/symbol coded 8-PSK scheme (equivalent to the coded 8-PSK schemes mentioned

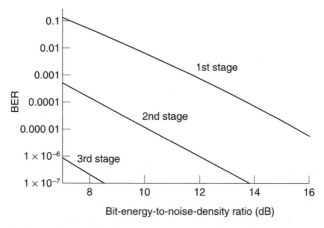

Figure 9.26 Estimated stage BERs for multilevel coded 8-PSK with rate 2/3 constraint length 7 codes on each level

above), we might use a rate 2/3 punctured convolutional code on each of the three levels. For constraint length 8, this allows a minimum Hamming distance of 8. The simulated BER performance with constraint length 5 is approximately the same as the optimized TCM scheme at a constraint length of 6.

However, Fig. 9.26 shows that with this scheme the stage BERs are very unequal. Hence, a significant improvement can be obtained by changing the minimum Hamming distances of the component codes so as to equalize them close to some target BER. Figure 9.27 shows the same BERs for a multi-level code optimized for BER $= 10^{-3}$ [9.20]. This improves on the equal distance coded scheme by some 2.5 dB at the target BER, although asymptotically it is much poorer.

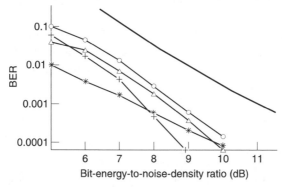

Figure 9.27 Simulated stage BERs (+, stage 1; ○, stage 2; *, stage 3) and total BER (△), compared with estimated total BER (continuous line) for code {3/8, 3/4, 7/8}, constraint length 7

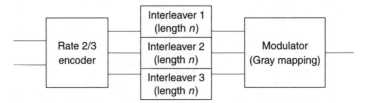

Figure 9.28   Interleaved coded modulation: separate interleavers

An alternative approach is to use a single convolutional code and apply interleaving at the bit level such that each bit of the code is transmitted on a separate (and independently fading) channel symbol. The original proposal was to use separate interleavers for the different levels of modulation, as shown in Fig. 9.28. Note that Gray coding is used in the modulator (rather than mapping by set partitioning), since we no longer make use of the differences in Euclidean distance in the constellation sub-sets. It is clear, however, that the structure of Fig. 9.28 may be reduced to that of 9.27 [9.21]: in effect we have returned to separate encoding and modulation, with an interleaver between. In the receiver, however, we must ensure that the demodulator calculates the correct metric values to the decoder, based on distances from the sub-sets according to Gray coding. The approach is known as *bit interleaved coded modulation*. It has the disadvantage over both the multilevel and the trellis codes that the decoding delay caused by the interleaver must be increased by a factor of about 3, since we must now ensure that the three bits transmitted on the same symbol are sufficiently separated in the code sequence that the correlation of their fading has no effect.

For a constraint length 7, rate 2/3 coded 8-PSK scheme of this sort the required bit-energy-to-noise-density for BER $= 10^{-3}$ is about 9 dB, a little poorer than the optimized multilevel scheme [9.22]. However it has also been noted that a rate 1/2 code could be used with a 16-PSK or 16-QAM modulator, giving the same rate in bits per symbol [9.23]. This would increase the minimum Hamming distance, from 6 to 10 in the example considered. This gives slightly better performance than the optimized multilevel scheme. However, the interleaving delay is further increased.

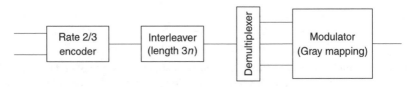

Figure 9.29   Interleaved coded modulation: single interleaver

9.3.3 Correlated fading and interleaving

An important assumption in all the above was highlighted at the beginning of Section 9.3.1: that the symbols of the coded signals fade independently. In practice, of course, fading is very rarely so rapid that successive symbols of a modulated signal are uncorrelated (and if it were, it would cause insuperable difficulties in carrier recovery). Thus, in practice, successive symbols of the codeword must be separated in time by means of *interleaving*. At the receiver the reverse process, *de-interleaving*, reassembles the codewords for decoding. Figure 9.30 illustrates the process. (The symbols π and π^{-1} are commonly used for interleaver and de-interleaver, respectively.) The interleaver can be regarded as an array memory. The code symbols are read into the array horizontally, row-by-row. When it is full, they are then read out vertically, column-by-column. The de-interleaver works in the reverse order. (This is a *rectangular block interleaver*: there are other types, as we shall see in Chapter 11, but the basic principle is the same.) One codeword of the input code stream is shown shaded. Its symbols are distributed through the transmitted stream, and then reassembled in the de-interleaver, as shown. There will of course be a delay through the whole process, given essentially by the total size of the interleaver.

The size of the interleaver should be sufficient that all code symbols are separated by at least the coherence time of the channel, and therefore the number of rows L should be at least the coherence time. Clearly, the row length K should be equal to the block length for a block code (or at least a few constraint lengths for a convolutional code). The overall delay is then given by $N = KL$.

Many systems are subject to a delay limitation. For example, two-way speech services must have delay limited to a few hundred milliseconds at most, or normal conversation becomes very difficult. This means that the delay due to a single radio link is severely limited: in the third-generation personal communication systems it will be limited to 40 ms [9.24]. Many

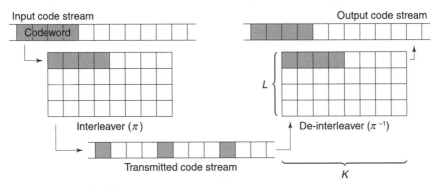

Figure 9.30 Interleaving

radio channels, however, fade much more slowly than this: even vehicle-mounted mobile systems must operate when the vehicle is stationary in traffic. In these cases the effect of implicit diversity is severely limited.

For this reason, many radio systems (including the second-generation standard GSM) allow *slow frequency hopping* (SFH) [9.25]. Here the carrier frequency changes at intervals in a predefined manner. (We ensure that other users also change frequencies simultaneously in a coordinated manner, so that there are no collisions.) Usually, one TDMA data burst is transmitted at each frequency. The frequencies should be separated by more than the coherence bandwidth of the channel, so that the fading is uncorrelated. This converts the implicit time diversity of the coded system into a form of time-frequency diversity, which may allow it to be exploited even in very slowly fading (or stationary) channels.

Nevertheless, even with frequency hopping, the extent of usable diversity may be somewhat limited in practice. The resulting correlation between code symbols will affect the performance of the codes and coded modulation schemes mentioned above: the full extent of the diversity advantage indicated above may not be achieved.

Example 9.5

In the second-generation digital mobile radio standard GSM [9.25A] FEC coding is used as described in Section 7.6.1. The mobile channel is commonly subject to rather severe multipath fading, whose fading rate depends on the speed of the mobile. In these circumstances the FEC coding can be exploited to provide an implicit diversity advantage, as mention in Section 9.3.1. However, and especially at low speeds, the fading of code symbols is strongly correlated. Thus interleaving is required to reduce this correlation, and obtain this diversity advantage.

We have shown in Section 7.6.1 how the digitally encoded speech data are FEC encoded to provide a total of 456 coded bits per speech frame. This is transmitted within the TDMA structure of GSM, which transmits the coded data in 114-bit TDMA time slots. Data from eight users are multiplexed onto one carrier, with a frame period of 4.615 ms. The delay limitation for transmission in GSM is 40 ms, which means that one speech frame can be transmitted over eight TDMA frames. (Note that there is a further delay of 20 ms due to the packetization of the speech signal.) The 456 bits are therefore interleaved over eight time slots using an 8×57 interleaver. The 57 bits are then further interleaved within the time slot using an 8×8 interleaver (which is not completely filled). Data from two successive speech frames are combined in each slot, giving the required total of 114 bits/slot. Figure 9.31 illustrates this process: (a) shows how the speech packet bits (0–455) are distributed into sections destined for slots labelled 0–7; (b) shows how the bits taken from the columns of the array

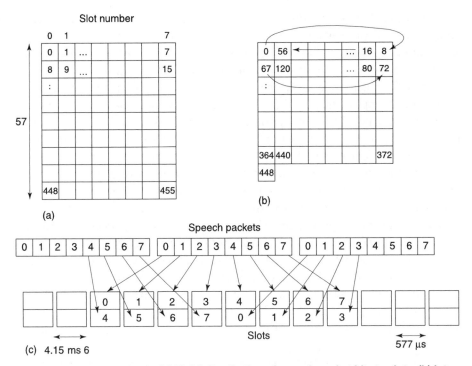

Figure 9.31 Interleaving in GSM: (a) distribution of speech packet bits to slots, (b) interleaving of bits within slot 0, (c) combining of speech packet bits in each slot

in (a) are interleaved within the slot. Slot 0 is illustrated, but the same pattern applies to all slots. The data are read into the array in the order shown, and read out by columns. Figure 9.31(c) shows how the 57 bits from each of two packets are combined to provide the 114 bits in each slot. Within the slot the bits from each packet are transmitted alternately.

At the receiver the coded speech packets are reassembled, the FEC code is decoded, and the speech signal is reconstructed.

Figure 9.31(b) shows that the bits whose fading is most highly correlated, because they are transmitted in succession, are separated by 64 places in the code sequence. Since the constraint length of the code is 5, and it is likely that the decoder has a truncation window length of 15 (Section 7.3.1), the correlation of these bits will probably have no effect on performance. We also observe that bits separated by 8 in the code sequence (such as bits 8 and 16) are transmitted 14 symbols apart on the channel (remembering that bits from a second speech packet are interleaved between those shown in Fig. 9.31(b)), which corresponds to 51.9 μs at the GSM channel rate of 270 ksymbols s^{-1}. Their correlation will thus have some effect on code performance. Adjacent bits in the code sequence are transmitted in successive packets, 4.6-ms apart.

As mentioned above (Section 9.1.1), the coherence time of the channel is given approximately by the inverse of the Doppler bandwidth. The maximum Doppler shift can be found from the conventional formula $\Delta f = (v/c)f$, where v is the mobile velocity, c is the speed of light $(3 \times 10^8 \, \mathrm{m \, s^{-1}})$, and f is the carrier frequency. For a mobile travelling at $50 \, \mathrm{km \, h^{-1}}$, with a carrier frequency of $2 \, \mathrm{GHz}$, the Doppler shift is $1.2 \, \mathrm{kHz}$, giving a coherence time of around $1 \, \mathrm{ms}$. Thus we can expect little correlation between bits of successive slots, but quite high correlation between bits of the same slot. Hence there will be some degradation of code performance. In particular, the maximum diversity factor is limited to the number of slots over which the speech packet is interleaved, i.e. 8. Note also that the last 78 bits of the packet are not encoded, so the interleaving does not provide a direct diversity advantage. However, it does mean that fading is likely to affect only part of these bits for any one speech packet, and hence it may result in a perceptual improvement in the speech quality.

At lower speeds, below about $10 \, \mathrm{km \, h^{-1}}$, successive time slots become largely correlated, so that nearly all the diversity advantage is lost. Here the SFH option in the GSM standard may be invoked. Frequencies are changed on a slot-by-slot basis, so that the eight slots over which a packet is interleaved are transmitted at eight different frequencies, on which the fading is expected to be uncorrelated.

9.3.4 Dispersion in coded systems

As mentioned above, in uncorrelated fading (or with sufficient interleaving) the i.s.i. introduced by dispersion on a wideband channel can be treated as another source of noise, uncorrelated with the data. If the dispersed components are subject to Rayleigh fading (which is due to a complex Gaussian process), then this noise will be Gaussian. From (9.16) and (9.17), the mean signal-to-interference ratio is:

$$\mathrm{SNR_{i.s.i.}} = \int_{-\infty}^{\infty} \overline{|h(\tau)|^2} g^2(t_\mathrm{s} - \tau) \, d\tau \Big/ \int_{-\infty}^{\infty} \overline{|h(\tau)|^2} \sum_{i \neq 0} g^2(iT + t_\mathrm{s} - \tau) \, d\tau \quad (9.24)$$

FEC coding is effective against this interference exactly as it is against any other source of uncorrelated interference, and hence we can use (9.24) together with the bounds on BER for coded systems to obtain an estimate of the irreducible BER of a coded system. Figure 9.32 [9.26] shows the irreducible BER against bit rate normalized to the coherence bandwidth for a rate $1/2$ constraint length 7 convolutional code, compared with uncoded transmission on a Rayleigh fading dispersive channel. It shows that whereas an uncoded system would be limited in data rate to a small fraction of the coherence bandwidth, with coding rates very close to the coherence bandwidth possible. Similar results would apply in coded modulation systems.

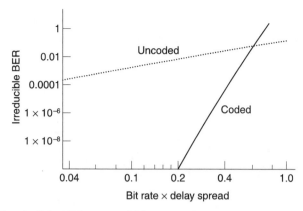

Figure 9.32 Irreducible BER using QPSK on a Rayleigh fading channel, with and without coding

9.3.5 Equalization in coded systems

However, to achieve rates greater than the coherence bandwidth, equalization is still required. Equalization and decoding could be applied separately, as shown in Fig. 9.33. A linear or non-linear equalizer could be used. However, as we have seen, a linear equalizer functions well only in some radio channels, and does not perform maximum likelihood signal detection. Non-linear equalizers perform better, and the MLSE is of course maximum likelihood by definition. However, in the structure of Fig. 9.33 these would pass hard decisions to the decoder, and would be obliged to treat the received signal as uncoded. Thus information is lost, and overall the receiver is not maximum likelihood. Simulation has shown that, in general, separate equalization and decoding performs poorly [9.4, 9.27].

A further problem arises in considering coded modulation. Figure 9.34 compares (as an example) a coded 8-PSK system with uncoded QPSK. Both transmit 2 bits/symbol, and we will assume that both use a non-linear equalizer, which makes symbol decisions. However, the coded 8-PSK equalizer must make decisions on an 8-PSK constellation in the presence of noise, and is therefore more likely to suffer errors. The decoder will then be obliged to use

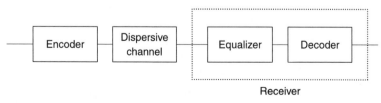

Figure 9.33 Separate equalization and decoding

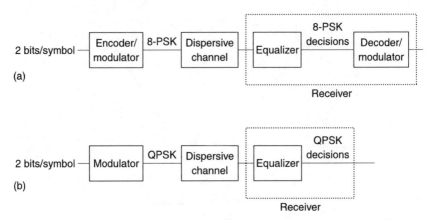

Figure 9.34   Coded 8-PSK compared (a) with uncoded QPSK, (b) with equalization

hard decisions, which as we have seen (Chapter 8) is severely sub-optimum for a coded modulation scheme.

We have noted above that the channel can be treated as a finite state machine. The number of states is M^L, where $M = 2^k$ is the constellation size and L is the length of the channel impulse response in symbol periods (i.e. the number of taps in the tapped delay-line model). For a convolutional code, the encoder also is an FSM, with (say) 2^m states. Thus we can treat the combination of encoder and channel as a single, much larger FSM, and perform MLSE upon its output using the Viterbi algorithm. However, the number of states in the joint machine is the product of those in the two separately, i.e. 2^{kL+m}. Since k in the coded modulation scheme is at least one greater than in an equivalent uncoded scheme, the number of states in the joint FSM is greater by a factor of at least 2^{L+m}. In most cases, this makes the full ML estimation of the joint system computationally quite impractical.

Thus the RSSE techniques mentioned in Section 9.2.4 become particularly attractive in coded systems. The M-algorithm has been used (see Chapter 7), along with a suitable pre-filter, with somewhat more success than for convolutional decoding alone [9.28]. Other RSSE techniques involve a grouping of trellis states, and calculating a metric to the closest of the joint states [9.29]. One particularly important version of this, sometimes known as *per-survivor processing* [9.30], considers only the trellis states due to the code, neglecting those due to the channel. The i.s.i. due to the channel is then calculated for each survivor path, and subtracted. Such techniques have been evaluated by simulation on various channels, and it has been found that none are wholly robust to all possible channels [9.4]. However, on most practical channels they are more robust than uncoded equalization schemes, and the benefit of the coding is retained.

Problems

9.1 For the COST 207 models in Table 9.4 find:
(a) the mean delay and delay spread;
(b) the coherence bandwidth;
(c) the 90% multipath power delay range, D_{90}.
Part (a) is simpler using a computer algebra package such as *Mathematica*. Otherwise, the following integrals may be useful in obtaining a good approximation:

$$\int_0^\infty \exp(-ax)\,dx = \frac{1}{a}, \qquad \int_0^\infty x\exp(-ax)\,dx = \frac{1}{a^2}$$

$$\int_b^\infty x\exp[-a(x-b)]\,dx = \frac{1+ab}{a^2}, \qquad \int_0^\infty (x-c)^2\exp(-ax)\,dx = \frac{2-2ac+a^2c^2}{a^3}$$

$$\int_b^\infty (x-c)^2\exp[-a(x-b)]\,dx = \frac{2+2a(b-c)+a^2(b-c)^2}{a^3}$$

9.2 Find the r.m.s. tap amplitudes in the tapped delay-line model of a COST 207 hilly terrain channel if the symbol rate is 1 Msymbol s^{-1} and rectangular pulse shaping is used.
Again, if this is solved manually, the following integrals may be useful:

$$\int_0^1 t^2\exp(-at)\,dt = \frac{2-(2+2a+a^2)\exp(-a)}{a^3}$$

$$\int_0^1 (1-t)^2\exp(-at)\,dt = \frac{2-2a+a^2-2\exp(-a)}{a^3}$$

9.3 Derive the delay spreads of the two-ray and exponential power-delay profiles (9.9) and (9.11). You may use the integrals given in Problem 9.1.

9.4 By considering the Doppler shift and the power received from each direction, derive the Doppler spectrum given in (9.14) and Fig. 9.8. If you have access to a computer algebra or numerical integration package, you might also calculate and plot the autocorrelation function of the fading envelope (the inverse Fourier transform of the Doppler power spectrum), and hence find the coherence time of the channel, defined more precisely as the time shift for which the correlation drops by 50%.
Find also the autocorrelation function and coherence time for the Gaussian and the first-order Butterworth Doppler spectra, as a function of the 3-dB cut-off frequency of the spectra. If a computer algebra package is not available, the following inverse Fourier transforms

may help:

$$\mathbf{F}^{-1}[\exp(-f^2)] = \int_{-\infty}^{\infty} \exp(-f^2)\exp(-2\pi jf\tau)\,df = \frac{1}{\sqrt{2\pi}}\exp(-\pi^2\tau^2)$$

$$\mathbf{F}^{-1}\left(\frac{1}{1+f^2}\right) = \pi\exp(-2\pi|\tau|)$$

9.5 Find the signal-to-i.s.i. ratio for a system with rectangular pulse shaping on a channel with exponential power-delay profile. Determine how it varies with the product of symbol rate and delay spread. Assuming a Rayleigh fading channel with 1-μs delay spread, find the maximum data rate using coherent BPSK for BER $\leq 10^{-3}$.

9.6 Find the required total bit-energy-to-noise-density ratio using BPSK for BER $= 10^{-6}$ on a Rayleigh fading channel with 1, 2, 4 and 8 branch diversity, compared with a non-fading channel.

9.7 A mobile radio system operating at a carrier frequency of 1 GHz has a Butterworth Doppler spectrum with cut-off frequency ν_{max}. A power control system varies the transmit power in 1-dB steps every 4 ms. Estimate the maximum mobile speed that will allow the transmitter to track the average fading rate.

9.8 A channel response is modelled as a tapped delay line with tap weights {0.75, 1, 0.5, 0.3, 0.3} (all real). Find the frequency response of a zero-forcing equalizer for this channel, and hence estimate the noise enhancement caused by such an equalizer.

The frequency response of a filter with z-domain transfer function $H(z)$ is given by $|H[\exp(2\pi jf)]|$.

Find also, by means of a series expansion of the z-transform, the tap weights of an FIR filter to implement this equalizer, and estimate the number of taps required.

9.9 Find a decision feedback equalizer with six feed-forward taps for the channel {0.7, 1, 0.5}, with $N_0 = 0.1$. Estimate the noise enhancement factor for the feed-forward filter. Compare this with the performance of a linear zero-forcing equalizer for the same channel.

9.10 What maximum data rate could have been used in GSM (for the same equalizer complexity) if the worst case channel had been the bad urban COST 207 channel?

9.11 Estimate the required bit-energy-to-noise-density ratio to achieve a BER of 10^{-6} with coded QPSK on a Rayleigh fading channel, using the (2, 1, 7) convolutional code of Table 7.3. Comment on interleaver requirements to achieve this performance.

9.12 What would be the maximum data rate for BER $\leq 10^{-3}$ with the system of Problem 9.5 if the (2, 1, 7) convolutional code were used with BPSK?

References

9.1 Burr, A.G. (1996) The multipath problem: an overview. In *IEE Colloquium on Multipath Countermeasures*, London, 23 May 1996, Colloquium Digest 1996/120.

9.2 Clarke, R.H. (1968) A statistical theory of mobile radio reception. *Bell System Technical Journal*, **47**: 957–1000.

9.3 Zhang, W. (1994) Simulation and modelling of multipath mobile channels. In *Proceedings of the 44th IEEE Vehicular Technology Conference*, Stockholm, June, pp. 160–4.

9.4 Thorlby, J.P. (1996) Equalisation techniques for coded modulation. PhD thesis, University of York.

9.5 Bello, P.A. (1963) Characterization of randomly time-variant linear channels. *IEEE Transactions on Communication Systems*, **CS-11**: 36–393.

9.6 COST 207 (1989) *Digital Land–Mobile Radio Communications*, Commission of the European Communities.

9.7 Burr, A.G. (1993) Narrow band modulation and coding schemes for radio LAN. In *4th European Conference on Radio Relay Systems*, Edinburgh, 11–14 October, pp. 51–6.

9.8 Rappaport, T.S., Seidel, S.Y. and Takamizawa, K. (1991) Statistical channel impulse-response models for factory and open plan building radio system design. *IEEE Transactions on Communications*, **39**(5): 794–807.

9.9 Saleh, A.A.M. and Valenzuela, R.A. (1987) A statistical model for indoor multipath propagation. *IEEE Journal of Selected Areas in Communications*, **SAC-5**: 128–37.

9.10 Proakis, J.G. (1995) *Digital Communications*, 3rd Edition, McGraw-Hill.

9.11 Lee, W.C.Y. (1982) *Mobile Communications Engineering*, McGraw-Hill.

9.12 Hulbert, A.P. (1993) Myths and realities of power control. In *IEE Colloquium on Spread Spectrum Techniques for Radio Communication Systems*, April, Colloquium Digest 1993/095.

9.13 Pearce, D.A.J., Burr, A.G. and Tozer, T.C. (1998) Capacity of TDMA cellular systems with slow Rayleigh fading countermeasures. In *Proceedings PIMRC'98*, Boston, September, Vol. 3, pp. 1240–4.

9.14 Qureshi, S.U.H. (1985) Adaptive equalisation. *Proceedings of the IEEE*, **73**(9): 1349–87.

9.15 Belfiore, C.A. and Park, J.H. (1970) Decision feedback equalisation. *Proceedings of the IEEE*, **58**(5): 779–85.

9.16 Forney, G.D. Jr (1972) Maximum-likelihood sequence estimation of digital sequences in the presence of intersymbol interference. *IEEE Transactions on Information Theory*, **18**: 363–78.

9.17 Schlegel, C. and Costello, D.J. (1989) Bandwidth efficient coding for fading channels: code construction and performance analysis. *IEEE Journal of Selected Areas in Communications*, **7**: 1356–68.

9.18 Divsalar, D. and Simon, M.K. (1988) The design of trellis coded MPSK for fading channels: performance criteria. *IEEE Transactions on Communications*, **36**: 1004–12.

9.19 Seshadri, N. and Sundberg, C.-E.W. (1992) Multilevel coded modulations for fading channels. *Proceedings of the 5th International Tirrenia Workshop*, Elsevier, pp. 305–16.

9.20 Burr, A.G. (2000) Design of optimum M-PSK codes for the Rayleigh fading channel. *IEE Proceedings – Communications*, **147**(1): 13–17.

9.21 Caire, G., Taricco, G. and Biglieri, E. (1998) Bit-interleaved coded modulation. *IEEE Transactions on Information Theory*, **44**(3): 927–46.

9.22 Zehavi, E. (1992) 8-PSK trellis codes for a Rayleigh channel. *IEEE Transactions on Communications*, **40**(5): 873–84.

9.23 Hansson, U. and Aulin, T. (1995) Channel symbol expansion diversity. *Electronics Letters*, **31**(18): 1545–6.

9.24 ITU-R (1994) *Provisional Draft New Recommendation on Procedure for Selection of Radio Transmission Technologies for FPLMTS*, COST 231 TD(94)106, Darmstadt, 6–8 September.

9.25 Olofsson, H., Naslund, J. and Skold, J. (1995) Interference diversity gain in frequency hopping GSM. In *Proceedings IEEE 45th Vehicular Technology Conference*, July, Vol. 1, pp. 25–8.

9.25A Hodges, M.R.L. (1990) The GSM radio interface. *British Telecom Technology Journal*, **8**(1): 31–43.

9.26 Burr, A.G. (1996) The multipath problem: an overview. In *IEE Colloquium on Multipath Countermeasures*, London, 23 May, Colloquium Digest 1996/120.

9.27 Burr, A.G. and Thorlby, J.P. (1991) Effect of dispersive fading channels on block coded modulation. In *Sixth International Conference on Mobile Radio and Personal Communications (IEE)*, Warwick, 9–12 December.

9.28 Aulin, T.M. (1999) Breadth-first maximum likelihood sequence detection: Basics. *IEEE Transactions on Communications*, **47**(2): 208–16.

9.29 Eyuboglu, M.V. and Qureshi, S.U.H. (1988) Reduced-state sequence estimation with set partitioning and decision feedback. *IEEE Transactions on Communications*, **36**(1): 13–20.

9.30 Raheli, R., Polydoros, A. and Tzou, C.K. (1995) Per-survivor processing – a general approach to MLSE in uncertain environments. *IEEE Transactions on Communications*, **43**(2–4): 354–64.

Chapter 10

OFDM

With the current rapid expansion in radio communication, modulation and coding for radio communications is also a rapidly changing field. In these two final chapters we focus on two areas that have recently attracted a great deal of attention, namely orthogonal frequency division multiplexing (OFDM) and turbo-codes. In this chapter we describe OFDM [10.1].

Although it is an old technique, dating back at least to the 1950s [10.2], OFDM has attracted a lot of attention in the past few years because it was chosen initially for digital audio broadcasting (DAB) [10.3], and more recently also for digital video broadcast (DVB) [10.4]. It was also proposed for third-generation digital mobile radio [10.5], but was not taken up in any of the main systems. Other proposed applications include upstream communications on cable TV systems, an environment which is also subject to a form of multipath due to reflections from mismatched cable junctions [10.6], and digital subscriber line (DSL) signalling in its various forms, including asymmetric DSL (ADSL) [10.7]. It is particularly well-suited to multimedia systems, in which information of all kinds is treated simply as a digital data stream, because it is readily adaptable to the requirements of different services.

As we have seen in the last chapter, conventional modulation schemes are limited in their maximum data rate on multipath channels by the inter-symbol interference (i.s.i.) caused by the multipath dispersion. Without equalization, the lower limit on symbol period is given by the channel delay spread. On the channels frequently encountered in personal communication systems, this may limit the data rate to a few tens of $kbit\,s^{-1}$. Of course equalization may be applied in order to increase data rates, but at the cost of a complexity in the receiver, which may increase rapidly with the product of data rate and delay spread. An equalizer also normally requires a training sequence to allow it to adapt to the channel. To implement true multimedia services in radio systems much higher data rates are likely to be required.

The principle of OFDM [10.1] is to split the data stream into parallel sub-channels, each of which is modulated onto one of a set of carriers, chosen so that the modulated signals are orthogonal to one another. In this way the symbol rate on each sub-channel is greatly reduced, and hence the effect of i.s.i. due to channel dispersion is reduced. Guard intervals can also be inserted to reduce i.s.i. further. The technique can also be used to provide additional robustness due to diversity in the presence of narrowband fades or interferers. Coding is essential in this case to allow this diversity to be taken advantage of. As mentioned, OFDM has been adopted for digital broadcasting, both audio and TV, as well as being proposed for mobile radio. The rationale for this is to avoid the effects of dispersion due to multipath propagation, and of the very similar effects of quasi-synchronous broadcasting on the same frequency.

10.1 Description

In fact, OFDM has a long history. A similar technique was first proposed by Mosier and Clabaugh in 1958 [10.2]. A few years later Chang [10.8] and Saltzberg [10.9] suggested the use of orthogonal signals for the sub-channels, allowing a considerable increase in bandwidth efficiency. An early application was to HF signalling in military communications. More recently interest has been re-awakened by its application in a variety of modern communication systems, as mentioned above.

The principle of OFDM is to divide the incoming data stream into a number of sub-channels, each of which is then modulated onto one of a set of closely spaced sine wave carriers. At the receiver these are separately demodulated, and the original data stream is reconstituted (Fig. 10.1). In the earliest systems the sub-channels were separated at the receiver by filtering, requiring a guard band between them. Strictly, of course, this is multi-carrier modulation rather than OFDM. It was Chang and (independently) Saltzberg who realized that if the sub-channel spacing was equal to the symbol rate on each (Fig. 10.2(a)), then the modulated signals would be orthogonal, and could readily be separated by correlation, using a conventional matched filter, or correlator. This led to true OFDM, and increased the bandwidth efficiency significantly.

In practice, of course, modern OFDM systems are not implemented using separate modulators, filters and demodulators. The modulation and demodulation can be performed jointly using an inverse discrete Fourier transform

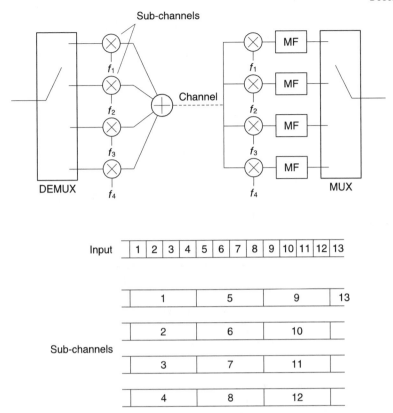

Figure 10.1   Principle of OFDM: MUX, multiplexer; MF, matched fitter; DEMUX, demultiplexer

(IDFT) and a DFT, respectively. In fact, the renewed popularity of OFDM dates from the point at which digital signal processing (DSP) devices capable of performing these transformations became readily available [10.10].

It should be noted that OFDM does not in itself provide any spectrum spreading. The bandwidth of a basic OFDM system is identical to that of a single carrier system carrying the same data rate and using the same modulation. The overall system bandwidth is merely divided between the sub-channels. This is of course an advantage in that bandwidth efficiency is not reduced, but it also means that no additional diversity advantage may be available on fading channels through the use of OFDM alone.

The rationale behind this process is that each channel has a reduced symbol rate relative to the delay spread of the channel, and therefore is less affected by channel dispersion. However, with the scheme so far described there is still some remanent i.s.i. and, more seriously, the dispersion also leads to interference between sub-channels, or inter-channel interference (i.c.i.). It was soon realized that this could be eliminated by the introduction of a guard interval, or cyclic extension (Fig. 10.2(b)), at the cost of a small reduction in bandwidth

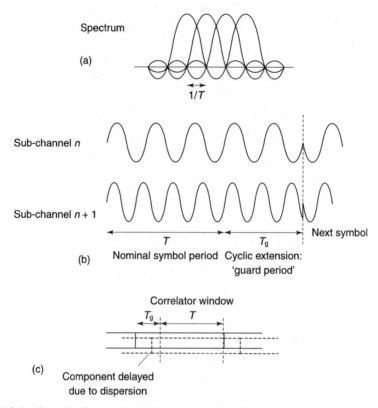

Spectrum

(a)

$\overleftrightarrow{1/T}$

Sub-channel n

Sub-channel $n + 1$

Next symbol

T T_g

(b)   Nominal symbol period   Cyclic extension:
'guard period'

Correlator window

T_g T

(c)
Component delayed
due to dispersion

Figure 10.2   Use of orthogonal carriers and cyclic extension

efficiency. The principle here is to extend the transmitted signal beyond the nominal symbol period into a guard interval, so as to provide a cyclic signal. The receiver correlator, however, only integrates over the nominal symbol period (Fig. 10.2(c)). Thus any signals delayed by channel dispersion remain orthogonal, eliminating both i.s.i. and i.c.i., provided the delay is less than the guard interval. The guard interval is therefore always implemented in OFDM systems operating on a dispersive channel.

However, such systems still have poor performance on a fading channel, even if the fade affects only some sub-channels. This is because the overall BER of the system is close to that of the poorest sub-channel. For this reason the systems proposed for broadcast applications employ FEC coding, and are known as coded orthogonal frequency division multiplex (COFDM). Provided the bits of a given codeword are distributed across the sub-channels, the inherent diversity provided by the code yields a very significant diversity improvement. Note, however, that this is only available if the total bandwidth is much greater than the coherence bandwidth of the channel.

Most modulation schemes may be used on the sub-channels, provided the requirements of orthogonality are maintained. (This, in practice, means that linear modulation is used.) The modulation scheme will determine the spectrum efficiency and bit-energy-to-noise-density requirement of the scheme. Indeed, except for the overhead introduced by the guard period, these parameters will be the same in a basic OFDM system as in a single carrier system using the same modulation. Thus for applications where a high bandwidth efficiency is required, such as video transmission, a multilevel modulation scheme such as 16-QAM or 64-QAM is used, while for mobile radio applications, where more robust modulation is required, QPSK might be used.

It is possible to generalize the concept of OFDM using signals other than sine waves to carry the information. In principle, any orthogonal set of signals may be used as carriers, or 'bearers'. For example, the Walsh–Hadamard set has been proposed, in the context of a hybrid OFDM/spread spectrum system [10.11, 10.12]. The use of wavelets has also been proposed, taking advantage of their time-frequency localization [10.13]. The disadvantage of most alternative bearers is that the property of the cyclic extension that completely eliminates i.s.i. and i.c.i. is lost, as will be seen in the next section.

The Walsh–Hadamard-based systems described, represent one version of the hybrid OFDM/spread spectrum, but in fact a wide range of alternative proposals exist. For example spreading may be applied prior to combining the channels [10.11], or to the whole multiplex afterwards [10.14]. The object is to provide a broader spectrum, and thus to provide diversity advantages on a frequency-selective fading channel. This is currently a very active research area.

Multiple access can be provided in OFDM systems in the same way as in single carrier systems, i.e. using TDMA, FDMA or CDMA (in the case of OFDM/spread spectrum systems) [10.15, 10.16]. There are, however, some variations of FDMA which become possible in OFDM. For example, instead of using one completely separate OFDM system per user, the signal at the network hub can be treated as a single OFDM multiplex, from which each user selects the required sub-channels. These sub-channels then do not need to be contiguous in frequency. We will call this approach 'joint FDMA'. This allows increased frequency diversity on the signals for each user, and also reduces the complexity of the hub. However, for use on the uplink (user-to-hub) it would require rather accurate modulator frequency control.

10.2 Basic analysis

In this section we analyze a basic OFDM system, to show how the guard period eliminates multipath effects. This will also show why sinusoids are the optimum bearers for the sub-channels.

However, we adopt a very general system model initially, in which the bearers will be denoted as $c_k(t)$, $k = 0 \cdots K - 1$. The bearers for the ith symbol are defined over the interval $iT_s \leq t < iT_s + T$, with a cyclic extension in negative time such that $c_k(t) = c_k(T + t)$, $T - T_s \leq t - iT < 0$. Here $T_s > T$ is the symbol period, and $T_g = T_s - T$ is the guard period.

The ith symbol transmitted on the kth bearer is denoted by d_{ki}, and may be complex. We will normally consider without loss of generality the 0th symbol, which we may denote as simply d_k. The transmitted signal for the ith symbol is thus:

$$s_i(t) = \sum_{k=0}^{K-1} d_{ki} c_k(t), \quad iT_s - T_g < t \leq iT_s + T \tag{10.1}$$

We will model the channel initially in terms of a single multipath component, introducing a delay τ and a frequency shift ω_d relative to the line-of-sight signal component, with (complex) fading envelope h (h_k for the kth sub-channel), and subject to additive white Gaussian noise (AWGN) $\eta(t)$. (For normalization we may assume that $|h_k|^2 = 1$; the fading in different sub-channels may or may not be correlated.) Later we will combine this component with the signal and other multipath components. Then the received signal:

$$x_i(t) = s_i(t - \tau)h \exp(j\omega_d t) + \eta(t) \tag{10.2}$$

Note that the phase shift in the carrier introduced by the delay is incorporated in the phase of the fading envelope h.

The receiver effectively forms the correlation between the received signal and each of the bearers, using only the interval $iT_s \leq t < iT_s + T$. Thus the output of the lth channel:

$$C_{il} = \int_{iT_s}^{iT_s + T} x_i(t) c_l^*(t) \, dt \tag{10.3}$$

where $c_l^*(t)$ denotes the complex conjugate of the lth bearer signal. To show the required properties of the bearers, we will first consider the case when $\tau < T_g$ and $\omega_d = 0$, and also neglect the thermal noise. At this point, too, we will set $i = 0$ and drop the subscript. Then:

$$C_l = \int_0^T x(t) c_l^*(t) \, dt = \int_0^T hs(t - \tau) c_l^*(t) \, dt = \int_0^T \sum_{k=0}^{K-1} h_k d_k c_k(t - \tau) c_l^*(t) \, dt$$

$$= \sum_{k=0}^{K-1} h_k d_k \int_0^T c_k(t - \tau) c_l^*(t) \, dt = \sum_{k=0}^{K-1} h_k d_k r_{kl}(\tau) \tag{10.4}$$

Because of the cyclic extension, $r_{kl}(\tau)$ is the cyclic cross-correlation function of the kth and the lth bearers. It is clear that if $r_{kl}(\tau) = 0$, $k \neq l$, $\forall \tau$, then $C_l = hd_l r_{ll}(\tau)$, and the data can be separated perfectly. It can be proven that the sinusoids spaced at intervals of frequency $1/T$ are the only full set of functions having this property perfectly [10.17]. Hence the sinusoids are in this sense the optimal set of bearers.

Thus we may complete our system model by defining the bearers to be sinusoids, using the complex exponential form:

$$c_k(t) = \exp\left(2\pi j \frac{kt}{T}\right) \tag{10.5}$$

and we may readily verify the properties of the bearers:

$$r_{kl}(\tau) = \begin{cases} T \exp\left(-2\pi jk \dfrac{\tau}{T}\right), & k = l \\ 0, & k \neq l \end{cases} \tag{10.6}$$

Thus we see that if sine waves are used as bearers, separated in frequency by $1/T$, and with cyclic extension, then provided there is no Doppler shift and the maximum multipath delay is less than the guard period T_g, there will be no interference at all. However, practical radio channels do not have a finite maximum delay: they tend to have an infinite impulse response with typically an exponential decay (see Section 9.1.2). They will also have finite Doppler shift, if the terminal is moving (Section 9.1.3), and even in some circumstances in fixed systems. In the general case this will result in interference, both the return of i.s.i. and a new i.c.i., from one sub-channel to another, because the sub-channels have ceased to be truly orthogonal.

10.3 Effect of excess multipath delay and Doppler

We now analyze the system for this more general case of excess multipath delay and/or Doppler, i.e. where $\tau > T_g$ and/or $\omega_d \neq 0$. More detail of this analysis is given in [10.18]. From Fig. 10.2(c) we note that if $\tau > T_g$ the current symbol (we have assumed that this is the 0th) no longer fills the receiver correlator window, and instead a portion of the previous (the -1th) is also present. Then:

$$\begin{aligned} C_l &= \int_0^{\tau - T_g} x_{-1}(t) c_l^*(t)\, dt + \int_{\tau - T_g}^T x_0(t) c_l^*(t)\, dt \\ &= \sum_{k=0}^{K-1} h_k d_{-1,k} \int_0^{\tau - T_g} c_k(t - \tau) c_l^*(t) \exp(j\omega_d t)\, dt \\ &\quad + \sum_{k=0}^{K-1} h_k d_{0,k} \int_{\tau - T_g}^T c_k(t - \tau) c_l^*(t) \exp(j\omega_d t)\, dt \end{aligned} \tag{10.7}$$

The bearers are no longer orthogonal over these sub-intervals, or with the frequency-shift term present, and hence interference results. This can conveniently be separated into i.s.i., due to the first term of the above equation, and i.c.i., due to all elements of the second term except the lth. The power of these components (taking $|d_k|^2$ as unity) can be determined as:

$$I_s(k, l) = \frac{1 - \cos[2\pi\xi(p + \psi)]}{\pi^2(p + \psi)^2} \tag{10.8}$$

$$I_c(k, l) = \frac{1 - \cos[2\pi(1 - \xi)(p + \psi)]}{\pi^2(p + \psi)^2} \tag{10.9}$$

where $p = l - k$, $\xi = (\tau - T_g)/T$, and $\psi = f_d T$. Note that $I_c(l, l) = S(l)$, the signal power. Assuming that the sub-channel data is uncorrelated, and/or the sub-channels are subject to uncorrelated fading, the interference from different sub-channels adds incoherently and hence the total i.s.i, i.c.i. and signal power, respectively, are given by summing over all sub-channels. For a large multiplex, assuming that the sub-channel in question is not close to the edge, we can approximate the i.s.i. and i.c.i. powers as sums to (plus and minus) infinity. Note that since the argument of the sum is even in p, a sub-channel at the edge of the multiplex will experience a signal-to-interference ratio 3-dB better than this.

Both sums do in fact yield a closed-form solution, but unfortunately it is too complex to transcribe here. However, the two special cases $\psi = 0$ (zero frequency shift) and $\xi = 0$ (zero excess delay) are more amenable.

For the zero frequency-shift case we obtain some remarkably simple solutions, for a restricted range of ξ:

$$I_s = \sum_{p=-\infty}^{\infty} \frac{1 - \cos(2\pi\xi p)}{\pi^2 p^2} = \xi, \quad 0 \le \xi \le 1 \tag{10.10}$$

$$I_c = 2\sum_{p=1}^{\infty} \frac{1 - \cos[2\pi(1 - \xi)(p + \psi)]}{\pi^2(p + \psi)^2} = 1 - \xi^2, \quad 0 \le \xi \le 1 \tag{10.11}$$

$$S = \underset{\psi \to 0}{Lt} \left\{ \frac{1 - \cos[2\pi\psi(1 - \xi)]}{\pi^2\psi^2} \right\} = 1 - \xi^2, \quad 0 \le \xi \le 1 \tag{10.12}$$

Figure 10.3 shows the variation of these quantities with excess delay up to T. Figure 10.4 shows that the approximation given by the sum to infinity is accurate for relatively modest multiplex size.

In the zero-excess-delay case we obtain:

$$I_s = \sum_{p=-\infty}^{\infty} \underset{\xi \to 0}{Lt} \left\{ \frac{1 - \cos[2\pi\xi(p + \psi)]}{\pi^2(p + \psi)^2} \right\} = 0 \tag{10.13}$$

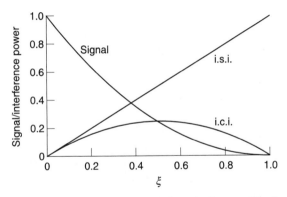

Figure 10.3   Signal, i.s.i. and i.c.i. power plotted against normalized excess delay

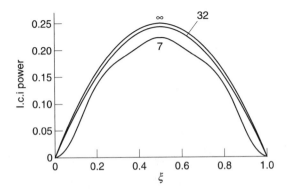

Figure 10.4   The i.c.i. for various sizes of multiplex

i.e. there is no i.s.i. (which is not unexpected)

$$I_c = \sum_{p=-\infty, p\neq 0}^{\infty} \frac{1 - \cos[2\pi(p+\psi)]}{\pi^2(p+\psi)^2} = \frac{\Psi^{(1)}(1-\psi)\cos(2\pi\psi)}{\pi^2} \qquad (10.14)$$

where $\Psi^{(1)}(\cdot)$ denotes the first logarithmic derivative of the digamma function.

$$S = \frac{1 - \cos(2\pi\psi)}{\pi^2\psi^2} \qquad (10.15)$$

The variation of signal and i.c.i. with ψ is plotted in Fig. 10.5.

Figure 10.6 shows the variation of signal-to-i.c.i. ratio with normalized r.m.s. Doppler shift. Two models of Doppler shift are used: the first contains a pair of discrete Doppler shifts, equal and opposite, while the second contains a continuous 'spread' of frequencies, with a Gaussian distribution. The result shows that the shape of these distributions does not make much difference, and that there is in any case little effect provided the symbol rate is at least 50 times the maximum frequency shift. For frequency shifts due to Doppler, this is likely to be the case in many radio systems.

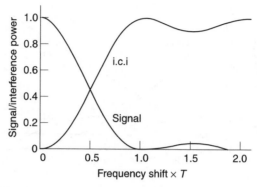

Figure 10.5 Signal and interference power plotted against frequency shift $\times T$ (i.e., ψ)

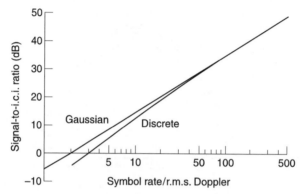

Figure 10.6 Variation of signal-to-i.c.i. ratio with r.m.s. Doppler shift, for zero excess delay

10.4 Effects of multipath on coded and uncoded systems

Here we give some results for three illustrative OFDM systems, all using QPSK and transmitting 1 bit/symbol on each sub-channel (and therefore involving 50% redundancy) [10.19]. These results are summarized in Table 10.1. In scheme A, the redundancy is fully employed in the guard interval, which

Scheme	Guard interval/symbol period	Code rate
A	0.5	1 (uncoded)
B	0.333	3/4
C	0	1/2

Table 10.1 Three schemes at rate 1 bit/symbol/sub-channel

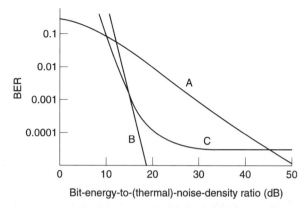

Figure 10.7   Performance of Schemes A–C of Table 10.1 subject to excess dispersion with delay spread $= 0.05 \times$ symbol period, and zero frequency shift

occupies 50% of the symbol period. In scheme C, it is given to the coding, and there is no guard period. Scheme B shares redundancy: there is both coding and a guard period.

We evaluate the BER performance of these schemes on a channel with exponential power-delay profile, using the estimates of BER taken from Section 7.4.2. The code is the rate 1/2 constraint length 7 convolutional code, punctured in scheme B to provide rate 3/4. The results are shown in Figs 10.7–10.9.

Figure 10.7 shows the performance of schemes A–C in thermal noise and subject to dispersion in excess of the guard period, but with zero frequency shift. In scheme C, we observe an irreducible error rate floor (it is present in

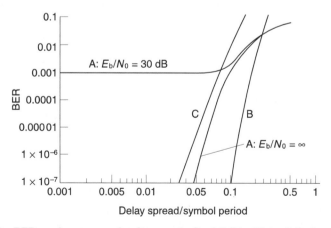

Figure 10.8   BER performance of schemes A–C of Table 10.1 plotted against delay spread normalized to symbol period, for bit-energy-to-thermal-noise-density 30 dB (except where stated)

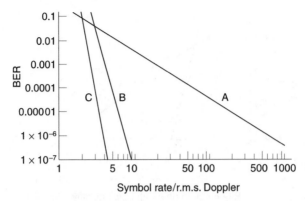

Figure 10.9 BER performance of Schemes A–C of Table 10.1 subject to Doppler frequency shift (discrete channel), zero excess dispersion

the other schemes, but at a much lower level). Figure 10.8 gives the same results, this time plotted against delay spread normalized to the symbol period. The irreducible BER for scheme A is given, in addition to the result for bit-energy-to-noise-density ratio 30 dB. These results show the importance of both coding and a guard period: the lowest irreducible BER is given by scheme B, which involves both. In fact, in terms of irreducible BER, the uncoded scheme A is better than scheme C. However, from Fig. 10.7 coding is clearly essential if low BER is to be achieved without excessive signal-to-thermal-noise ratio requirements.

Conversely, Fig. 10.9 shows the performance of the schemes with no excess dispersion, but in the presence of Doppler frequency shift. Here the guard period has only a small effect on i.c.i., and hence the optimum scheme is scheme C, which has the most powerful FEC coding. Again, some degree of coding is clearly essential to achieve low BER on a channel affected by Doppler shift.

Example 10.1

Consider a 64 sub-channel OFDM system, intended for mobile data broadcasting, using scheme B on a channel characterized by the COST 207 typical urban (TU) model (see Chapter 9), with a mobile terminal travelling at up to $130\,\text{km h}^{-1}$. The required BER is 10^{-6}. Find the maximum and minimum data rate.

Solution The dispersion on this channel is exponential with delay spread 1 μs. If the required BER is 10^{-6} or better, then from Fig. 10.8 a symbol rate in excess of $100\,\text{ksymbol s}^{-1}$ is possible, allowing a data rate of $6.4\,\text{Mbit s}^{-1}$. Extrapolating from Fig. 10.7, the required bit-energy-to-thermal-noise-density ratio would be of the order of 20 dB. The total bandwidth occupied is slightly over 6.4 MHz. Maximum Doppler shift is given by:

$$\Delta f = \frac{\nu}{\lambda} = \frac{\nu f_c}{c}$$

For a mobile travelling at $130\,\text{km}\,\text{h}^{-1}$, operating at 1.8 GHz, the Doppler shift would be 216 Hz. From Fig. 10.9 this yields a minimum symbol rate of about $2\,\text{ksymbol}\,\text{s}^{-1}$, and indicates that for a broadband system the i.c.i. due to Doppler is not likely to be a problem.

Example 10.2(a)

Consider the 8k mode of the Digital Video Broadcast (Terrestrial) standard, DVB-T [10.4]. The two possible modes of the standard are: the '8k' mode, designed for single frequency networks (SFNs), where multiple transmitters may be used to transmit the same signal sharing the same frequency, and the '2k' mode, which was a technologically simpler system intended for earlier introduction where SFNs were not required. Choose a suitable symbol period, and assume mobile operation of the standard at $130\,\text{km}\,\text{h}^{-1}$.

Solution A SFN will result in a severely delayed copy of the transmitted signal due to the next nearest transmitter: to avoid this a guard interval of 200 μs is required. To provide acceptable spectral efficiency the guard interval must not be more than one-quarter of the useful symbol interval T. This gives a minimum T of 800 μs. For compatibility with the MPEG-2 coded video standard [10.20], a useful data rate of about $10\,\text{Mbit}\,\text{s}^{-1}$ was required when operating with QPSK (modulation orders up to 64-QAM can also be used). This means that $800 \times 10/2 = 4000$ carriers are required. Allowing for additional overheads, the next largest power of 2 is 8192, and so this was chosen.

The actual choice of T is 896 μs, with guard period 224 μs. This is clearly sufficient to overcome normal multipath, which in the worst-case COST 207 model [10.21] has a maximum delay of 20 μs. (However, a broadcast system typically serves a much larger area than the mobile systems which the COST models were intended to simulate, and so a larger delay spread may be expected). I.s.i. and i.c.i. due to multipath can therefore be neglected. Assuming a transmit frequency of 850 MHz (at the top of the UHF terrestrial television band), if the signal is received in a vehicle travelling at $130\,\text{km}\,\text{h}^{-1}$ ($36\,\text{m}\,\text{s}^{-1}$), maximum Doppler is 102 Hz. The symbol rate $1/T$ is $1.12\,\text{ksymbol}\,\text{s}^{-1}$. Assuming FEC coding as powerful as that used in scheme B above (which is likely), from Fig. 10.9 the performance is acceptable – but only just so. The DVB-T system is not really designed for high speed mobile reception.

We will return to this worked example in Example 10.2(b).

10.5 Application of FEC coding

Having shown above that FEC coding is essential, in this section we consider in more detail how it can be applied in OFDM systems. In particular, we consider how the coded bits should be mapped onto the modulated symbols on each sub-channel. This covers such issues as interleaving and the application of coding to higher-order modulation schemes, i.e. coded modulation.

We noted in Section 9.3.1 that FEC coding of Hamming distance d_H potentially provides d_H-fold diversity combining on a fading channel. This, however, assumes that the bits of the code sequence fade independently. In many cases, sub-channels are also relatively slowly fading. Hence the code sequences must be interleaved across the sub-channels rather than in time. Moreover, since sub-channel bandwidths are narrow, neighbouring sub-channels are also likely to be strongly correlated. Therefore adjacent bits of the code sequence should be separated by at least the coherence bandwidth of the channel. This applies also to bits transmitted on the same symbol, such as the two bits of a QPSK symbol. This suggests an interleaving scheme of the sort illustrated in Fig. 10.10. Here the columns represent sub-channels, and the rows symbol periods. The two halves of each square represent the two bits carried by a QPSK symbol. The numbers give the order of bits in the code sequence. The scheme illustrated ensures that adjacent bits in the code sequence are separated in frequency by at least three sub-channels. Here there is no element of interleaving in time: if the channel is changing fairly rapidly, and if delay restrictions allow it, this could also be added. Note that the maximum diversity order k_{max} (whatever the code minimum distance) is given by:

$$k_{max} \leq \frac{W}{\Delta f} = W\Delta \tag{10.16}$$

where W is the total multiplex bandwidth, Δf is the coherence bandwidth, and Δ is the delay spread, since this is the maximum number of independently fading symbols that can be combined. Frequency-selective fading across the band is *required* to provide the diversity advantage of OFDM.

A further issue is the mapping of the code sequence onto higher-order modulation schemes. This is in fact very similar to the design of coded modulation

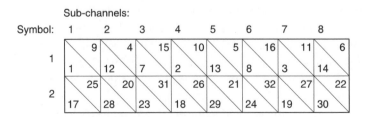

Figure 10.10 Example interleaving scheme for QPSK system

schemes for fading channels, as discussed in Section 9.3.2. Thus the same schemes may be used: in particular multilevel coded modulation or bit inter-leaved coded modulation.

Note, as mentioned in Section 9.3.1, that to implement optimum combining requires the attenuation of each symbol – in this case each sub-channel – to be taken into account. The phase must be corrected, as described in Section 10.6, and the signal must further be weighted by the channel attenuation (i.e. symbols which are already attenuated should be further attenuated at the decoder). This implements maximum ratio combining. Hence channel state information is required for the decoder; in most systems this may readily be provided by the pilot symbols used for equalization (Section 10.6).

Example 10.2(b)

FEC coding and interleaving in DVB-T.

The DVB-T system employs constraint length 7 convolutional inner codes. A range of modulation schemes may be used from QPSK to 64-QAM, all with Gray-coded constellation mapping. The code sequence is demultiplexed into streams destined for each bit of the constellation label, and separate bit interleavers are applied to each. A further pseudo-random interleaver is then applied to the channel symbols. Thus bit-level interleaving is applied, as recommended above, and sufficient symbol-level interleaving is provided to take full advantage of any frequency diversity available in the multiplex. The total signal bandwidth is 7 MHz; if the delay spread is around 2 μs, then the maximum diversity order is 14. The inner code may have a minimum distance up to about 10; so in this case this is the maximum diversity order that is likely to be achieved.

The standard also allows for an (optional) outer Reed–Solomon code: a (255, 239) code shortened to (204, 188), whose symbols are $\log_2(256) = 8$ bits long, i.e. 1 byte. This fits with the MPEG-2 packet, which is 188 bytes. The error-correcting power $t = (204 - 188)/2 = 8$ symbols. An outer interleaver may also be used between the outer and inner encoders. This is a convolutional interleaver [11.10], see Section 3.3, operating on bytes, which preserves the burst-error correcting property of the RS code (Section 6.3.6). The convolutional encoder can be modelled as a set of I multiplexed delay lines, each having a delay that is a multiple of M bytes, as shown in Fig. 10.11. In this case I is 12 and M is 17, so that the maximum delay through the interleaver is $12 \times 17 = 204$, or one code block.

This outer code may also increase the effective diversity order a little, but as we have seen the frequency diversity available from the multiplex is only a little larger than the diversity provided by the inner code. The total transmission period of one code block is $204 \times 17 = 3468$ byte periods, or about 3.5 ms at the minimum data rate (about 8 Mbit s^{-1}). Over this period there is unlikely

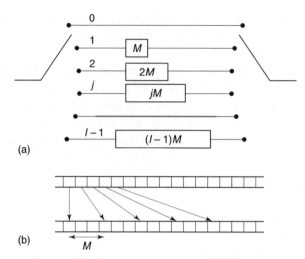

Figure 10.11   Convolutional interleaver: (a) equivalent structure, (b) operation

to be much fading in the time domain, so there is little scope for additional time diversity as a result of the outer code.

An alternative FEC scheme for DVB-T using turbo-codes is described in [10.22].

We will return to this worked example in Example 10.2(c).

10.6   Equalization

The robustness of OFDM to multipath dispersion does not mean that no account need be taken of its effect. The frequency response of the channel will cause attenuation and phase shift that will both vary between sub-channels, which can be corrected by means of equalization. However, this takes the form simply of the reversal of these phase and amplitude effects on each sub-channel so as to recreate the original signal before demodulation.

This does, however, require knowledge of the channel frequency response at the receiver. This is normally provided by the insertion of pilot symbols at intervals on each sub-channel. The pilot symbols allow what is effectively carrier phase and amplitude estimation for each sub-channel: they are the equivalent of a preamble for carrier recovery in a single carrier system. This allows coherent demodulation: an alternative would clearly be to use non-coherent demodulation, and in particular differential demodulation. This avoids the necessity for equalization and, in particular, avoids the need for pilot symbols. The resulting reduction in overhead can at least partially offset the relative degradation of differential demodulation compared with coherent [10.23].

Example 10.2(c)

Pilot symbols in DVB-T.

For example, Fig. 10.12 shows the distribution of pilot symbols in the DVB multiplex [10.4]. 'Scattered' pilot symbols are distributed throughout the multiplex, every 12th sub-channel and every fourth symbol, as shown. 'Continual' reference signals are transmitted on certain sub-channels (177 out of 6817 sub-channels in the '8k' system). The symbol transmitted in each is taken from a pseudo-random sequence, and the pilots are also transmitted at higher power than other symbols.

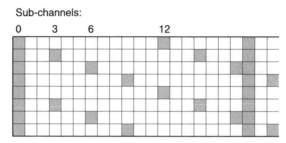

Figure 10.12   Distribution of pilot (or reference) symbols (shaded) in DVB-T

Note that not all carriers are covered: the distribution is designed to provide an adequate sampling of the channel response, both in frequency and in time. Responses of sub-channels between the pilots are obtained by interpolation. Clearly, the density of samples required depends on how rapidly the channel varies, in time and in frequency.

10.7   Synchronization

Carrier recovery, if required, is provided by the pilot symbols, as discussed in Section 10.6. However, symbol timing recovery is still needed. The presence of the cyclic extension in OFDM, however, provides redundancy in the signal that can be exploited to extract timing information [10.24]. The cyclic extension means that the last period T_g is identical to the first within each symbol. This can be exploited by calculating the correlation between signal segments of length T_g separated by T, as shown in Fig. 10.13. Figure 10.13(a) shows the structure of the correlator, while 10.13(b) illustrates its operation. The shaded section denotes the cyclic extension, which is a copy of the first interval T_g of the symbol. The circuit returns the correlation between the two sections of signal bracketed. When they are aligned as shown, the correlation is maximum; when the two sets of brackets fall in different symbols the

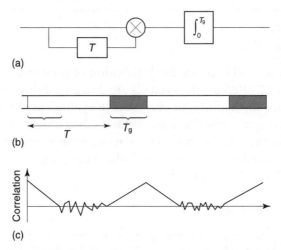

(a)

(b)

(c)

Figure 10.13 Using cyclic extension for time synchronization: (a) synchronizer structure, (b) synchronizer operation, (c) correlation output

correlation is small and random (due to correlation between random data), as shown in Fig. 10.13(c). Thus the maximum of the correlator output indicates the optimum timing alignment.

10.8 Signal envelope

One significant drawback of OFDM is the envelope of the signal. It consists of a (possibly large) number of sine waves of random relative phase, depending on the data. These may add in phase at certain points in the symbol, resulting in a possible peak amplitude of N times the sub-channel amplitude A, where N is the number of sub-channels. The r.m.s. amplitude, however, is $A\sqrt{N}$, resulting

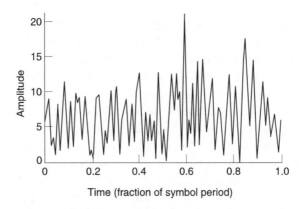

Figure 10.14 Envelope of OFDM symbol with 64 sub-carriers of unit amplitude

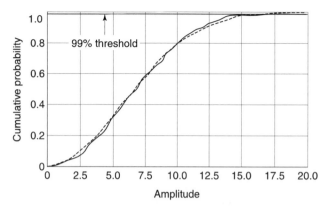

Figure 10.15   Cumulative distribution function of 64 sub-carrier OFDM, compared with Rayleigh distribution, showing also 99% probability threshold

in a possible peak-to-mean ratio of $\sqrt{N}$. In fact, the OFDM signal has a waveform very like white noise, and hence a Rayleigh distributed amplitude. Figure 10.14 shows the amplitude of one OFDM symbol with 64 sub-channels, and Fig. 10.15 compares the cumulative distribution function of its amplitude with the Rayleigh distribution. We note that amplitude excursions are, in practice, rarely greater than about three times the r.m.s. amplitude (which is 8 in Fig. 10.14), and 10.15 shows that it exceeds 18 only 1% of the time.

However, to amplify this signal without distortion requires a very linear power amplifier and/or a very large back-off. This is not too important in broadcasting applications where only a few fixed transmitters are required, in which cost and power efficiency are not of the essence, but is much more significant in fixed access or (especially) in mobile systems. Without the back-off, non-linear effects like those described in Chapter 3 will occur: namely spectral re-growth outside the band and self-interference to the OFDM symbols. (Constellation distortion is not likely to be significant.) A number of techniques have been developed to minimize the peak-to-mean ratio:

- Signal coding: a code is applied (analogous to an FEC code) which excludes sub-channel data combinations giving rise to large peaks. The disadvantage of this approach is that the power of this code for error correction may then be reduced [10.25].
- Choice of signal frequencies: only a sub-set of the sub-channels is used, again chosen to minimize peak-to-mean ratio. Again, this increases the overhead.
- Truncate amplitude peaks in the signal, then bandpass filter to remove the resulting out-of-band components. This leaves in-band self-interference, and also reduces signal power.

- Add a band-limited signal to cancel amplitude peaks. This also results in in-band self-interference, which must be counteracted with FEC coding [10.26].

References

10.1 Zou, W.Y. and Wu, Y. (1995) COFDM: an overview. *IEEE Transactions on Broadcasting*, **41**(1): 1–8.

10.2 Mosier, R.R. and Clabaugh, R.G. (1958) KINEPLEX, a bandwidth-efficient binary transmission system. *AIEE Transactions*, **76**: 723–8.

10.3 Le Floch, B., Lassalle, R. and Castelain, D. (1989) Digital sound broadcasting to mobile receivers. *IEEE Transactions on Consumer Electronics*, **3**: 493–503.

10.4 European Standard EN 300 744 V1.1.2 (1997-08), *Digital Video Broadcasting (DVB); Framing Structure, Channel Coding and Modulation for Digital Terrestrial Television*, obtainable from http://www.etsi.org/eds/eds.htm

10.5 van de Beek, J.-J., Börjesson, P.O., Edfors, O. *et al.* (1996) *A Conceptual Study of OFDM-based Multiple Access Schemes: Parts 1–4*, ETSI STC SMG2 meetings 18–20, Technical reports Tdoc 116/96, 166/96, 250/96, May–December.

10.6 Barsellotti, J. and Langlais, B. (1995) Paddling upstream: overcoming problems in the CATV return path. In *19th Montreaux Television Symposium*, 8–13 June.

10.7 Czajkowski, I.K. (1999) High-speed copper access: a tutorial overview. *Electronics and Communication Engineering Journal*, **11**(3): 125–48.

10.8 Chang, R.W. (1966) Synthesis of band-limited orthogonal signals for multichannel data transmission. *Bell System Technical Journal*, **45**: 1775–96.

10.9 Saltzberg, B.R. (1967) Performance of an efficient parallel data transmission system. *IEEE Transactions on Communication Technology*, **COM-15**: 805.

10.10 Weste, N. and Skellern, D.J. (1998) VLSI for OFDM. *IEEE Communications Magazine*, **36**(10): 127–31.

10.11 Muller, T., Rohling, H. and Grunheid, R. (1995) Comparison of different detection algorithms for OFDM–CDMA. In *Proceedings of IEEE Vehicular Technology Conference VTC'95*, p. 835.

10.12 Zhang, H. and Rutkowski, D. (1995) Orthogonal sequency division modulation. In *Proceedings of IEEE Vehicular Technology Conference VTC'95*, p. 810.

10.13 Tzannes, M.A., Tzannes, M.C., Proakis, J. and Heller, P.N. (1994) DMT systems, DWMT systems and filter banks. In *Proceedings of SUPERCOMM/ICC'94*, Vol. 1, New Orleans, pp. 311–15.

10.14 Vandendorpe, L. (1995) Multitone spread spectrum communications systems in a multipath Rician fading channel. *IEEE Transactions on Vehicular Technology*, **44**(2): 327–37.

10.15 Muller, T., Bruninghaus, K. and Rohling, H. (1996) Performance of coherent OFDM–CDMA for broadband mobile communications. *Wireless Personal Communications*, **2**: 295–305.

10.16 Rohling, H. and Grünheid, R. (1997) Performance comparison of different multiple access schemes for the downlink of an OFDM communication system. In *Proceedings IEEE VTC'97*, Phoenix, May, pp. 1365–9.

10.17 Burr, A.G. (1993) Design of orthogonal sequences: a geometric approach. In M.J. Ganley (Ed.), *Cryptography and Coding*, IMA/Oxford University Press.

10.18 Burr, A.G. (1999) Performance analysis of COFDM for broadband transmission on a fading multipath channel. *Wireless Personal Communications*, **10**(1): 3–17.

10.19 Burr, A.G. (1997) Performance of COFDM for multimedia transmission on the personal communication channel. In *Proceedings IEEE International Conference on Universal Personal Communications*, San Diego, October.

10.20 MPEG-2 ISO (International Standards Organization) ISO/IEC 13818, (1995) *Coding of Moving Pictures and Associated Audio*, Geneva.

10.21 Bello, P.A. (1963) Characterizaton of randomly time-variant linear channels. *IEEE Transactions on Communication Systems*, **CS-11**: 36–393.

10.22 Burr, A.G. (1999) Performance of Turbo-coded OFDM. In *IEE Colloquium on Turbo-coding in Digital Broadcasting – Can it Double Capacity?*, London, 22 November, Digest 99/165.

10.23 Engels, V. and Rohling, H. (1995) Multilevel differential modulation techniques (64-DAPSK) for multicarrier transmission systems. *European Transactions on Telecommunication,* **6**(6): 633–40.

10.24 Van de Beek, J.-J., Sandell, M. and Borjesson, P.O. (1997) Tracking of time and frequency offset in the uplink of an OFDM-based system for UMTS. *IEEE Transactions on Signal Processing*, **45**(7): 1800–5.

10.25 Shepherd, S., Orriss, J. and Barton, S. (1998) Asymptotic limits in peak envelope power reduction by redundant coding in orthogonal frequency-division multiplex modulation. *IEEE Transactions on Communications*, **46**(1): 5–10.

10.26 May, T. and Rohling, H. (1998) Reducing the peak-to-average power ratio transmission systems. In *Proceedings IEEE VTC'98*, Ottawa, May, pp. 2474–8.

Chapter 11

Turbo-codes

As we saw in Chapter 5, Claude Shannon described bounds on the capacity of a communication channel in 1948, and even showed that codes existed that could in principle achieve them – namely random codes [11.1]. However, for more than 40 years following his work, it was found to be very difficult to approach the bounds in practice, with codes that were decodable with a reasonable degree of computational effort. It seemed that every class of code that had a computationally feasible decoding algorithm could not approach the Shannon bound in performance. This led one researcher to comment (in view of the fact that there must be an infinite number of very long random codes that do achieve the Shannon bound) that 'all codes are good, except for the ones we can think of' [11.2].

In fact, it was long conjectured that the *computational cut-off rate* [11.3, p. 184], another information theoretic concept, constituted a bound on codes that could be practically decoded. This rate had been achieved quite early on using long convolutional codes with sequential decoding, but was still a few dB from the Shannon bound.

Hence considerable excitement, not to mention a degree of scepticism, was aroused in 1993 at the International Conference on Communications (held that year in Geneva) when a paper was presented [11.4] describing codes that were claimed to approach within 0.7 dB of the Shannon bound. The authors were Claude Berrou, Alain Glavieux and P. Thitimajshima, from École Nationale Supérieure Télécommunications (ENST) de Bretagne, Brest, France, a group previously little known in the coding community. However, their work was soon replicated by many other researchers, and in the past few years 'turbo-codes', as their inventors named them, have become a major focus of coding research and development, and achieved practical application within a few years of their discovery, for example in the Mars Pathfinder space mission of 1996–1998 [11.5]. Their use for similar deep space communication systems has now been standardized by the Consultative Committee on Space Data Systems (CCSDS) [11.6]. They are also likely to appear in the standards for third-generation mobile radio systems, UMTS/IMT-2000 [11.7], and are under consideration for digital broadcasting applications, among many others.

Despite the suddenness with which they burst on the coding community, 'turbo-codes' are really a natural development of two somewhat older concepts, namely *concatenated coding* and *iterative decoding*. In fact, the term 'turbo-code' is something of a misnomer when applied to the code: it refers more to the principle of iterative decoding than to the codes themselves. In this chapter we therefore begin by considering concatenated codes and array codes, and developing the iterative decoder for these codes, by which the composite code can be decoded using separate decoders for the component codes. A vital element of this decoder is the *soft in, soft out* (SISO) component decoder, which we consider in Section 11.3 in its main form (the MAP decoder) and some of its variants. We then proceed in Section 11.4 to the 'turbo-codes' described by Berrou *et al.* An important part of these is the interleaver that occurs between the component encoders: in Section 11.5 we consider alternative forms of these and their effect on code performance. In Section 11.6 we describe the performance achieved by turbo-codes, and compare it with various information theoretic bounds. Section 11.7 extends our consideration to more bandwidth efficient systems: 'turbo-coded modulation'. In the final section we consider briefly other applications of the 'turbo-principle', including 'turbo-product codes', which are really simply conventional array codes iteratively decoded. In spite of its relatively recent origin, this field of research has developed very rapidly, and thus in many of these areas we can do no more than outline the main principles, directing the reader to the original papers for more detail.

11.1 Concatenated coding and array codes

Concatenated coding has been known for many years as a method of combining two or more relatively simple codes to provide much more powerful coding. The principle is simple: it is illustrated in Fig. 11.1. The output of the first (*outermost*) encoder is simply fed to the input of the second, and so on. In the decoder, the last (or *innermost*) code is decoded first, its output is fed to the next, and so on to the outermost decoder. Thus the effective code on the channel is much longer than any of the *component* codes, while it can be

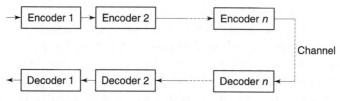

Figure 11.1   Principle of concatenated coding

decoded by the relatively simple component decoders. For example, we might use a $(31, 27)$ 2-error correcting Reed–Solomon (RS) code as the outer code, and a $(15, 5)$ 3-error correcting BCH code as the inner. The symbols of the RS code correspond to 5 bits each, i.e. to one codeword of the inner code. The composite code therefore has a total length of $31 \times 15 = 465$ bits, including 135 data bits. Error correcting power is more difficult to evaluate, since it depends on the distribution of the errors: the code will in fact only guarantee to correct 6 bit errors, but will normally correct many more than that. Other combinations are of course possible: for example the inner code might be a convolutional code. In fact, the most powerful code available before the advent of turbo-codes used a concatenation of a constraint length 7 convolutional inner code and a Reed–Solomon outer code: this code was used in a number of deep space missions (see Section 7.6.2).

This concept in its simplest form has a number of disadvantages. First, apart from the innermost decoder, all the decoders receive only hard decisions: they cannot perform soft decision decoding. Hence overall decoding cannot be maximum likelihood. Second, decoding errors in the inner code tend to give rise to error bursts, which the outer code may not be able to cope with.

One class of concatenated code which avoids at least the second of these problems is the *array* or *product code* [11.8, 11.9]. This is most easily illustrated for a concatenation of two codes, as in Fig. 11.2, although the principle can extend to more. We feed the data for one code (say the outer code) into the

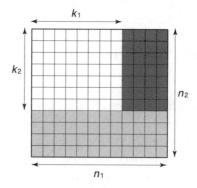

Figure 11.2   Two-dimensional array code

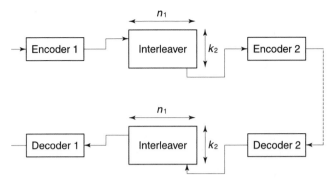

Figure 11.3   Encoder/decoder for array code

rows of an array, usually one codeword into each row (i.e. k_1 bits). This is the unshaded part of Fig. 11.2. We then generate the $n_1 - k_1$ parity check bits for each codeword, and put them into the shaded area on the right of the array. Finally, we use a second encoder to generate check bits for the columns of the array (including the parity check bits of the row code), and put the result into the lower shaded part of the array. Thus the whole array forms an $(n_1 \times n_2, k_1 \times k_2)$ code. It includes an $((n_1 - k_1) \times (n_2 - k_2))$ block of 'checks on checks' in the bottom right-hand corner of the array. Note that if the codes are linear, and the same code is used for all columns and all rows, then the same set of 'checks on checks' is generated if the columns are encoded first.

This code can be generated by a concatenation of the two encoders, but this time including an interleaver, as shown in Fig. 11.3. The interleaver is $n_1 \times k_2$, and the codewords generated by the first code are fed into its rows. It is then read out column-by-column, and fed to the second encoder, which generates the check bits for the bottom part of the array. This is then decoded in the reverse order, with a de-interleaver between.

Now if a word error occurs in decoder 2, this will corrupt, in effect, one column of the array. This, however, will affect only one bit of each codeword of code 1, and decoder 1 should be able to deal with this. We may also say that the de-interleaver has broken up error bursts due to the decoding errors in the inner code. We will revisit these codes in Section 11.8.

11.2   Iterative decoding

The optimum decoder for the joint code would find the maximum-likelihood solution for the whole code array at once, but of course this would be prohibitively complex. In the decoder of Fig. 11.3, however, decoder 1 must still work with hard decisions from decoder 2, and therefore information will be lost.

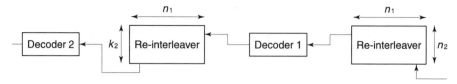

Figure 11.4   Alternative decoder

Note that it would be equally possible to perform the decoding in the opposite order, as shown in Fig. 11.4. In this structure the rows of the array are fed first into decoder 1 (after appropriate reordering using a de-interleaver). They are then re-interleaved, and the columns are decoded.

These two decoders behave differently with the same received signal. Figure 11.5 shows two error patterns in the received data. Taking the hard decision decoding case for the moment, and assuming that both row and column codes can correct single errors, then the decoder of Fig. 11.3 (column first) will successfully decode the pattern in (a), but the pattern in (b) will result in two column errors, which in turn are likely to give rise to several row errors. Conversely, the row-first decoder of Fig. 11.4 will decode the pattern in (b), but fail on the pattern in (a). Clearly, it would be helpful to combine the information generated by each decoder. This can be done by feeding the same signal to both decoders, but using the output of one to assist in the operation of the other.

It would also be helpful to be able to use soft information from the output of one decoder in the next decoder in a concatenated scheme. Such information could, in principle, be available: for example if a received signal is close in Euclidean distance to the decoded word, then we have a much higher degree of confidence regarding that word than if the signal is close to the boundary of the decision region.

We therefore require a decoder for each component code that can yield soft information at its output on the reliability of its decisions. It should also accept

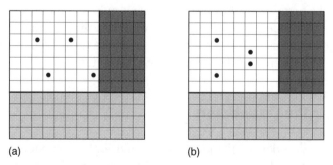

(a)   (b)

Figure 11.5   Two error patterns for an example in which row and column codes will correct single errors. The pattern in (a) will be decoded correctly if columns are decoded first, and in (b) if rows are decoded first

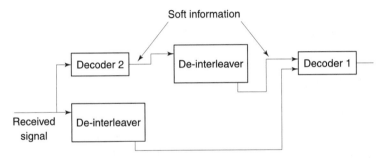

Figure 11.6   Joint decoder using soft information

additional information at its input taken from the previous decoder. We may then construct a decoder for the joint code, which is able to make use of information from each of the component decoders, as shown in Fig. 11.6.

However, this decoder still does not make use of the soft information from decoder 1 in decoding code 2. This could be done by feeding the soft output of decoder 1 back into decoder 2, and performing another iteration of the decoding, as shown in Fig. 11.7. Further iterations can then be performed, each resulting in a further refinement of the data estimate, eventually converging (in most cases) on a solution with a small number of data errors. Typically eight or more iterations may be used.

Figure 11.7 shows the form in which the decoder is normally implemented: a pipelined architecture in which the data is transferred to additional hardware

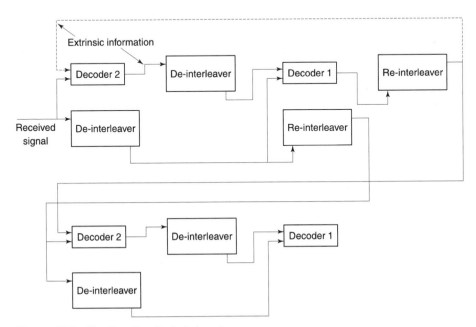

Figure 11.7   The iterative (turbo) decoder

for each additional iteration, while subsequent data blocks are processed in the first set of hardware. The diagram is, however, sometimes drawn as a single set, with feedback from the output to the input of decoder 2, indicating that the same data could be processed repeatedly by the same hardware. It is this decoder structure that led to the term 'turbo' as applied to iterative decoding, by analogy with a turbo-engine, in which a part of the energy at the output is fed back to the input to assist in the operation of the engine [11.4]. Hence, the term really applies to the decoding, not to the codes themselves.

The operation of the iterative decoder can also be understood in terms of the code array of Fig. 11.2. The decoder first performs row decoding, which generates initial estimates of the data in the array. For each data bit there will be both a tentative decision and a reliability estimate for that decision. The columns may then be decoded, working from the original input signal, but taking into account the information from the first decoding. This is known as a priori information on the data. This second decoding in its turn will further refine the data decision and its reliability estimate. There will then be information available that was not used in the first row decoding, so the row decoding is repeated, and so on, until the data estimates have converged.

The a priori information for the next decoder can be obtained from the log likelihood of the data symbols at the output of the previous decoder. However, this embodies all the information available to the decoder, both from the received data symbol and from the redundant symbols associated with that decoder. We must forward to the next decoder only that information which comes from the redundancy, since the information from the data symbol is already available to it. This is called the *extrinsic information* [11.4], and is obtained by subtracting the log likelihood obtained from the data symbol from the total log likelihood at the decoder output. (The information from the code stream is called the *intrinsic* information.) This will be illustrated in Example 11.1 below.

11.3 The SISO decoder

A vital part of the iterative decoder is evidently a decoder for the component codes which accepts soft a priori information at its input from previous decoding attempts (in addition to the input signal), and generates soft information at its output on the reliability of its decisions. The most common form of this is widely known as a *maximum a posteriori* (MAP) decoder or, more generally and perhaps more accurately, a *soft in, soft out* (SISO) decoder. In Appendix 2 we describe in more detail the exact operation of this algorithm and several of its variants, the log-MAP, the max-log-MAP and the soft output Viterbi (SOVA) algorithms.

Figure 11.8   Inputs and outputs of soft in, soft out decoder

The preferred form for this soft information is as log likelihood ratios (LLRs), which encapsulate reliability information (see Section 5.6.3). Hence the decoder, viewed as a 'black box', takes the form shown in Fig. 11.8. Its inputs are a vector **r** of received symbol values from the channel, and a vector λ_i of a priori LLRs for the corresponding data symbols. Its outputs are similarly a vector of data symbol estimates **d̂**, and a vector λ_o of their LLRs after decoding. Of course the data estimates are given by the sign of the LLRs, and hence only one actual output is required, although we may also need to derive the extrinsic information for use in the iterative decoder described above.

The MAP/SISO decoder is usually implemented using the Bahl–Cocke–Jelinek–Raviv (BCJR) [11.10] algorithm (see Section A2.1), also known as the *forward–backward* algorithm, for reasons that will shortly become apparent. It operates on a trellis representation of the code, which is usually convolutional. (The trellis is usually terminated by adding 'tail bits', as described in Section 7.3.1.)

Figure 11.9 shows an example trellis. Consider, for example, the trellis section outlined. Those branches shown dashed correspond to data '1' at this point. However, their likelihood depends not only on their probability in this trellis section, but on the probabilities of the paths through the whole trellis of which they are part. Hence the LLR is given by the ratio of the sum of probabilities of all trellis paths which include one of the dashed branches, to those of all paths including one of the solid branches. To evaluate this, we must find the relative probabilities of paths leading to the nodes on the left of the trellis, and also of those leading from the nodes on the right to the termination of the trellis. The former probabilities, usually denoted by α for each node, can be determined by a forward pass through the trellis similar to that employed by the Viterbi algorithm, but the latter, denoted by β, is best

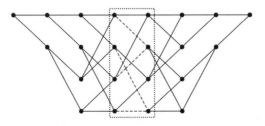

Figure 11.9   Example trellis to illustrate the BCJR algorithm

obtained by a backward pass using the same algorithm, from the termination back to the start. Hence 'forward–backward'. The probabilities of each branch given the received signal are similarly denoted by γ.

The LLR of a given symbol can then be calculated from the relative probabilities of the nodes on the left and right of the corresponding trellis section, and from the probabilities of the branches of the section given the received code symbols (the αs, βs and γs). Here we also take into account the a priori information, since the information that the symbol is more likely to be '1' than '0' will increase the probabilities of the dashed branches, and affect the overall LLR.

More detail of the MAP algorithm, including the derivation of the αs, βs and γs, and a pseudo-code representation of the algorithm, are given in Appendix A2. The algorithm is frequently simplified by working in terms of LLRs, rather than direct probabilities, which converts multiplications to summations, and avoids exponentiations. This results in the log-MAP algorithm, described in Appendix A2.3. While the transformation to log likelihoods simplifies multiplication, it considerably complicates additions. A further simplification, called the max-log-MAP algorithm, is also possible, and is obtained by approximating this sum by the maximum of the log likelihoods. It is described in Section A2.4, where we show that it gives the same decisions as the Viterbi algorithm, and indeed requires the same calculations as the Viterbi algorithm, although two passes are still required. A final simplification, described in Section A2.5, is essentially an elaboration of the Viterbi algorithm, called the *soft output Viterbi algorithm* (SOVA), and provides some soft output information. For the two last algorithms this will not be as accurate as that provided by the MAP or log-MAP algorithms.

We now give a simple example of the decoding of a concatenated code, in order to illustrate both soft output decoding based on log likelihoods, and iterative decoding using extrinsic information.

Example 11.1

Consider what is probably the simplest possible non-trivial concatenated code: a 2×2 array to which a single parity check code is added on both rows and columns (excluding the checks on checks). The example codeword is:

$$
\begin{array}{cc|c}
1 & 1 & 0 \\
0 & 1 & 1 \\
\hline
1 & 0 &
\end{array}
$$

This codeword is transmitted, mapping '1' $\Rightarrow +1$ and '0' $\Rightarrow -1$, and noise of mean power 0.5 is added (so that the signal-to-noise ratio is 3 dB), resulting in the received signals:

$$
\begin{array}{cc|c}
1.38 & 0.67 & -0.88 \\
-1.68 & -0.17 & 1.47 \\
\hline
-0.03 & -2.21 &
\end{array}
$$

Note that this would be received incorrectly without coding, and that it could not be decoded by hard decision decoding of the row and column codes. Use iterative decoding to obtain an improved decoding.

Solution The log likelihood ratios of the data alone are given by:

$$
L_{ij}^{d} = \log \left\{ \frac{\exp[-(r_{ij}-1)^2/2\sigma^2]}{\exp[-(r_{ij}+1)^2/2\sigma^2]} \right\} = \frac{(r_{ij}+1)^2 - (r_{ij}-1)^2}{2\sigma^2} = \frac{2r_{ij}}{\sigma^2} \qquad (11.1)
$$

where the subscripts denote the position of the data in the array. This yields the likelihoods:

$$
\begin{array}{cc}
5.46 & 2.65 \\
-6.67 & -0.66
\end{array}
$$

We now calculate the log likelihoods by decoding the horizontal code. For each symbol we find the ratio of the total likelihoods of those codewords in which it is '1' to those in which it is '0':

$$
L_{ij}^{h} = \log \left[\frac{P(\mathbf{r}|d_{ij} = 1 \,\&\, d_{i,3-j} = 1 \,\&\, d_{i,3} = 0) + P(\mathbf{r}|d_{ij} = 1 \,\&\, d_{i,3-j} = 0 \,\&\, d_{i,3} = 1)}{P(\mathbf{r}|d_{ij} = 0 \,\&\, d_{i,3-j} = 1 \,\&\, d_{i,3} = 1) + P(\mathbf{r}|d_{ij} = 0 \,\&\, d_{i,3-j} = 0 \,\&\, d_{i,3} = 0)} \right]
$$

$$
= \log \left\{ \left(\exp\left[-\frac{(r_{ij}-1)^2 + (r_{i,3-j}-1)^2 + (r_{i,3}+1)^2}{2\sigma^2} \right] \right. \right.
$$

$$
\left. + \exp\left[-\frac{(r_{ij}-1)^2 + (r_{i,3-j}+1)^2 + (r_{i,3}-1)^2}{2\sigma^2} \right] \right) \Big/
$$

$$
\left(\exp\left[-\frac{(r_{ij}+1)^2 + (r_{i,3-j}-1)^2 + (r_{i,3}-1)^2}{2\sigma^2} \right] \right.
$$

$$
\left. \left. + \exp\left[-\frac{(r_{ij}+1)^2 + (r_{i,3-j}+1)^2 + (r_{i,3}+1)^2}{2\sigma^2} \right] \right) \right\} \qquad (11.2)
$$

Note that by Bayes theorem $P(\mathbf{d}|\mathbf{r})P(\mathbf{r}) = P(\mathbf{r}|\mathbf{d})P(\mathbf{d})$, and we are here assuming that $P(\mathbf{d})$ is the same for all data (i.e. we have no a priori information about $\mathbf{d}$), and that $P(\mathbf{r})$ is the same for all data.

Applying this to our received codeword we have:

$$
\begin{array}{cc}
7.76 & 6.01 \\
-6.02 & 4.82
\end{array}
$$

We can use the results of this decode as a priori information to improve our decoding of the vertical code. However, some of the information has come from the received data symbols, which are also available to the vertical decoder, so we should not provide this information again. Accordingly, we calculate the *extrinsic information* resulting from the horizontal decoding, by simply subtracting the horizontal decoding log likelihoods from the data log likelihoods. (Note that since log likelihoods effectively have the dimensions of information, this can genuinely be understood in terms of subtraction of information.) The extrinsic information here is:

$$\mathbf{L}^{\mathrm{e}} = \mathbf{L}^{\mathrm{h}} - \mathbf{L}^{\mathrm{d}} = \begin{bmatrix} 2.29 & 3.36 \\ 0.66 & 5.47 \end{bmatrix}$$

We can apply this as a priori information in calculating the vertical log likelihoods:

$$L_{ij}^{\mathrm{v}} = \log \left[\frac{\begin{array}{l} P(\mathbf{r}|d_{ij}=1 \, \& \, d_{3-i,j}=1 \, \& \, d_{3,j}=0)P_{\mathrm{p}}(d_{ij}=1)P_{\mathrm{p}}(d_{3-i,j}=1) \\ +P(\mathbf{r}|d_{ij}=1 \, \& \, d_{3-i,j}=0 \, \& \, d_{3,j}=1)P_{\mathrm{p}}(d_{ij}=1)P_{\mathrm{p}}(d_{3-i,j}=0) \end{array}}{\begin{array}{l} P(\mathbf{r}|d_{ij}=0 \, \& \, d_{3-i,j}=1 \, \& \, d_{3,j}=1)P_{\mathrm{p}}(d_{ij}=0)P_{\mathrm{p}}(d_{3-i,j}=1) \\ +P(\mathbf{r}|d_{ij}=0 \, \& \, d_{3-i,j}=0 \, \& \, d_{3,j}=0)P_{\mathrm{p}}(d_{ij}=0)P_{\mathrm{p}}(d_{3-i,j}=0) \end{array}} \right]$$

$$= L_{ij}^{\mathrm{e}} + \log \left\{ \left(\exp \left[L_{3-i,j}^{\mathrm{e}} - \frac{(r_{ij}-1)^2 + (r_{3-i,j}-1)^2 + (r_{3,j}+1)^2}{2\sigma^2} \right] \right. \right.$$

$$\left. + \exp \left[-\frac{(r_{ij}-1)^2 + (r_{3-i,j}+1)^2 + (r_{3,j}-1)^2}{2\sigma^2} \right] \right) \Big/$$

$$\left(\exp \left[-\frac{(r_{ij}+1)^2 - (r_{3-i,j}-1)^2 + (r_{3,j}-1)^2}{2\sigma^2} \right] \right.$$

$$\left. \left. + \exp \left[L_{3-i,j}^{\mathrm{e}} - \frac{(r_{ij}+1)^2 + (r_{3-i,j}+1)^2 + (r_{3,j}+1)^2}{2\sigma^2} \right] \right) \right\}$$

(11.3)

Note that this contains a component directly due to the extrinsic information, which can be discounted immediately, along with the component obtained from the received data symbols. Then the new estimate of the extrinsic information:

$$\mathbf{L}^{\mathrm{e}\prime} = \mathbf{L}^{\mathrm{v}} - \mathbf{L}^{\mathrm{d}} - \mathbf{L}^{\mathrm{e}} = \begin{bmatrix} -0.13 & 4.80 \\ 0.13 & 5.95 \end{bmatrix}, \quad \mathbf{L}^{\mathrm{v}} = \begin{bmatrix} 5.33 & 7.45 \\ -6.55 & 5.29 \end{bmatrix}$$

This can then be used in the next horizontal decode, and so on. It might appear here that the extrinsic information from the previous iteration has been added in and then immediately subtracted again, and therefore will have no overall effect. However, although the extrinsic information for a given symbol is immediately subtracted from that symbol, it nevertheless has an effect on other symbols through the term $L_{3-i,j}^{e}$ in Equation (11.3). In the example, the likelihoods for the next iteration are:

$$\mathbf{L}^h = \begin{bmatrix} 8.93 & 6.00 \\ -11.51 & 4.78 \end{bmatrix}, \quad \mathbf{L}^v = \begin{bmatrix} 5.33 & 7.41 \\ -6.55 & 5.28 \end{bmatrix}$$

at which point the decoding has converged, and in this case decoding is correct.

11.4 Parallel-concatenated convolutional codes

The original 'turbo-codes' of Berrou, Glavieux and Thitimajshima did not in fact use concatenated block codes in the form of array codes, as we have used above, but *parallel concatenated recursive-systematic convolutional codes* (PC-RSC codes). (It has subsequently been shown that the turbo-decoding principle applied to array codes can yield practically as good results, as we shall see in Section 11.7). The principle of parallel concatenation is to encode the same information simultaneously in two encoders, but one of the encoders is fed via an interleaver. The interleaver means that the same data symbol appears in two different contexts in the code stream, and hence can be iteratively decoded in the same way as above. The recursive-systematic code (RSC, see Section 7.1.3) allows the data symbols to be separated from the code symbols. The data is sent only once: only the parity symbol from each RSC is sent.

Note that parallel concatenation could equally well be applied to the array code of Fig. 11.2. The data are applied to the row encoder, resulting in the $((n_1 - k_1) \times k_2)$ block of parity check digits on the right-hand side of the array. In parallel it is interleaved and fed in column order to the column encoder, resulting in the $((n_2 - k_1) \times k_1)$ block of parity digits below the data array. Only the $((n_1 - k_1) \times (n_2 - k_2))$ block of 'checks on checks' at the bottom right of the array is missing.

The recursive-systematic code also has another property which contributes to the overall performance of the turbo-code. In the non-recursive encoder, a data sequence of finite weight (finite number of '1's) will always result in a code sequence of finite weight, because the encoder will always return to the zero state when the last data '1' is shifted out. Because of the feedback, however, an input data sequence that leaves the encoder in a non-zero state will continue indefinitely to generate code '1's even if the subsequent data stream remains at zero. (We may describe this as a sequence that does not *terminate* the encoder.) Hence a finite weight data sequence may, in principle, produce an infinite weight code sequence. For example, consider the encoder shown in Fig. 11.10. This is similar to that of Fig. 7.5, except that for

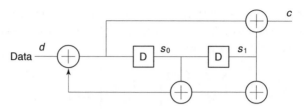

Figure 11.10   A four-state recursive-systematic encoder for a turbo-code

reasons which will shortly become clear, the feedback and feedforward generators are reversed. If the data sequence $1000\cdots$ is input, then the state of the
encoder (expressed in terms of the pair $\{s_0, s_1\}$, follows the sequence 10, 11,
01, $10\cdots$ and so on, indefinitely. (In fact for this feedback generator, although
not for that of Fig. 7.5, the encoder cycles through all possible non-zero states,
producing a repetitive sequence of period $2^{\nu-1} - 1$, called an *m-sequence*. Such
generators exist for all encoders, and tend to result in the best turbo-codes.)
Further, even if the code sequence is finite, a low weight data sequence may
produce a high weight code sequence. In Fig. 11.10, the data sequences
$10010\cdots$, $1000001\cdots$, etc., terminate the encoder producing code sequences
$11110\cdots$, $11101110\cdots$. In general, the weight of the code sequence will tend
to increase with the non-zero length of the data sequence (i.e. the span
between the first and the last '1'). As we will see, this behaviour combined
with the effect of the interleaver gives rise to the distance structure of the
turbo-code.

The resulting structure is shown in Fig. 11.11. It would naturally generate a
rate 1/3 code: two parity bits for each data bit. However, for the Berrou *et al.*
code one of the parity bits is punctured alternately for each data bit (cf. Section
7.5), so that a rate 1/2 code results [11.4, 11.11]. Higher rate codes can also be
produced using other, more drastic, puncture patterns. Alternatively (and
equivalently), we may replace the component encoder with a higher rate
encoder [11.12]. However, for reasons explored in Section 11.6, it is best not
to puncture the data stream.

The interleaver (denoted by π in the diagram) is not usually the straightforward rectangular interleaver that we have used up to this point. It is a
pseudo-random block interleaver: the data are read into it by rows and

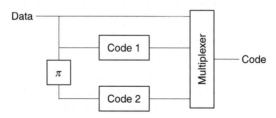

Figure 11.11   Parallel concatenated encoder

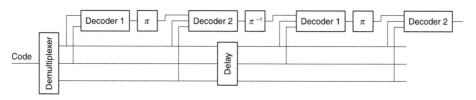

Figure 11.12   Decoder for parallel concatenated code

columns, as conventionally, but are read out in a pseudo-random order. The interleaver should also be as large as possible: the Berrou *et al.* code used a 65 536 interleaver. Various types of interleaver have been proposed: we will consider some of them and their effect on performance in the next section.

Figure 11.12 shows the decoder for this 'turbo-code'. Code 1 is first decoded, using the relevant set of parity bits and a SISO decoder. Again it is extrinsic information that is passed between decoders, rather than the decoded data. The extrinsic information from the first decoder is interleaved using the same pseudo-random order as the interleaver in the encoder, so that it appears in the same order as the parity of code 2. Code 2 can then be decoded in the same way, resulting in a refinement of the data estimate. This is then used to provide a priori information for a second iteration of Code 1, and so on. Two complete iterations are shown; many more are usually needed.

Figure 11.13 illustrates the principle of the code. It shows the two data sequences that might be fed simultaneously to the two decoders, one shaded grey (which is fed to code 1), the other shaded diagonally (fed to code 2). The bit shaded both grey and diagonally is the first bit of both sequences. Hence this bit is decoded first in the context of the grey sequence, which leads to one estimate of its LLR, then in the context of the diagonally shaded sequence, which leads to an independent estimate, just as in the case of the array code. A low correlation between the estimates (which is necessary for the efficient operation of the iterative decoder) is provided by the

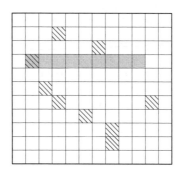

Figure 11.13   Sequences for parallel concatenated code in pseudo-random interleaver

interleaver, which ensures that these two sequences do not intersect again for some distance.

Note that normally the data are encoded and decoded interleaver-load by interleaver-load, rather than continuously, as the architecture and the use of convolutional codes might suggest. The trellises of the encoders are usually terminated by the addition of appropriate tail bits at the end of these blocks. Similarly, the decoders work on one block at a time, applying the forward–backward algorithm to each. In fact these blocks are encoded and decoded completely independently, so that turbo-codes are in effect block codes, albeit with an extremely long block length.

As our consideration of array codes has shown, PC-RSC codes are not the only codes to which the iterative decoding algorithm can be applied to achieve near-Shannon-limit performance. In fact, a wide range of structures have now been developed, including serially concatenated convolutional codes, and a variety of hybrids of parallel and serial concatenation [11.13].

11.5   Interleavers and distance spectra

The interleaver is clearly a vital constituent of the turbo-coder, and is one of the essential ingredients that result in the remarkable performance of turbo-codes. As we have seen above, the interleaver for parallel concatenated codes (the usual form of turbo-codes) is not a simple block (or rectangular) interleaver, but pseudo-random. The exact characteristics of the interleaver are very important in determining the performance of the code, and hence there has been much research into the optimum choice of interleaver [11.14, ch. 3].

The interleaver has a fundamental influence on the distance (or weight) spectrum of the code (cf. Sections 5.7 and 7.4), and in particular on the overall minimum distance. This also largely determines the BER performance of the code, although, as we will see, the operation of the iterative decoder is also important. In this section we will examine the distance spectra of some codes and the relationship with the interleaver.

Since it is difficult to calculate the distance spectrum of a turbo-code using a particular interleaver (it is best done by generating sample codewords), the concept of the *uniform interleaver* has been introduced [11.15]. The uniform interleaver is a probabalistic device that maps a data sequence of weight w to any other sequence of the same weight with equal probability – it might be regarded as a truly random, rather than merely pseudo-random, interleaver. It is not useful in practice, but only as a device to calculate bounds on distance spectra of actual codes.

For a uniform interleaver it may readily be shown that the expected *conditional weight distribution* of the parallel concatenated code, i.e. the average number of sequences of total weight d and data weight w:

$$A^{C_P}(w, d) = {}^N C_w \Pr\{[wt(C_1) + wt(C_2) = d]|wt(D) = w\}$$

$$= \sum_{d_1=0}^{d} \frac{A^{C_1}(w, d_1)A^{C_2}(w, d - d_1)}{{}^N C_w} \tag{11.4}$$

where $A^{C_{1,2}}(w, d_1)$ denotes the conditional weight distribution of the component codes C_1, C_2; and D denotes the data sequence. Note that for the purposes of this calculation C_1 contains the systematic data stream as well as the first component parity stream, while C_2 consists of the second parity stream only.

This calculation indicates how the interleaver combined with the properties of the RSC component code results in an advantageous distance structure. Consider a data sequence that terminates the first component encoder, resulting in a finite and low weight code output. This is then interleaved and fed to the second encoder. For a randomly chosen interleaver, the probability that it will also terminate the second encoder and produce a second low weight code sequence is small. Hence even if there are code sequences of low weight (which is to say pairs of codewords with small Hamming distance), the multiplicity of such words is small, which results in a low BER.

By an argument similar to the one Shannon used in establishing his bound on code performance (see Section 5.5.2) we may show that the distance spectrum of Equation (11.4) results in an upper bound on the BER of a turbo-code using the 'best' interleaver. Since it is an average over all possible interleavers, there must be at least one actual interleaver that performs at least as well as this.

However, unlike the Shannon bound, this bound does not appear to be very tight. Figure 11.14 compares the uniform interleaver bound with the estimated distance spectrum using a pseudo-random interleaver (that defined in [11.11])

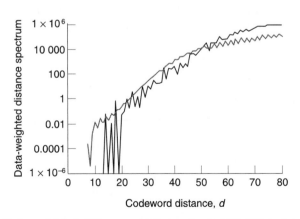

Figure 11.14 Data-weighted distance spectrum of a length 256 turbo-code using an actual interleaver (black line) compared with uniform interleaver bound (grey line), plotted on a log scale

and four-state component codes [11.16]. (Note that the error-weighted distance spectrum does not consist only of integers, since it is weighted by the proportion of the data bits in the block that are in error. The uniform bound, being a statistical average, is also not constrained to have only integer values.) The distance spectrum of the actual code was estimated by exhaustive search of codewords with low data weights, and Monte Carlo estimation for other codewords. We observe that for smaller distances the actual distance spectrum generally falls below the bound, and most significantly that the minimum distance is in fact 14, while the bound suggests it might be as low as eight. As we will see below, these differences result in a significant difference between the BER of the actual code and the uniform interleaver bound, especially at higher signal-to-noise ratios.

These results suggest that, in fact, the choice of interleaver is very important, since there are interleavers that perform noticeably better than the average (and, presumably, many that perform noticeably worse). This has led to further research in the subject. We have noted above that low weight data sequences may result in high or even (potentially) infinite weight code sequences when applied to the RSC encoder. The task of the interleaver is to ensure that those that result in low weight code sequences in one encoder do not also give rise to low weights in the other encoder. There are a number of possible choices of interleaver.

The most obvious is the conventional rectangular, or block interleaver. However, this has a major drawback. Consider a pair of weight 2 data sequences which map into the interleaver as shown in Fig. 11.15, and suppose that the data sequence $10010\cdots$ terminates the encoder producing a low weight sequence. Then when read out and encoded by rows, two low weight non-zero code sequences will be generated. However, when read out by columns the same pair of data sequences are generated, which will also produce two low weight code sequences from the second encoder. Moreover, there are a large number of such patterns, since this block of '1's would

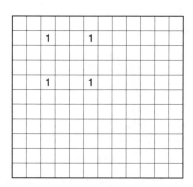

Figure 11.15   Data sequence in rectangular interleaver (remainder of interleaver is filled with '0's)

result in the same code weight wherever in the interleaver it was placed. This effect is especially important for large interleavers.

This behaviour is partly due to the uniformity of the structure of the rectangular interleaver, in that a pattern that gives a low weight codeword when placed in one part of it will do so throughout the interleaver. It is unlikely to occur in a pseudo-randomly generated interleaver. Berrou and Glavieux described a suitable pseudo-random interleaving algorithm for their original turbo-code [11.11]: this was used in the code of Fig. 11.14. It produces good interleavers (not necessarily the best) for lengths which are powers of 2, but appears to work less well for other lengths. Other pseudo-random algorithms have been developed, for example the JPL algorithm [11.17]. Other interleavers are described in [11.14].

A desirable property of an interleaver is clearly to 'spread' the data sequence so that sequences with short non-zero spans are interleaved to form long spans. This will tend to cause data sequences with low weight in one encoder to give high weight in the other encoder. (It does not, however, rule out the behaviour illustrated above for the rectangular interleaver.) We may define a *spreading factor S* for an interleaver [11.14] as:

An interleaver has a *spreading factor S* if any data sequence of non-zero span less than S is interleaved to form a sequence of span greater than S, and *vice versa*.

Example 11.2

Find the spreading factor of a rectangular interleaver.

Solution   Consider a $k_1 \times k_2$ rectangular interleaver, where $k_1 \times k_2 = N$, as shown in Fig. 11.16. Consider pairs of data '1's that are $l - 1$ places apart when read out horizontally (i.e. they have a non-zero span of l). Clearly if the $l - 1$ places do not overlap the end of a row, as in the pair of positions labelled 'a' in the diagram, then the interleaved sequence, read out vertically, will put these data '1's $l' - 1 = (l - 1) \times k_1$ places apart. If the sequence does overlap the end of a row, as in case 'b', then the interleaved '1's will be $l' - 1 = (k_2 - l - 1) \times k_1 - 1$ places apart, $l - 1 \leq k_2$. Only if $l - 1 = k_2$, as in 'c', will the interleaved sequence have a very small non-zero span. Hence, we can state that for $l - 1 < k_2$, $l' - 1 > k_1$. If we start with the sequence read out vertically, we simply reverse the positions of k_1 and k_2, and hence we can also state that for $l' - 1 < k_1$, $l - 1 > k_2$. Hence, in either case, if the non-zero span (l or l') of the input sequence is less than $\min(k_1 + 1, k_2 + 1)$, then the non-zero span of the interleaved sequence (l' or l) is greater than this. Hence:

$$S = \min(k_1 + 1, k_2 + 1) \tag{11.5}$$

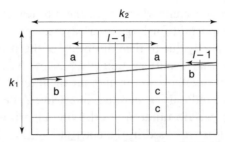

Figure 11.16   Rectangular interleaver to illustrate calculation of spreading factor

In fact the spreading factor obtained by a square interleaver, with $k_1 = k_2 = \sqrt{N}$ is the largest possible for given interleaver size. However, as we have already seen, the rectangular interleaver gives quite poor results in a turbo-code. This is largely because all sequences with a given non-zero span tend to interleave to sequences with only a small number of different non-zero spans. In the example above we saw that non-zero spans $l < k_2 + 1$ all interleave to give non-zero spans of exactly $(l-1) \times k_1 + 1$ or exactly $(k_2 - l - 1) \times k_1$. This means that if a given input sequence does result in a low weight code sequence, then there will be a large number of other sequences that interleave to the same non-zero span, and therefore may also give low weight code sequences. Hence, the multiplicity of such sequences may be large. This has led some researchers to formulate another parameter, the *dispersion* of an interleaver [11.14], which measures the number of different non-zero spans resulting from input sequences of the same non-zero span. However, it is not as useful as the spreading factor in assessing interleavers. However, choosing an interleaver that is both pseudo-random and has a good spreading factor seems likely to lead to desirable properties: this results in the *spread-random* or *S-random* interleaver [11.14, 11.18].

In practice, random and spread-random interleavers must usually be implemented using a look-up table (which is drawn up using random number generators). For a large interleaver this gives rise to complexities, and it is often preferred to use a simple algorithm to obtain the index for reading out the data from the interleaver. The Berrou interleaver [11.11] and the JPL interleaver [11.6] are examples of random-like interleavers which can nevertheless be defined using such an algorithm. Another rather important interleaver of this type is that used in the UMTS standard.

Example 11.3

Description of an UMTS interleaver.

As mentioned above, the third-generation mobile radio system UMTS includes a turbo-code as one of its options for FEC code. The standard defines the interleaver used in full detail [11.7], for a wide range of possible interleaver sizes (which are referred to in the standard as K). Here we will describe the principles behind it, without going into the detail, and illustrate with reference to a length 1024 interleaver.

The interleaver is based on a conventional rectangular interleaver, with either 10 or 20 rows ($R = 10$ or 20), depending on the interleaver size. The number of columns, C, is chosen to be one more, one less, or equal to a prime number, p, whichever gives the size closest to that required. The input data is then read into an $R \times C$ array along the rows. If the interleaver size $K \neq RC$, then part of the interleaver is left empty.

For example, for interleaver length $K = 1024$, R is specified as 20. The next greater prime number than $1024/20$ is $p = 53$, but a row length $C = p - 1 = 52$ gives $RC = 1040$, which is closer to 1024.

The data are then permuted within the rows, and the rows themselves are also permuted, before the data are read out by columns. It is clearly this permutation that ensures that the interleaver performs better than a simple rectangular interleaver.

The permutation along the rows (called the *intra-row permutation* in the standard) can be regarded as two successive permutations, although it is not described in this way in the standard. The first operates on all rows, so that in effect it permutes the columns. The ith column after permutation is taken from the original position $c(i)$, where:

$$c(i) = [g_0 \times c(i - 1)] \bmod (p)$$

where the columns are numbered 0 to $C - 1$. For $p = 53$ the standard specifies $g_0 = 2$, and the permutation pattern is:

{0, 1, 3, 7, 15, 31, 10, 21, 43, 34, 16, 33, 14, 29, 6, 13, 27, 2, 5, 11, 23, 47, 42, 32, 12, 25, 51, 50, 48, 44, 36, 20, 41, 30, 8, 17, 35, 18, 37, 22, 45, 38, 24, 49, 46, 40, 28, 4, 9, 19, 39, 26}

Note that this type of permutation, in which whole columns are moved, will not avoid the problem illustrated in Fig. 11.15, since the pattern given there would still be read out by columns to form two low weight code sequences. For this reason the rows are permuted again, but this time a different permutation is applied to each row. A set of numbers p_j, $j = 0 \cdots R - 1$, relatively prime to $p - 1$ are chosen, and the ith row is further permuted according to the function:

$$c_j(i) = (i \times p_j) \bmod (p - 1)$$

Thus, for example, overall the first row is permuted according to the pattern:

{1, 14, 37, 41, 44, 33, 38, 2, 28, 21, 29, 35, 13, 23, 4, 3, 42, 5, 17, 26, 46, 8, 6, 31, 10, 34, 52, 39, 16, 12, 9, 20, 15, 51, 25, 32, 24, 18, 40, 30, 49, 50, 11, 48, 36, 27, 7, 45, 47, 22, 43, 19, 0} while the pattern of the second is:

{1, 19, 43, 22, 47, 45, 7, 27, 36, 48, 11, 50, 49, 30, 40, 18, 24, 32, 25,
51, 15, 20, 9, 12, 16, 39, 52, 34, 10, 31, 6, 8, 46, 26, 17, 5, 42, 3, 4, 23,
13, 35, 29, 21, 28, 2, 38, 33, 44, 41, 37, 14, 0}

It is interesting to note that this does not necessarily give a very large spreading factor: in the example, S is only 4. However, the performance of the resulting turbo-code is good, giving a lower error floor than an S-random interleaver of the same length with spreading factor 19, and much better performance than the 32×32 rectangular interleaver, which has the maximum possible spreading factor of 33. The interleaver also has the advantage that it is largely deterministically defined, using only a few look-up tables, while an S-random interleaver would require a comparatively large look-up table for each possible interleaver length. The UMTS interleaver is defined for every possible length between 320 and 5114 bits.

11.6 Performance of turbo-codes

It was, of course, the performance of turbo-codes, attaining close to the Shannon bound, that caused such an explosion of interest in the topic. This was first demonstrated by simulation, rather than by any form of theoretical analysis: it was only later that some degree of theoretical understanding of the reasons for their performance was attained. There are, in fact, two aspects to the performance of turbo-coding: first, the structure of the codes themselves and, second, the performance and, especially, the convergence of the iterative decoding algorithm. These are still extremely active areas of research, and definitive theories are not yet available, but we will review the main principles briefly, and describe the empirical results that have been obtained by simulation.

As we have seen in Chapter 5, the performance of any code depends on its structure, in terms of the minimum distance and the distance spectrum. In calculating the BER, rather than the word or event error probability, the number of bit errors in each erroneous codeword is also important.

It is interesting to note that in turbo-codes, as in concatenated codes in general, the minimum distance may not be very large. We noted above for the example of the concatenated $(31, 27)$ RS code and $(15, 5)$ BCH code (an overall $(465, 135)$ code) that the error-correcting power was 6, corresponding to a minimum distance of 13. While this is still a matter of controversy, because as we have seen it depends on the exact structure of a large pseudo-random interleaver, something similar seems to apply to PC-RSC turbo-codes: the minimum distance may be no more than 10 or 20.

The reason for this may be observed from the structure of the encoder. As usual, we take the all-zeros word as a reference: a turbo-code is just as much a linear code as any other convolutional code. For a recursive code there will be a number of possible data sequences (terminating sequences) which return the encoder to the zero state after a relatively short period, resulting in a short path with weight close to the minimum distance of the component code. Such sequences, however, are 'scrambled' by the interleaver, so that when they are presented to the second encoder, it is unlikely that they will also be such as to result in a low weight code sequence from this encoder. While it is unlikely, it is not however impossible, and for a large interleaver there may well be a few possible data sequences that result in low weight sequences from both codes.

This being so, how is it that turbo-codes achieve such good performance? The answer appears to be that the number of such data sequences is very small (because as we have seen their probability is small), and thus that each codeword has only a very small number of neighbours at the minimum distance. Thus the error probability contribution is small. It is this contribution that results in the 'error floor' that has been observed in some turbo-codes.

The absolute lower limit on the minimum distance is thus only the sum of the minimum distances of the component codes. However, if the interleaver has a non-zero spreading factor (as described in Section 11.5), then, by definition, any data sequence with non-zero span less than S will interleave to give a span greater than S. Since the code weight of the component code is roughly proportional to the non-zero span, this will result in a minimum distance some-what larger than this absolute minimum, which tends to increase with S.

Note also that where low weight code sequences occur, they usually affect only a few data bits because the data weight is small. Hence the number of data errors arising from a word error associated with them is small, much smaller than the number of bits per word. Equation (5.39) gave an estimate of the BER:

$$P_b \leq \sum_j e_j Q\left(\frac{d_j}{2\sigma}\right) \tag{11.6}$$

where e_j is the sum of the number of bit errors corresponding to all erroneous codewords at distance d_j from the correct word, divided by the number of data bits per word. In terms of the conditional weight distribution calculated in Equation (11.4) we may write:

$$e_j = \sum_{w=1}^{N} \frac{w}{N} A^{C_p}(w, d = j) \tag{11.7}$$

For turbo-codes, the number of bit errors associated with the minimum distance word is usually of the order of four or less, whereas the number of bits per word is the size of the interleaver. Thus e_j is usually very small, resulting in a very low error floor. Much larger values occur at larger distances, because there are many more possible sequences of higher weight. This, of

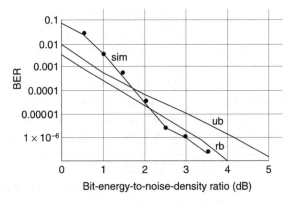

Figure 11.17   Simulated BER (sim) of rate 1/3 length 256 turbo-code compared with uniform interleaver bound (ub) and union bound obtained from pseudo-random interleaver (rb)

course, approaches the structure of a random code, and we know from Shannon's work that random codes have good performance.

Figure 11.17 shows the performance of the code whose distance spectrum is shown in Fig. 11.14. The union bound of (11.6) has been used to obtain bounds from both the estimated actual distance spectrum and the uniform interleaver bound, and these are compared with simulation results using the iterative MAP decoder. We note that, as expected, the uniform interleaver bound gives a quite pessimistic estimate of BER; that based on the estimated spectrum is quite close to the simulation, at least at high signal-to-noise ratios. We note that the BER reaches an 'error floor' at around 2.5-dB E_b/N_0, due to the minimum distance of the code. For larger interleavers this error floor is likely to be much lower. The uniform interleaver approach enables us to relate the level of the error floor to the size of the interleaver, giving the so-called 'interleaver gain'. This depends on the structure of the encoder, but for PC-RSC codes the error floor varies inversely with the interleaver size.

The code used here has very simple constituent codes: performance improves rapidly with larger numbers of states. For example, for 16-state codes with an interleaver length 1000, BER $= 10^{-6}$ can be achieved at about 0.4 dB, only about 0.9 dB from the Shannon bound.

The second issue concerns the performance of the decoding algorithm. In using Equation (11.6) we are in effect assuming that the iterative algorithm achieves maximum likelihood (ML) performance. Comparison with simulation appears to show that, in practice, it does for most cases, but theoretical studies have shown that convergence of the algorithm is not in fact guaranteed. The rate of convergence also depends on the code. Figure 11.18 shows the simulation results for the Berrou *et al.* code, after 1, 2, 3, 6 and 18 decoder iterations. Convergence to very close to the Shannon bound is clear, although a law of

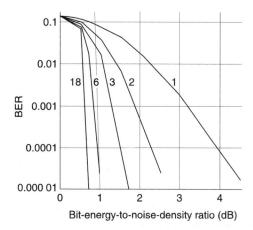

Figure 11.18   Simulation results for Berrou _et al._ code, with different numbers of decoder iterations

diminishing returns operates after about six iterations. (Note that the Shannon bound for this code, being rate 1/2, is 0 dB.)

Figure 11.17 shows, however, that the iterative decoder does not in fact always achieve ML decoding. For E_b/N_0 below 2 dB the simulated BER is above the union bound. Since the union bound is an upper bound for ML decoding, this is clearly not achieved in this range. It is clearly important to ensure that the iterative decoder approaches as closely as possible to ML performance, which may require careful attention to the details of decoding, for example in the way extrinsic information is passed on. The interleaver may also influence the operation of the algorithm, since it depends on the lack of correlation between the extrinsic information extracted from the two decoders, which requires the code sequences to be independent as far as possible.

The iterative decoder also clearly requires that the component codes can be decoded separately. An extreme example of this is explored in [11.16], where alternative puncture patterns are investigated: an alternative pattern is considered which punctures the data stream completely, leaving the two component code streams unaffected. The rate of this code is also 1/2, and it in fact has a higher minimum distance than the conventional rate 1/2 punctured code. However, its performance is extremely poor, which can be attributed to the fact that the effective rate of the two component codes when presented to their decoders is unity, and hence no error correction is possible, and no valid extrinsic information can be passed on to the second decoder.

The iterative decoder has been described as a version of a more general algorithm known as _belief propagation_ [11.19, 11.20], in which the codes are described in the form of a diagram known as a _Tanner graph_. This consists of a network of nodes, which represent data symbols, and branches, which

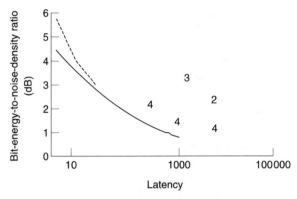

Figure 11.19 Bounds on required bit-energy-to-noise-density ratio versus latency, compared with some results for turbo-codes

represent the relationships between code and data symbols. Ideally, the belief propagation algorithm would operate on a Tanner graph which takes the form of a tree, with no loops in it, but for a turbo-code the graph has loops. The algorithm can still be applied, but the loops require an iterative approach: hence iterative decoding. The design of the interleaver should also ensure that the loops are long, which again relates to the independence of the extrinsic information from the two decoders.

The large interleavers of turbo-codes result in a significant latency, and hence overall delay. This may rule them out for some delay-limited applications, such as speech, although it is possible to trade complexity of component codes against interleaver size. There is in any case an information-theoretic limit to the coding gain for given latency [11.21], which is related to the limit on gain for a given block length, since a decoder must operate on a sufficiently long 'window' on the code sequence. The additional delay due to the iterative decoder we may treat as a processing delay, rather than inherent latency, since it could in principle be performed 'off-line' at a higher rate.

Figure 11.19 compares some results obtained for turbo-codes for $BER = 10^{-3}$ with the theoretical bounds for the same BER, showing that some turbo-codes are within about 1 dB of the bounds. Result marked '1' is for the Berrou *et al.* code [11.4]; '2' is from [11.22], '3' from [11.23]; while the results marked '4' are obtained by Valenti and Woerner [11.24] using three different interleaver lengths.

11.7 Turbo-coded modulation

The turbo-codes as so far described are binary, and thus provide relatively low bandwidth efficiency. In this section we consider how they can be employed in

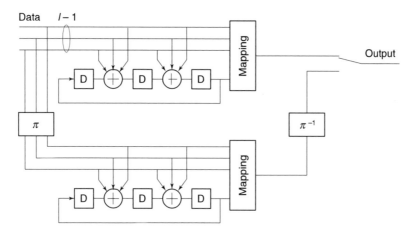

Data $l-1$

Mapping

Output

π

π^{-1}

Mapping

Figure 11.20   Turbo trellis coded modulation encoder

coded modulation schemes, to extend the benefits of turbo-codes to systems in which spectral efficiencies around or greater than $1\,\mathrm{bit\,s^{-1}\,Hz^{-1}}$ are required.

There are two basic approaches to what might be called 'turbo-coded modulation', based, respectively, on trellis coded modulation and on multilevel coded modulation. The distinction is basically whether one turbo-code or multiple separate codes are used. A version of the former approach, which we will call turbo trellis coded modulation (T-TCM) was the earliest to be described [11.25]. A different but equivalent version is described in [11.26]. In T-TCM (as described in [11.26]), two trellis coded modulation encoders in recursive-systematic form (RS-TCM) are employed (see Section 8.2.1), as illustrated in Fig. 11.20. For a modulation scheme with 2^l constellation points, $l-1$ data bits are input per symbol, and are fed to two identical RS-TCM encoders, the second via an interleaver operating on groups of $l-1$ bits. The encoders generate an additional code bit, so that the resulting l bits can be mapped (by set partitioning – see Section 8.1.3) to a modulated symbol. Note that the output of both encoder/modulators contains the systematic information as well as the code bits. The output of the second encoder/modulator is then de-interleaved to regenerate the original order. To avoid duplication of the systematic information, alternate symbols are selected from the two encoded symbol streams. The interleaver must also be designed with the constraint that even positions are interleaved to even positions, and odd to odd. The decoder is equivalent to the normal turbo-decoder except that the component decoders are TCM decoders, and the details of interleaving and de-interleaving are different (in view of the de-interleaver in the encoder).

The alternative approach is multilevel turbo-coded modulation (ML-TCM), introduced by Wachsmann and Huber [11.27]. Here, the MLCM approach is employed (Section 8.4), using binary turbo-codes as the component codes.

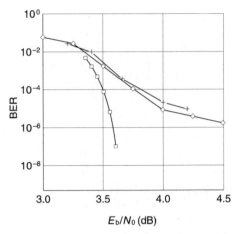

Figure 11.21 Comparison of turbo-coded modulation schemes, after: □ [11.12], ◇ [11.27], + [11.29]

Puncturing must be employed to yield the required rates for the component codes. Multistage decoding may then be employed, in which the stage decoders are binary turbo-codes. The demodulators must of course return soft information on each level of decoding, preferably log likelihood information according to Section 5.6.3.

Figure 11.21 compares these schemes, including a second, more complex version of T-TCM known as PCTCM [11.28]. All three use 8-PSK modulation and have a rate of 2 bits/symbol. The T-TCM scheme uses eight-state trellises and a length 2048 interleaver, while the ML-TCM scheme uses a 16-state trellis and a total interleaver length of 2000. The PCTCM scheme has a 16-state trellis and 4096 length interleaver, and maps the coded bits onto pairs of 8-PSK symbols, treated as a four-dimensional constellation. The diagram suggest that while the more complex PCTCM scheme is much better than the other two, T-TCM and ML-TCM have quite similar performance, although ML-TCM uses more complex component encoders. This suggests that the T-TCM approach may represent a good compromise between complexity and performance.

11.8   'Turbo-product codes', and other applications of the 'turbo-principle'

As we have seen, the term 'turbo' strictly applies only to the turbo-decoder, and hence the turbo-principle is really that of iterative decoding. This has other applications than decoding of turbo-codes. The most obvious of these is perhaps the decoding of other types of concatenated code, especially array

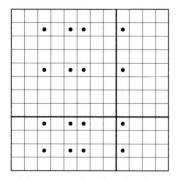

Figure 11.22   Pattern of minimum weight sequences in product code

or product codes. In fact, these codes with iterative decoding are now generally referred to as 'turbo-product codes' [11.30].

Pyndiah [11.30] describes an iterative decoding algorithm for such codes. Since the component codes are now block codes (in this case BCH codes) the Chase algorithm, adapted to provide a soft output, is used for the component decoders. Otherwise the decoder structure is exactly as described in Section 11.2 above. It is instructive, however, to compare the simulation results from [11.30] with a union bound, which is quite readily obtainable for these codes.

The distance spectrum of these product codes may readily be calculated as follows. Minimum weight sequences must have a pattern within the array of the form shown in Fig. 11.22 (in which the minimum distance of row and column codes is assumed to be 4). Clearly, the minimum distance of the product code:

$$d_p(\min) = d_1(\min)d_2(\min) \tag{11.8}$$

Also, if the number of minimum distance row and column codewords is $A_1(d_1(\min))$ and $A_2(d_2(\min))$, respectively, then the multiplicity in the product code is:

$$A_p[d_p(\min)] = A_1[d_1(\min)]A_2[d_2(\min)] \tag{11.9}$$

and in general the multiplicity in the product code:

$$A_p(d_p = d_1d_2) = A_1(d_1)A_2(d_2) \tag{11.10}$$

This has been used to calculate the distance spectra of various product codes based on extended BCH (including Hamming) codes. The distance spectra of the component codes can be obtained using the formulae in [11.31] p. 177.

Example 11.4

Estimate the BER of the product code $(BCH(32, 26, 4))^2$ using turbo coding.

Solution The BCH(31, 26, 3) code is of course a Hamming code, whose weight distribution may be obtained by noting that its dual weight spectrum may be obtained from the polynomial:

$$B(z) = 1 + z^{31}$$

from whence the weight spectrum polynomial for the Hamming code can be obtained using the MacWilliams identity ([11.31] p. 76):

$$A(z) = \frac{(1+z)^n}{2^{n-k}} B\left(\frac{1-z}{1+z}\right)$$

Hence we obtain the weight spectrum of the extended code as:

$$A_2(z) = A_1(z) = 1240z^4 + 27\,776z^6 + 330\,460z^8 + 2\,011\,776z^{10} + 7\,063\,784z^{12}$$
$$+ 14\,721\,280z^{14} + 18\,796\,230z^{16} + 14\,721\,280z^{18} + 7\,063\,784z^{20}$$
$$+ 2\,011\,776z^{22} + 330\,460z^{24} + 27\,776z^{26} + 1240z^{28} + z^{32}$$

(in which the coefficient of z^n gives the multiplicity of codewords of weight n). Hence, using (11.6), the error-weighted distance spectrum of the product code ([BCH(32, 26, 4)]^2 = (1024, 676, 16)) is:

$$e_d = \{0, 0, 0, 0, 0, 0, 0, 0, 0, 0, 0, 0, 0, 0, 0, 0, 24025, 0, 0, 0, 0, 0, 0, 0, 1614480,$$
$$0, 0, 0, 0, 0, 0, 0, 25610650, 0, 0, 0, 27123264, 0, 0, 0, 0, 0, 0, 0, 0, 0, 0, 0,$$
$$860517840, 0, 0, 0, 0, 0, 0, 0, 0, 0, 0, 0, 0, 0, 0, 0, 6825238225, 0, 0, 0, 0, 0,$$
$$0, 0, 0, 0, 0, 0, 0, 0, 0, 0, 0, 0\}$$

This may be used to calculate a union bound on the BER, as described in Section 5.7. The result is shown in Fig. 11.23, compared with the simulation results given in [11.30] for this code, and the uncoded result.

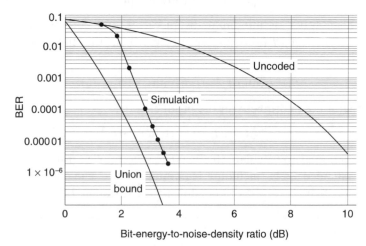

Figure 11.23 Union bound on BER of [BCH(32, 26, 4)]^2 product code, compared with simulation results of [11.30]

The results show quite good agreement between the bound and the simulation, except that they do not converge as closely as for the parallel concatenated turbo-codes. This is probably because the component decoders used are based on the Chase algorithm, which are sub-optimum. Note also that the gap between simulation and bound increases at higher BER, which suggests that the iterative decoding algorithm may not converge at these levels.

Iterative decoding has also been applied to equalization. We have already seen (Section 9.3.4) how coded transmission on a dispersive channel can be treated as a concatenation of two codes: we may apply soft output decoding and iteration to the joint decoding/equalization problem. In the same way, it can also be used for joint synchronization and decoding; and can also be applied to multistage decoding of multilevel coded modulation schemes, resulting in decoding that approaches the ML performance. It has been applied to separation of interfering signals, such as the self-interference of a CDMA system, resulting in close to ML multi-user detection.

In fact, iterative decoding can be applied to nearly any group of processes in the chain of receiver functions, which should ideally be performed jointly: instead they are performed separately, with iterative decoding, and in many cases performance is as good as the optimum joint technique, usually with much reduced complexity. In this way, it is likely that the 'turbo-principle' will find very wide application in communications.

References

11.1   Shannon, C.E. (1948) A mathematical theory of communication. *Bell System Technical Journal*, **27**: 379–423, 623–56.
11.2   Battail, G. (1992) We can think of good codes, and even decode them. *Eurocode'92*, Udine, Italy, November.
11.3   Blahut, R.E. (1987) *Principles and Practice of Information Theory*, Addison-Wesley.
11.4   Berrou, C., Glavieux, A. and Thitimajshima, P. (1993) Near Shannon limit error-correcting coding: turbo codes. In *Proceedings IEEE International Conference on Communications*, Geneva, Switzerland, 1064–70.
11.5   Divsalar, D. and Pollara, F. (1995) Low-rate turbo codes for deep space applications. In *Proceedings IEEE International Symposium on Information Theory (ISIT'95)*, Whistler, September, p. 35. See also http://techreports.jpl.nasa.gov/, Technical Report 95-0487, and http://www.jpl.nasa.gov/
11.6   Consultative Committee on Space Data Systems (1999) *Recommendation for Telemetry Channel Coding*, CCSDS 101.0-B-4, May. See http://www.ccsds.org
11.7   3GPP *Multiplexing and Channel Coding (FDD)*, Technical Specification Group Radio Access Network, document number 3G TS 25.212, version 3.0.0, 3rd Generation Partnership Project (3GPP) obtainable at: ftp://ftp.3gpp.org/
11.8   MacWilliams, F.J. and Sloane, N.J.A. (1977) *The Theory of Error-Correcting Codes*, North-Holland.

11.9 Elias, P. (1954) Error-free coding. *IRE Transactions on Information Theory*, **4**: 29–37.

11.10 Bahl, L., Cocke, J., Jelinek, F. and Raviv, J. (1974) Optimal decoding of linear codes for minimizing symbol error rate. *IEEE Transactions on Information Theory*, **20**: 284–7.

11.11 Berrou, C. and Glavieux, A. (1996) Near optimum error correcting coding and decoding: turbo-codes. *IEEE Transactions on Communications*, **44**(10): 1261–71.

11.12 Benedetto, S., Garello, R. and Montorsi, G. (1998) A search for good convolutional codes to be used in the construction of turbo codes. *IEEE Transactions on Communications*, **46**(9): 1101–5.

11.13 Divsalar, D. and Pollara, F. (1997) Hybrid concatenated codes and iterative decoding. In *Proceedings IEEE International Symposium on Information Theory (ISIT'97)*, September, p. 10.

11.14 Heegard, C. and Wicker, S.B. (1999) *Turbo Coding*, Kluwer.

11.15 Benedetto, S. and Montorsi, G. (1996) Unveiling turbo-codes: some results on parallel concatenated coding schemes. *IEEE Transactions on Information Theory*, **42**(6): 409–28.

11.16 Burr, A.G. and White, G.P. (1999) Comparison of iterative decoder performance with union bounds for short frame turbo-codes. *Annales des Telecommunications*, **54**(3–4): 201–7.

11.17 Dolinar, S., Divsalar, D. and Pollara, F. (1998) *Code Performance as a Function of Block Size*, TMO progress report 42-133, JPL, May. See http://www.jpl.nasa.gov/

11.18 Dolinar, S. and Divsalar, D. (1995) *Weight Distributions for Turbo-codes Using Random and Non-Random Permutations*, TDA progress report 42-121, JPL, August. See http://www.jpl.nasa.gov/

11.19 McEliece, R.J., MacKay, D.J.C. and Cheng, J.F. (1998) Turbo decoding as an instance of Pearl's 'belief propagation' algorithm. *IEEE Journal on Selected Areas in Communications*, **16**(2): 140–52.

11.20 Wiberg, N. (1996) Codes and decoding on graphs. PhD thesis no. 440, Linköping University, Sweden.

11.21 Burr, A.G. (1997) Turbo-coded modulation. *Proceedings First International Seminar on Turbo-coding and Related Topics*, ENST Brest, France, September, pp. 111–18.

11.22 Barbulescu, A.S. and Pietrobon, S.S. (1994) Interleaver design for turbo codes. *Electronics Letters*, **30**(25): 2107–8.

11.23 Jung, P. and Naßhan, M. (1994) Performance evaluation of turbo codes for short frame transmission systems. *Electronics Letters*, **30**(2): 111–13.

11.24 Valenti, M.C. and Woerner, B.D. (1997) Variable latency turbo codes for wireless multimedia applications. *Proceedings First International Seminar on Turbo-coding and Related Topics*, ENST Brest, France, September, pp. 216–19.

11.25 Goff, S., Glavieux, A. and Berrou, C. (1994) Turbo codes and high spectral efficiency modulation. In *Proceedings IEEE International Conference on Communications*, May, pp. 645–9.

11.26 Robertson, P. and Wörz, T. (1998) Bandwidth efficient turbo trellis-coded modulation using punctured component codes. *IEEE Journal Selected Areas in Communications*, **16**(2): 206–18.

11.27 Wachsmann, U. and Huber, J. (1995) Power and bandwidth efficient digital communication using turbo codes in multilevel codes. *European Transactions on Telecommunications*, **6**(5): 557–67.

11.28 Benedetto, S., Divsalar, D., Montorsi, G. and Pollara, F. (1996) Parallel concatenated trellis coded modulation. In *Proceedings IEEE International Conference on Communications*, p. 974.

11.29 Robertson, P., Höher, P. and Villebrun, E. (1997) Optimal and sub-optimal maximum a posteriori algorithms suitable for turbo decoding. *European Transactions on Telecommunications*, **8**(2): 119–25.

11.30 Pyndiah, R. (1998) Near optimum decoding of product codes: block turbo codes. *IEEE Transactions on Communications*, **46**(8): 1003–10.

11.31 Lin, S. and Costello, D.J. (1983) *Error Control Coding: Fundamentals and Applications*, Prentice-Hall.

Appendix 1

Finite field theory

A1.1 Finite fields

In this appendix we deal with the theory of finite or Galois fields, which as mentioned in Section 6.3.4 are the basis of BCH and Reed–Solomon codes. As stated there, finite fields are closed groups for which two operations, termed 'addition' and 'multiplication', are defined [6.3, pp. 19–40]. More formally, a finite field may be defined by the following set of properties:

(1) There are two defined operations: *addition* ('+') and *multiplication* ('×').
(2) The field is *closed* under these operations: i.e. the sum or product of two elements of the field is always another element.
(3) The field contains the *additive identity* or 'zero' element, such that $a + 0 = a$, and the *multiplicative identity* or 'unity', such that $a \times 1 = a$.
(4) For every element a there is an *additive inverse* element $(-a)$, such that $a + (-a) = 0$, and (except for '0') a *multiplicative inverse* a^{-1} such that $a \times a^{-1} = 1$.
(5) The associative $a + (b + c) = (a + b) + c$, $a \times (b \times c) = (a \times b) \times c$, commutative $a + b = b + a$, $a \times b = b \times a$, and distributive $a \times (b + c) = a \times b + a \times c$ laws apply.

It turns out that only certain field sizes can satisfy all these properties. The simplest cases have size equal to a prime number, say p, in which case the elements are the integers from 0 to $p - 1$. Addition and multiplication are ordinary, real number, addition and multiplication taken modulo-p (i.e. we take the remainder of the result on division by p), and the additive and multiplicative identities are simply '0' and '1', respectively. The finite field of size p is referred to as GF(p) (for 'Galois field'). The simplest such field is the field of binary numbers GF(2), containing '0' and '1'. Here addition is of course modulo-2, multiplication is ordinary multiplication (which happens also to be equivalent to the logical AND function), and an element's additive inverse is itself.

In a prime number field, there is always at least one element whose powers constitute all the non-zero elements of the field: i.e. when we successively multiply by this element, we cycle through all the field elements except '0'. Such an element is called *primitive*.

Example A1.1

List the elements of the finite field GF(5). Define addition and multiplication, and find additive and multiplicative inverses. What primitive elements are there in the field?

Solution   Elements: 0, 1, 2, 3, 4

Addition:

	0	**1**	**2**	**3**	**4**
0	0	1	2	3	4
1	1	2	3	4	0
2	2	3	4	0	1
3	3	4	0	1	2
4	4	0	1	2	3

Multiplication:

	0	**1**	**2**	**3**	**4**
0	0	0	0	0	0
1	0	1	2	3	4
2	0	2	4	1	3
3	0	3	1	4	2
4	0	4	3	2	1

Additive and multiplicative inverses:

	0	**1**	**2**	**3**	**4**
Additive	0	4	3	2	1
Multiplicative	–	1	3	2	4

Primitive elements 2 and 3:

$$2^0 = 1 \qquad 3^0 = 1$$
$$2^1 = 2 \qquad 3^1 = 3$$
$$2^2 = 4 \qquad 3^2 = 4$$
$$2^3 = 3 \qquad 3^3 = 2$$
$$2^4 = 1 \qquad 3^4 = 1$$
$$2^5 = 2 \qquad 3^5 = 3$$

etc.

Note that 4 is not primitive, since:

$$4^0 = 1 \qquad 4^1 = 4$$
$$4^2 = 1 \qquad 4^3 = 4$$

etc.

However, except for the rather simple case of GF(2), prime number fields are of little interest in coding theory. More significant are *extension fields*, whose size is an integer power of a prime number, say p^q, and in particular *binary extension fields*, where the prime number $p = 2$. In this case the elements are the polynomials of order up to $q - 1$ whose coefficients are taken from GF(p). We will use X as the dummy variable, to avoid confusion with x, the dummy variable used in the polynomial representation of codes in Section 6.1.3.

In these fields 'addition' is addition of polynomials taking the coefficients modulo-p; 'multiplication' is similarly multiplication of polynomials. However, it is clear that the product of two polynomials in the field may have order greater than $q - 1$. Hence, when this occurs we take the result 'modulo some *irreducible polynomial*'. This is a polynomial of order q which does not have any factors in the field (except, of course, unity). Suitable irreducible polynomials for binary extension fields for q up to 16 are tabulated in Table A1.1. Like the prime fields described above, extension fields have at least one primitive element.

q	Polynomial	q	Polynomial
3	$1 + X + X^3$	10	$1 + X^3 + X^{10}$
4	$1 + X + X^4$	11	$1 + X^2 + X^{11}$
5	$1 + X^2 + X^5$	12	$1 + X + X^4 + X^6 + X^{12}$
6	$1 + X + X^6$	13	$1 + X + X^3 + X^4 + X^{13}$
7	$1 + X^3 + X^7$	14	$1 + X + X^6 + X^{10} + X^{14}$
8	$1 + X^2 + X^3 + X^4 + X^8$	15	$1 + X + X^{15}$
9	$1 + X^4 + X^9$	16	$1 + X + X^3 + X^{12} + X^{16}$

Table A1.1   Irreducible polynomials for binary extension fields

The polynomial notation for the field elements is rather clumsy: it is more convenient to convert them to numerical form. It is easy to express them in the form of a p-ary q-tuple of the polynomial coefficients (constant term first). In the case of binary extension fields this is a q digit binary number, which may readily be converted to decimal form, this time with the constant term treated as the least significant bit.

Example A1.2

GF(8) has $p = 2$ and $q = 3$. Its elements (in polynomial, binary and decimal form) are:

Polynomial	Binary	Decimal	Polynomial	Binary	Decimal
0	0, 0, 0	0	1	1, 0, 0	1
X	0, 1, 0	2	$1 + X$	1, 1, 0	3
X^2	0, 0, 1	4	$1 + X^2$	1, 0, 1	5
$X + X^2$	0, 1, 1	6	$1 + X + X^2$	1, 1, 1	7

From Table A1.1, an appropriate irreducible polynomial is $1 + X + X^3$. We will demonstrate multiplication in this field by testing the element $\alpha = X$ to see if it is primitive.

$$\alpha^0 = 1$$

$$\alpha^1 = X$$

$$\alpha^2 = X^2$$

$$\alpha^3 = X^3 \bmod (1 + X + X^3) = 1 + X$$

$$\alpha^4 = X + X^2$$

$$\alpha^5 = (X^2 + X^3) \bmod (1 + X + X^3) = 1 + X + X^2$$

$$\alpha^6 = (X + X^2 + X^3) \bmod (1 + X + X^3) = 1 + X^2$$

$$\alpha^7 = (X + X^3) \bmod (1 + X + X^3) = 1 = \alpha^0$$

Thus the powers of α cycle through all the non-zero elements of the field, and hence $\alpha = X$ is a primitive element of GF(8).

Addition in the field is defined as modulo-2 addition of the polynomial coefficients, or equivalently as bit-by-bit modulo-2 addition of the binary representation. This leads to the addition table shown in Table 6.4(a). As a further example of multiplication, consider:

$$(1 + X^2) \times (1 + X + X^2) = (1 + X + X^3 + X^4) \bmod (1 + X + X^3) = X + X^2$$

$$
\begin{array}{r}
X + 1 \\
X^3 + X + 1 \overline{\smash{\big)}\, X^4 + X^3 \qquad\quad + X + 1} \\
\underline{X^4 \qquad\quad + X^2 + X} \\
X^3 + X^2 \qquad\quad + 1 \\
\underline{X^3 \qquad\qquad + X + 1} \\
X^2 + X
\end{array}
$$

This calculation can be greatly simplified with the aid of the list of powers of α above, in which $1 + X^2 = \alpha^6$ and $1 + X + X^2 = \alpha^5$. Then $\alpha^6 \times \alpha^5 = \alpha^{11} = \alpha^4 = X + X^2$. Note that the table repeats after α^7, and hence the powers may be taken modulo-7 (or in general modulo-$(2^q - 1)$). This has been used to obtain the multiplication table, Table 6.4(b), using the decimal representation.

A1.2   BCH codes

We next consider how the theory of Galois fields can be used to construct the generator polynomials $g(x)$ for the BCH codes of Section 6.3.5. In general, a polynomial can have coefficients taken from any Galois field (including extension fields), and these are then said to be polynomials *over* that field. It is useful to consider the *roots* of the polynomial: the values of x for which $g(x) = 0$. These roots may, in general, be members of an appropriate Galois field. Now it can be shown that for a polynomial over GF(2) (i.e. coefficients are '0' and '1' only), if β is a root of $g(x)$, then so are $\beta^2, \beta^4, \beta^8, \ldots$, until the sequence repeats.

This means that we can construct a polynomial over GF(2) (such as the generator polynomial of a BCH code) from its roots. Just like polynomials whose coefficients are real numbers, a polynomial over a field can be constructed from the factors given by the full set of its roots:

$$g(x) = (x - \beta_1)(x - \beta_2) \cdots (x - \beta_m) \tag{A1.1}$$

where $\beta_1 \cdots \beta_m$ are the solutions to $g(x) = 0$, and m is the order of $g(x)$. If we choose roots so that if β is included, so are $\beta^2, \beta^4, \beta^8, \ldots$; then the resulting polynomial has coefficients '0' and '1', and so is suitable for a BCH code. We ensure this by constructing a minimum polynomial from a root β, which also contains β^2, β^4, etc.

For example, in GF(8), the minimum polynomial of $\beta = X$ is:

$$M_\beta(x) = (x - \beta)(x - \beta^2)(x - \beta^4) = (x - X)(x - X^2)[x - (X + X^2)]$$

$$= 1 + (\alpha^3 + \alpha^5 + \alpha^6)x + (0)x^2 + x^3 = 1 + x + x^3$$

No higher terms need be included since $\beta^8 = \beta$. In general, the minimum polynomial for a root in GF(2^q) will contain q terms, and hence also have order q.

We may now define a t-error correcting primitive BCH code of length $n = 2^q - 1$ as follows. Its generator polynomial $g(x)$ is the minimum-order polynomial over GF(2) whose roots include $\alpha, \alpha^2, \alpha^3, \cdots, \alpha^{2t}$, where α is a primitive element of GF(2^q).

To ensure $g(x)$ coefficients are in GF(2), we must include the minimum polynomials of each of these roots. However, to minimize the order we should omit repeated minimum polynomials. Hence, the generator polynomial becomes:

$$g(x) = \text{LCM}\left[\prod_{j=1}^{2t} M_{\alpha^j}(x)\right] \tag{A1.2}$$

The resulting code has minimum Hamming distance at least $2t + 1$, and $k \geq n - mt$.

Example A1.3
Construct length $n = 7$ single and double error correcting BCH codes.

Solution The field in question is GF($n + 1$) = GF(8), (see Example A1.2), in which a primitive element is $\alpha = X$. Then the minimum polynomials:

$$M_\alpha(x) = M_{\alpha^2}(x) = M_{\alpha^4}(x) = (x - \alpha)(x - \alpha^2)(x - \alpha^4) = 1 + x + x^3$$

$$M_{\alpha^3}(x) = (x - \alpha^3)(x - \alpha^6)(x - \alpha^5) = \alpha^0 + (\alpha^2 + \alpha^1 + \alpha^4)x$$

$$+ (\alpha^3 + \alpha^6 + \alpha^5)x^2 + x^3$$

$$= 1 + x^2 + x^3$$

For the single error correcting code $g(x) = \text{LCM}(M_\alpha(x)M_{\alpha^2}(x)) = 1 + x + x^3$. The order of this, which is equal to $n - k$, is 3, and hence $k = 4$. Thus this is in fact the (7, 4) Hamming code.

For the double error correcting code:

$$g(x) = \text{LCM}[M_\alpha(x)M_{\alpha^2}(x)M_{\alpha^3}(x)M_{\alpha^4}(x)] = (1 + x + x^3)(1 + x^2 + x^3)$$

$$= 1 + x + x^2 + x^3 + x^4 + x^6$$

Hence $n - k = 6$, leaving $k = 1$. This is in fact the length 7 repetition code, and actually has $d_{min} = 7$, so it will correct three errors.

A1.3 Reed–Solomon codes

Reed–Solomon codes are defined in a very similar way to BCH codes, except that the requirement that the generator polynomial be over GF(2) is relaxed. Hence, the polynomial coefficients are in general drawn from GF(2^q), and so must be the code and information symbols (as we have seen in Section 6.3.6). This also means that we can simply use the basic roots $\alpha, \alpha^2, \alpha^3, \ldots, \alpha^{2t}$ in the generator polynomial, rather than the minimum polynomials.

The generator polynomial of length $n = 2^q - 1$, t error correcting Reed–Solomon code with symbols in GF(2^q) is given by:

$$g(x) = \prod_{j=1}^{2t} (x - \alpha^j) \tag{A1.3}$$

where α is again a primitive element of GF(2^q).

Here it is evident that the order of $g(x)$ is always $2t$. Hence $k = n - 2t$, and $d_{min} = 2t + 1$.

Example A1.4

Construct the generator polynomial (over GF(8)) of the code used in Example 6.6.

Solution   Choose $\alpha = X$ as the primitive element. Then:

$$g(x) = (x - \alpha)(x - \alpha^2)(x - \alpha^3)(x - \alpha^4) = \alpha^3 + (\alpha^2 + \alpha + \alpha^0 + \alpha^6)x$$

$$+ (\alpha^0 + \alpha^6 + \alpha^5 + \alpha^5 + \alpha^4 + \alpha^3)x^2 + (\alpha + \alpha^2 + \alpha^3 + \alpha^4)x^3 + x^4$$

$$= (1 + X) + (X)x + (1)x^2 + (1 + X)x^3 + (1)x^4$$

$$= 3 + 2x + 1x^2 + 3x^3 + 1x^4$$

A1.4 BCH decoding

In this section we outline the principles of the techniques used to decode BCH codes. They are, of course, susceptible to the basic technique outlined in Section 6.2.3, but because of their algebraic structure there are also other more efficient techniques available. This has been a very active area of research ever since BCH codes were discovered, so a full description of these techniques is well beyond the scope of this book.

First, we introduce another way of expressing the syndrome of a BCH code. Let $\beta_1, \beta_2, \ldots, \beta_J$ be the roots from which the generator polynomial is constructed (these are α and α^3 in the code of Example A1.3). Represent the received codeword as $r(x) = c(x) + e(x)$, as in Equation (6.15). Then we may divide the syndrome into J components, each obtained by substituting one of these roots into $r(x)$:

$$\mathbf{s} = \{\mathbf{s}_1, \mathbf{s}_2 \cdots \mathbf{s}_J\} = \{r(\beta_1), r(\beta_2) \cdots r(\beta_J)\} = \{e(\beta_1), e(\beta_2) \cdots e(\beta_J)\} \qquad (A1.4)$$

The last step follows since the βs are, by definition, roots of $c(x)$, and hence $c(\beta_j) = 0, j = 1 \cdots J$. The $\mathbf{s}_j$s are binary q-tuples (expressed in binary form in the same way as the roots in the table of Example A1.3), and thus the syndrome $\mathbf{s}$ has total length $Jq = n - k$. It may be shown that it is the same syndrome that results from multiplication by the transpose parity check matrix, as in Equation (6.13).

Suppose the received word has errors in positions $\varepsilon_1, \varepsilon_2, \ldots, \varepsilon_t$: that is:

$$e(x) = x^{\varepsilon_1} + x^{\varepsilon_2} + \cdots + x^{\varepsilon_t} \qquad (A1.5)$$

Then:

$$\mathbf{s}_1 = \beta_1^{\varepsilon_1} + \beta_1^{\varepsilon_2} + \cdots + \beta_1^{\varepsilon_t}$$
$$\mathbf{s}_2 = \beta_2^{\varepsilon_1} + \beta_2^{\varepsilon_2} + \cdots + \beta_2^{\varepsilon_t} \qquad (A1.6)$$
$$\vdots$$
$$\mathbf{s}_J = \beta_J^{\varepsilon_1} + \beta_J^{\varepsilon_2} + \cdots + \beta_J^{\varepsilon_t}$$

which is a system of J equations in the unknowns $\varepsilon_1, \varepsilon_2, \ldots, \varepsilon_t$, from which one or more solutions is obtainable. In general there may be many solutions, of which we normally extract the one indicating the fewest errors. Since the code is binary, if we know the locations of the errors we may correct them.

Example A1.5

Demonstrate syndrome decoding of the received word 1011011 in the (7, 1) BCH code.

Solution The (7, 1) BCH code constructed in Example A1.3 was designed as a double error correcting code, although we found that it is actually the 7-bit repetition code. Suppose that the word 1111111 is transmitted, but received with two errors, as 1011011.

This code is constructed from two roots: $\beta_1 = \alpha$ and $\beta_2 = \alpha^3$. Hence:

$$\mathbf{s}_1 = r(\alpha) = 1 + \alpha^2 + \alpha^3 + \alpha^5 + \alpha^6 = X^2 = 0, 0, 1$$
$$\mathbf{s}_2 = r(\alpha^3) = 1 + \alpha^6 + \alpha^9 + \alpha^{15} + \alpha^{18} = X^2 = 0, 0, 1$$

We next set up the system of Equations (6.30):

$$0, 0, 1 = \mathbf{s}_1 = \alpha^{\varepsilon_1} + \alpha^{\varepsilon_2}$$

$$0, 0, 1 = \mathbf{s}_2 = \alpha^{3\varepsilon_1} + \alpha^{3\varepsilon_2}$$

Substituting for α^{ε_2} from the first equation into the second:

$$\mathbf{s}_2 = \alpha^{3\varepsilon_1} + (\mathbf{s}_1 - \alpha^{\varepsilon_1})^3 = \mathbf{s}_1^3 + \mathbf{s}_1^2\alpha^{\varepsilon_1} + \mathbf{s}_1\alpha^{2\varepsilon_1}$$

$$(0, 0, 1) = (1, 0, 1) + (0, 1, 1)\alpha^{\varepsilon_1} + (0, 0, 1)\alpha^{2\varepsilon_1}$$

Solve this by trial and error:

$$\varepsilon_1 = 0: \quad (1, 0, 1) + (0, 1, 1) + (0, 0, 1) \neq (0, 0, 1)$$

$$\varepsilon_1 = 1: \quad (1, 0, 1) + (0, 1, 1) \times (0, 1, 0) + (0, 0, 1) \times (0, 0, 1)$$

$$= (1, 0, 1) + (1, 1, 1) + (0, 1, 1) = (0, 0, 1)$$

i.e. $\varepsilon_1 = 1$ is a solution. Then $\alpha^{\varepsilon_2} = \mathbf{s}_1 - \alpha^{\varepsilon_1} = (0, 0, 1) + (0, 1, 0) = (0, 1, 1) = \alpha^4$. Hence $\varepsilon_2 = 4$. Errors are in bits 1 and 4 (starting at 0), and so we obtain the corrected codeword as 1111111.

Of course for larger t a more formal approach to solving these equations is required. Several of these have been found, for example the iterative algorithm of Berlekamp [A1.1; A1.2, p. 155], and the shift-register synthesis approach of Massey [A1.3]. A different approach that has become more popular recently is termed *frequency domain*, because a transform analogous with the discrete Fourier transform (DFT) can be established over the Galois field [A1.4, p. 84]. This gives an efficient decoding procedure for both BCH and Reed–Solomon codes [A1.4, p. 86 ff].

Reed–Solomon codes admit of the same decoding procedure as BCH codes, except that since they are non-binary it is necessary to determine what the errors are, as well as to locate them. For this reason the frequency domain approaches are to be preferred for Reed–Solomon codes especially.

References

A1.1 Berlekamp, E.R. (1968) *Algebraic Coding Theory*, McGraw-Hill, New York.
A1.2 Lin, S. and Costello, D.J. (1983) *Error Control Coding: Fundamentals and Applications*, Prentice-Hall.
A1.3 Massey, J.L. (1969) Shift register synthesis and BCH decoding. *IEEE Transactions on Information Theory*, **15**: 122–7.
A1.4 Sweeney, P. (1991) *Error Control Coding: an Introduction*, Prentice-Hall.

Appendix 2

The MAP algorithm

A2.1 Principle of MAP algorithm

The MAP algorithm [A2.1, A2.2] returns the log likelihood ratio of each decoded bit given the signal amplitudes for the whole codeword. Consider one trellis section of a terminated trellis:

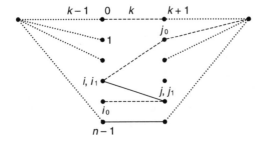

The trellis states before and after the period of interest are represented by the nodes, numbered as shown. The solid lines within the trellis section denote transitions corresponding to data '1'; dashed lines correspond to data '0'. The dotted lines on the left and right of the trellis section shown denote all possible paths, respectively, from the start of the trellis to each state (hereafter called the *prefix* paths), and from each state to the end of the trellis (the *suffix* paths), which is assumed to be terminated in a known state. The probability of the path to state i given the received signal, i.e. the a posteriori probability that the encoder is in this state at the beginning of the current trellis section, will be denoted by $\alpha(i)$. Similarly the probability that the encoder is in state j after the trellis section, given the received signal for the latter part of the trellis, is $\beta(j)$. We will denote the branch beginning in state i and ending in state j as $b(i,j)$.

Appendix 2: The MAP algorithm

The previous state of a branch corresponding to data d, $d = 0, 1$, and ending in state j is denoted by $p(j, d)$ and, conversely, the next state of a branch beginning in state i is $q(i, d)$. In the diagram above, and in the sequel, $p(j, d) = i_d$, $q(i, d) = j_d$, $d = 0, 1$.

The likelihood ratio of the data corresponding to the current trellis section is given by the ratio of the sum of the probabilities of all paths through the trellis including a solid branch in this section, to those including a dashed branch. This is given by:

$$\Lambda(d_k) = \frac{\sum_{i=0}^{n-1} \alpha_k(i)\gamma_k(i,j_1)\beta_k(j_1)}{\sum_{i=0}^{n-1} \alpha_k(i)\gamma_k(i,j_0)\beta_k(j_0)} \tag{A2.1}$$

where $\gamma_k(i, j_d) = P(b(i, j_d)|\{i, r\})$, the probability of branch $b(i, j_d)$ given that the encoder is in state i and given the received signal r.

We can also extend the prefix paths to the nodes at the right of the current section, and hence calculate the αs for the next trellis section. This can be used to define a recurrence relation from which αs for the whole trellis can be derived:

$$\alpha_{k+1}(j) = \alpha_k(i_1)\gamma_k(i_1, j) + \alpha_k(i_0)\gamma_k(i_0, j) \tag{A2.2}$$

where $i_d = p(j, d)$, $d = 0, 1$. Similarly, we can extend the suffix paths back to the left hand nodes, and calculate the βs for the previous section:

$$\beta_{k-1}(i) = \beta_k(j_1)\gamma_k(i, j_1) + \beta_k(j_0)\gamma_k(i, j_0) \tag{A2.3}$$

We can therefore calculate the αs for the whole trellis by applying (A2.2) over a forward pass through the trellis, and the βs by applying (A2.3) over a backward pass. For this reason the algorithm is sometimes known as the *forward–backward* algorithm. The forward pass can be initialized by assuming that the encoder started in a known state, the zero state. In a turbo-code, one encoder can also be returned to the zero state by adding appropriate tail bits, and for this code the backward pass can also be initialized. The second encoder cannot be returned to zero in this way, because the tail bits that zero one encoder will not necessarily zero the other. In this case the code is usually left unterminated, and the backward pass is initialized with the αs from the forward pass.

$\gamma_k(i, j_d) = P(b_k(i, j_d)|\{i, r_k\})$ is the a posteriori probability of the branch $b_k(i, j)$, given the received signal for trellis section k, r_k. Using Bayes theorem, we may write:

$$\gamma_k(i, j_d) = P[b_k(i, j_d)|\{i, r_k\}] = \frac{P[r_k|b(i, j_d)]P[b_k(i, j_d)]}{P(r_k)}$$

$$= \frac{P[r_k|b(i, j_d)]}{P(r_k)} P(d_k = d) \tag{A2.4}$$

In conventional coding, we have no a priori information about the bit, and hence we assume that $P(d_k = d) = P(d_k = d) = \frac{1}{2}$. In a turbo-decoder, however, we have extrinsic information from the other decoder, which can be used to provide this information. This is usually in the form of a likelihood ratio, $\Lambda_p(d_k)$, from which we can obtain:

$$P(d_k = 1) = \frac{\Lambda_p(d_k)}{1 + \Lambda_p(d_k)} \tag{A2.5}$$

Note that $P(r_k)$ is a constant for a given trellis section, and can therefore be neglected (treated as unity) for the purposes of comparison of different branches. On a Gaussian channel, we also note that:

$$P[r_k|b_k(i,j_d)] \propto \exp[-|r_k - s(i,j_d)|^2/2\sigma^2] = \exp[-\delta_k^2(i,j_d)/2\sigma^2] \tag{A2.6}$$

where $s(i,j_d)$ is the transmitted signal corresponding to the branch $b(i,j_d)$, and $\delta_k(i,j_d)$ denotes the Euclidean distance of the received signal from this transmitted signal. Again, the proportionality factor is constant over the trellis section, and can be ignored.

Further, if the transmitted signal is constant amplitude, i.e. $|s(i,j_d)| = c$, $\forall i, d$, then:

$$\exp[-\delta_k^2(i,j_d)/2\sigma^2] = \exp[-\{|r_k|^2 + |s(i,j_d)|^2 - 2\,\mathrm{Re}[r_k^* s(i,j_d)]\}/2\sigma^2]$$
$$\propto \exp\{\mathrm{Re}[r_k^* s(i,j_d)]/\sigma^2\} \tag{A2.7}$$

In a turbo-code, the received and transmitted signals for each component code contain two elements: the *systematic* (data) symbol and a *parity check* symbol. We may distinguish these using the subscripts s and c, respectively. The overall squared Euclidean distance is the sum of the Euclidean distances for the systematic and the parity check parts. Then we may rewrite (A2.6), splitting it into two terms:

$$P[r_k|b_k(i,j_d)] = \exp[-\delta_{ks}^2(i,j_d)/2\sigma^2]\exp[-\delta_{kc}^2(i,j_d)/2\sigma^2] \tag{A2.8}$$

Now $s_s(i,j_d) = -1, +1, d = 0, 1$, independently of i. Hence $\delta_{ks}(i,j_d)$ is also independent of i, and the term can be written $\exp(-\delta_{ks}^2(d)/2\sigma^2)$. Thus we only need to calculate two values for the systematic part: $\exp(-\delta_{ks}^2(0)/2\sigma^2)$ and $\exp(-\delta_{ks}^2(1)/2\sigma^2)$. In fact, for binary turbo-codes based on the punctured rate 1/3 code (which have one parity bit per trellis section for each component code), there are also only two values of the parity check part, corresponding to parity '0' and '1', and hence only four values of γ:

$$\gamma_k = \exp(-|r_{ks} \pm 1|^2/2\sigma^2)\exp(-|r_{kc} \pm 1|^2/2\sigma^2)$$
$$= \exp[\mathrm{Re}(\pm r_{ks}^*)/\sigma^2]\exp[\mathrm{Re}(\pm r_{kc}^*)/\sigma^2] \tag{A2.9}$$

normalizing the transmitted signal-to-unit amplitude, and omitting the a priori information $P(d_k = d)$.

Note that the terms $\exp(-\delta_{ks}^2(1)/2\sigma^2)$ and $P(d_k = 1)$ occur in all the terms of the numerator of (A2.1), and similarly $\exp(-\delta_{ks}^2(0)/2\sigma^2)$ and $P(d_k = 0)$ in all terms of the denominator. Then we can rewrite (A2.1) as:

$$\Lambda(d_k) = \frac{P_p(d_k = 1)\exp[-\delta_{ks}^2(1)/2\sigma^2]\sum\limits_{i=0}^{n-1}\alpha_k(i)\exp[-\delta_{kc}^2(i,j_1)/2\sigma^2]\beta_k(j_1)}{P_p(d_k = 1)\exp[-\delta_{ks}^2(0)/2\sigma^2]\sum\limits_{i=0}^{n-1}\alpha_k(i)\exp[-\delta_{kc}^2(i,j_0)/2\sigma^2]\beta_k(j_0)}$$

$$= \Lambda_p(d_k)\Lambda_s(d_k)\frac{\sum\limits_{i=0}^{n-1}\alpha_k(i)\exp[-\delta_{kc}^2(i,j_1)/2\sigma^2]\beta_k(j_1)}{\sum\limits_{i=0}^{n-1}\alpha_k(i)\exp[-\delta_{kc}^2(i,j_0)/2\sigma^2]\beta_k(j_0)} \qquad (A2.10)$$

where P_p and Λ_p denote a priori probability and likelihood ratios, respectively; and Λ_s denotes the likelihood ratio as determined directly from the systematic bit. It is the remaining term that contains the information drawn from the component code, and thus it is this information that should be passed to the next decoder as the *extrinsic information*. The other two terms represent information that is also available to the next decoder.

A2.2   Summary of algorithm

1. Forward pass:
   Initialize $\alpha_0(0) = 1$, all other αs to zero
   For each trellis section, $k = 0 \cdots N - 1$:
   - Calculate the four values of γ from the received signal using (A2.8)
   - For each node, $i = 0 \cdots n - 1$:
     - Calculate $\gamma(i,j_d) = P[b(i,j_d)|\{i,r\}]$ making use of the four values of γ already calculated
   - For each node, $j = 0 \cdots n - 1$:
     - Calculate $\alpha_{k+1}(j)$ using (A2.2)
2. Backward pass:
   Initialize $\beta_N(0) = 1$, all others to zero, if trellis terminated, otherwise $\beta_N(i) = \alpha_N(i)$, $i = 0 \cdots n - 1$
   For each trellis section, $k = N \cdots 1$:
   - For each node, $j = 0 \cdots n - 1$:
     - Calculate $\beta_{k-1}(j)$ using (A2.3)
   - For each node, $j = 0 \cdots n - 1$:
     - Calculate the terms of the summations in (A2.1)
   - Calculate the likelihood ratio $\Lambda(d_k)$

- Subtract the a priori information to obtain the extrinsic information to be passed on to the next decoder.

A2.3   The log-MAP algorithm

The MAP algorithm involves a large number of multiplications and exponentiations, which are computationally intensive. It also works with probabilities and likelihood ratios which have a large range, and cause difficulties in computer storage. For this reason it is convenient to convert all likelihoods into logarithmic form, which removes the exponentiations and converts the multiplications to additions. This is known as the log-MAP algorithm [A2.3].

Unfortunately, it makes the computation of sums of likelihoods much more complex. In place of the addition of the likelihoods λ_1 and λ_2 in the form $\lambda = \lambda_1 + \lambda_2$, we have for the corresponding log likelihoods l_1 and l_2:

$$l = \ln(\exp l_1 + \exp l_2) = l_1 \coprod l_2 \qquad (A2.11)$$

where we have used the special symbol $\coprod$ to represent this operation. Note that the associative and commutative laws of arithmetic apply to this operation. We may then rewrite Equations (A2.1)–(A2.3):

$$L(d_k) = \frac{\displaystyle\coprod_{i=0}^{n-1} [A_k(i) + G_k(i,j_1) + B_k(j_1)]}{\displaystyle\coprod_{i=0}^{n-1} [A_k(i) + G_k(i,j_0) + B_k(j_0)]} \qquad (A2.12)$$

$$A_{k+1}(j) = [A_k(i_1) + G_k(i_1,j)] \coprod [A_k(i_0) + G_k(i_0,j)] \qquad (A2.13)$$

$$B_{k-1}(i) = [B_k(j_1) + G_k(i,j_1)] \coprod [B_k(j_0) + G_k(i,j_0)] \qquad (A2.14)$$

where L denotes the log likelihood ratio, $\ln(\Lambda)$, and similarly A, B and G are the natural logarithms of α, β and γ, respectively.

$$G_k(i,j_d) = \ln[\gamma_k(i,j_d)] = \ln\{P[r_k|b(i,j_d)]\} + \ln[P(d_k = d)] - \ln[P(r_k)]$$

$$= -\frac{\delta_k^2(i,j_d)}{2\sigma^2} + \frac{[L_p(d_k)|_{d=1}, 1|_{d=0}]}{1 \coprod L_p(d_k)} + c \qquad (A2.15)$$

where c is a constant for a given trellis section, derived from the constant of proportionality.

The function described in (A2.11) can be expressed as:

$$l = \ln(\exp l_1 + \exp l_2) = l_1 + \ln[1 + \exp(l_2 - l_1)] \qquad (A2.16)$$

If the arguments are sorted so that $l_1 \geq l_2$, then $\ln(1 + \exp(l_2 - l_1))$ can be regarded as a correction factor that will tend to zero as the difference between the arguments increases. In the diagram, the correction factor appears as the difference between the solid line (the exact expression) and the dotted line (an approximation given by $\max(l_1, l_2)$). An approximation to the correction factor can be obtained from a look-up table.

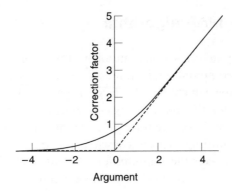

A2.4 The max-log-MAP algorithm

If the correction factor above is omitted, we have a very simple approximation to the function of Equation (A2.11):

$$l = \ln(\exp l_1 + \exp l_2) = l_1 \coprod l_2 = \max(l_1, l_2) \tag{A2.17}$$

Using this approximation throughout the log-MAP algorithm leads to the max-log-MAP algorithm [A2.4]. Equations (A2.12–A2.14) and (A2.1–A2.3) become:

$$L(d_k) = \frac{\overset{n-1}{\underset{i=0}{\max}}[A_k(i) + G_k(i,j_1) + B_k(j_1)]}{\overset{n-1}{\underset{i=0}{\max}}[A_k(i) + G_k(i,j_0) + B_k(j_0)]} \tag{A2.18}$$

$$A_{k+1}(j) = \max\{[A_k(i_1) + G_k(i_1,j)], [A_k(i_0) + G_k(i_0,j)]\} \tag{A2.19}$$

$$B_{k-1}(i) = \max\{[B_k(j_1) + G_k(i,j_1)], [B_k(j_0) + G_k(i,j_0)]\} \tag{A2.20}$$

The max operation in (A2.19) selects the most likely path to node j at each stage, and hence the most probable prefix path overall. Similarly, (A2.20) selects the most probable suffix path. The max operation in the numerator of (A2.18) then selects the most probable path overall which corresponds to data '1' in the current trellis section (the '1' path), while the denominator selects the most probable path which contains a '0' (the '0' path). The hard decision given by the decoder for that trellis section will therefore be the data corresponding to the most probable overall path through the trellis. Note that this will be the same path at every point in the trellis: for the full MAP algorithm we cannot identify one path selected by the decoder.

The max-log-MAP algorithm therefore outputs the ML code sequence over the whole trellis. The MAP algorithm, on the other hand, outputs the most probable symbol at each trellis period: it makes symbol-by-symbol decisions. The difference is subtle, and makes very little practical difference to the hard decisions made by the two decoders. It does, however, make a difference to the accuracy of the soft information returned by the decoder: the log likelihood ratio for each trellis period. In the MAP algorithm this is calculated taking into account all the possible paths through the whole trellis: in the max-log-MAP it takes into account only the most probable '1' path and the most probable '0' path.

A2.5 The SOVA algorithm

We have seen above that the max-log-MAP algorithm returns hard decisions corresponding to the ML code sequence. This is of course also characteristic of the Viterbi algorithm, which also returns the ML sequence. The resemblance is more direct than that, since the recursion defined by (A2.19) selects the metric corresponding to the ML path to node j, which in terms of the Viterbi algorithm is the *survivor* path. Thus the forward recursion performs the same operations as the Viterbi algorithm.

This suggests a further simplification of the max-log-MAP algorithm, which will bring its computational complexity close to that of the Viterbi algorithm. If we perform only the forward recursion, the hard decisions are unaffected, but the complexity is halved. Effectively we now have a Viterbi algorithm that has been amended to provide a soft output indicating the likelihood ratio of each symbol. This is known as the *soft output Viterbi algorithm* (SOVA), and is due to Hagenauer [A2.5, A2.6]. It also allows for the incorporation of the a priori information, the soft input to the decoder.

The algorithm now only provides one set of probabilities for each node of the trellis: the αs as calculated by the max-log-MAP algorithm. This prevents the use of the method of the MAP algorithm to calculate even an approximation to the likelihood ratio of the current bit. Instead we use the Viterbi algorithm to calculate (as far as possible) the likelihood of the most probable path containing a '1' at this point, and the most probable containing a '0'. Suppose the algorithm traverses the entire trellis, thereby tracing the ML path (the most probable). Now consider the survivor paths which have merged with this path at various points through the trellis. The set of these paths will certainly contain the second most probable path, and is likely to contain most of the most probable paths. (However, we cannot guarantee that the third most likely path, etc., is present, since this might have been eliminated at an earlier point in the second most likely path.) For a given trellis section we then find the most probable path from this set that contains a '1' at this point, and the most probable that contains a '0'. We may estimate the relative probabilities of these two paths from the difference of their metrics at the point at which they merge. This is the SOVA.

Clearly, it avoids the necessity for a second pass through the trellis required in the max-log-MAP. However, it does require a more complex version of the 'trace-back' procedure needed in the conventional Viterbi algorithm. Thus the complexity saving may not be as large as one might initially hope.

References

A2.1 Bahl, L., Cocke, J., Jelinek, F. and Raviv, J. (1974) Optimal decoding of linear codes for minimizing symbol error rate. *IEEE Transactions on Information Theory*, **20**: 284–7.

A2.2 Berrou, C., Glavieux, A. and Thitimajshima, P. (1993) Near Shannon limit error-collecting coding: turbo codes. In *Proceedings IEEE International Conference on Communications*, Geneva, Switzerland, pp. 1064–70.

A2.3 Robertson, P. (1994) Improving decoder and code structure of parallel concatenated recursive systematic (turbo) codes. In *Proceedngs IEEE International Conference on Universal Personal Communications (ICUPC'94)*, pp. 183–7.

A2.4 Robertson, P., Höher, P. and Villebrun, E. (1997) Optimal and sub-optimal maximum a posteriori algorithms suitable for turbo decoding. *European Transactions on Telecommunications*, **8**(2): 119–25.

A2.5 Hagenauer, J., Robertson, P. and Papke, L. (1994) Iterative (turbo) decoding of systematic convolutional codes with the MAP and SOVA algorithms. In *Proceedings ITG Conference on Source and Channel Coding*, München, October, pp. 21–8.

A2.6 Hagenauer, J. (1995) Source-controlled channel decoding. *IEEE Transactions on Communications*, **43**(9): 2449–57.

Index